FROM A
REALIST POINT OF VIEW:

Essays on the Philosophy of Science

William A. Wallace

Un[...] of America™

Library of Congress Catalog Card Number: 79-66154

FROM A REALIST POINT OF VIEW

ESSAYS ON THE PHILOSOPHY OF SCIENCE

FROM A REALIST POINT OF VIEW

ESSAYS ON THE PHILOSOPHY OF SCIENCE

BY

WILLIAM A. WALLACE

1979

P R E F A C E

The title of these essays bears obvious similarity to that of Willard Van Orman Quine's collection, *From a Logical Point of View* (Cambridge, Mass.: Harvard University Press, 1953). Actually the connection is rather tenuous, although it does suggest a different emphasis from Quine's when dealing with problems in the philosophy of science. Most of the work in the latter field has been done by logical empiricists, and it is the author's belief that they have now reached an impasse in their use of logical methods. Further advances, in his view, will result only if the focus is changed from the "logical" to the "real." Hence the title: *From a Realist Point of View: Essays on the Philosophy of Science.*

There are, of course, many varieties of realism, some making more extensive ontological claims than others. These essays propose to elaborate a variety referred to as moderate realism and usually associated with Aristotelian Thomism. Indeed the name of Aquinas appears consistently throughout these studies, so much so that the phrase "in the Thomistic tradition" could well be added to the title, were this not overburdening. The implied interest in Thomism, it should be stressed, is not antiquarian. Appropriately, perhaps, this volume appears on the centenary of *Aeterni Patris,* the encyclical published by Pope Leo XIII in 1879 to encourage the application of St. Thomas's thought to the solution of contemporary problems. The starting point of each essay is some present-day problematic in the philosophy of science. The moderate realism invoked in its solution is one judged by the author, on historical as well as on systematic grounds, to be apt and to have appeal for any serious seeker after truth, regardless of ultimate concern or religious commitment.

The essays reproduced herein have been elaborated over a period of twenty-five years and have appeared in a variety of publications. Most were prepared as invited papers or addresses, and bear the signs of their origin in the phraseology they employ. No attempt has been made to revise the papers or to impose a uniform style upon them. They have been grouped, however, into five sections or parts each with a unified theme, so as to present a coherent and more or less systematic philosophy of science when read consecutively. Since these essays represent but a small portion of the author's writing in the field, a bibliography has been added at the end of the volume giving a more extensive list of his publications by the year of their appearance. The papers reprinted here are included in that list, and the reader is directed to it for fuller particulars. (When several items were published in one year, lower case letters have been added for purposes of identification: thus 1964a is the first article to appear in 1964, 1964b the second, and so forth.) Two essays were written specially for this volume, and additions have been made to one other to improve the coverage and continuity of presentation.

Part I is entitled "Science and Philosophy" and is essentially propaedeutic in character. The first essay appeared under a slightly different title (1968c) as part of a memorial volume honoring Charles De Koninck and surveys various definitions of the philosophy of science. The second essay, given at a philosophy workshop at The Catholic University of America (1968d), builds on the first and proposes various pedagogical schemes for covering the content of the field. The third and concluding essay has not been published previously; it summarizes material covered in greater detail in 1977a, and otherwise explains fundamental concepts that are used in later essays.

"Methodology in Science" is the focus of the studies contained in Part II. Essay 4, originally given as an Aquinas Lecture at Dover, Massachusetts (1961a), surveys three divergent views of scientific method, viz, those of mathematical realism, fictionalism, and moderate realism. Following this is a paper devoted to the problem of measurement as related to sensible qualities, read to the Philosophy of Science Institute at St. John's University, New York (1965a). The sixth essay, which appeared in a commemorative issue of *The Review of Metaphysics* honoring St. Thomas (1974e), takes up problems of causality and its use in scientific explanation. The last study gives examples of a large number of demonstrations pertaining to the science of nature (1957a), and is illustrative of the ways in which Aristotelian canons of proof can be applied to trace the growth of certified knowledge

vi

throughout science's history.

Part III is central to the theme pervading all of the studies, that of realism in science. Its opening essay was a McAuley Lecture delivered at St. Joseph College in West Hartford, Connecticut (1964c), which surveys epistemological problems associated with gravitational attraction. Following this is a similar paper on the reality of elementary particles, read at an annual convention of The American Catholic Philosophical Association (1964a). The concluding essay, arguing in favor of cumulative growth in scientific knowledge, was an invited address to an International Congress, held in Rome and Naples, on the occasion of the seventh centenary of the death of Thomas Aquinas (1978c).

The next series of essays turns from problems of the physical sciences to those of the human sciences, under the rubric "Science and Man." Its first essay is an expanded version of a paper given at a workshop at Catholic University devoted to philosophy and technology (1964d), and proposes a model for man based on developments in cybernetics. After this comes a moral reflection on the atom bomb, written at the request of students who were aware of the author's knowledge of the circumstances of its use in World War II (1963e). The final essay in this part, new to this volume, grew out of lectures given to graduate students in the School of Nursing at Catholic University, and is based on materials developed at greater length in 1962a.

The concluding part addresses problems of ultimate explanation by exploring the relationships between science and God. The opening essay focuses on the concept of immateriality: it gives the complete text of an invited address to the convention of The American Catholic Philosophical Association devoted to that concept in 1978, a summarized version of which will be found in the *Proceedings 1978* when they appear. The second paper is a similar address given to an earlier convention of the same association (1972b). The concluding study is the oldest essay of the collection in time of composition: it revises the principal chapter of a dissertation entitled *Physics and God: The 'Prima Via' in the Light of Modern Science* and written at the Dominican House of Studies, Washington, D.C. (1956a). Consideration of the subject matter of this chapter sparked the author's interest in the history and philosophy of science, and led to most of the remaining publications listed in the bibliography.

The author wishes to thank the following for granting copyright permission to reprint the essays in this collection, as indicated:

Laval University Press, for Essay 1;

The Catholic University of America Press, for Essay 2 and part of Essay 11;

The Thomist Press, for Essays 4 and 16, which appeared in *The Thomist*, and for Essay 7, which was published in *The Thomist Reader 1957*;

The American Catholic Philosophical Association, for Essay 5, which appeared in its quarterly, *The New Scholasticism*, and for Essays 9, 14, and 15, which were printed in whole or in part in its various *Proceedings*;

The Metaphysical Society of America, for Essay 6, which appeared in its journal, *The Review of Metaphysics*;

St. Joseph College, West Hartford, Connecticut, for Essay 8, which was published as part of its series, *The McAuley Lectures*;

The International Thomistic Congress, Rome-Naples, 1974, for Essay 10; and

The Dominican Fathers of St. Joseph Province, for Essay 12.

William A. Wallace, O.P.

The Catholic University of America
Washington, D.C. 20064
June 1, 1979

TABLE OF CONTENTS

PART V: ULTIMATE EXPLANATION

x

PART I

SCIENCE AND PHILOSOPHY

ESSAY I :

DEFINING THE PHILOSOPHY
OF SCIENCE

W HAT is the philosophy of science? How is it related to other philosophical disciplines? Is there only one philosophy of science, or
are there many depending upon the ontological commitments of their
proponents? Is the philosophy of science a discipline at all, or is it merely
a disconnected series of topics discussed by amateur philosophers whose
major interest is science?

There seem to be no simple answers to these questions. If the
expression "philosophy of science" is taken in a sufficiently broad sense,
one can say that there are as many philosophies of science as there are
scientists, and almost as many as there are philosophers. In a more precise
sense, however, the philosophy of science may be said to be what is
practiced by one professionally competent in philosophy and in science,
who works in an area that is common to both. It is generally regarded as
a discipline or study concerned with philosophical problems raised by
modern science, such as the meaning of scientific concepts, laws, and
theories; the logical structure of science; and the methodology by which
it attains its results. Most of its practicioners may be broadly characterized as empiricists or as "scientific philosophers," although there are
also Kantians, Marxists, and Thomists who are interested in its problems.
Foremost among such Thomists was the late Charles De Koninck, to
whose memory these essays are dedicated. Perhaps more than any other
thinker, De Koninck was responsible for the spread of interest in the
philosophy of science among Catholic philosophers in the United States
and Canada. As a fitting testimonial to him, therefore, this article proposes to investigate the nature of the philosophy of science and to ascertain its proper relationship to other recognized branches of philosophy.
It aims to do this first by delineating the historical origins of the study,
then by sketching the rise of the movement under empiricist and positivist influences, and finally by evaluating the discipline that has evolved
through a comparative study of the views of Catholic philosophers who
have addressed themselves to its problems.

1

To locate the philosophy of science movement in its proper historical context, it is necessary to begin with the factors that led to the differentiation of science from philosophy. If the terms "philosophy" and "science" are taken as identically synonymous, then the philosophy of science is vacuously equivalent to the philosophy of philosophy or to the science of science. Presumably this is not what is intended by the expression, and thus it is necessary to discover wherein science differs from philosophy and how there can be a branch of philosophy that is concerned uniquely with science.

Remote Origins. The bifurcation between science and philosophy can conveniently be dated at about the 17th century. Until that time there was no separation between the two disciplines. A certain vagueness in the use of the terms had existed since their introduction among the Greeks, but for the most part "natural science" and "natural philosophy" were regarded through the centuries as coextensive in meaning. This terminological identification, in fact, persisted long after the world view on which it was based had been generally abandoned. Many universities in the 19th century listed courses in physics and chemistry under the catalogue title of "natural philosophy."

Among the scientists who contributed most to the separation of science from philosophy were Francis Bacon, Galileo Galilei, and Isaac Newton. The accent of these thinkers on the concrete as opposed to the universal, on the use of mathematical modes of reasoning, and on experimental methods prepared the groundwork for philosophers who would finally effect the separation. Foremost among such philosophers was René Descartes, whose subjectivism and mechanism exerted a marked influence on the course of intellectual history. Immediately after Descartes, in fact, philosophers aligned themselves into two divergent traditions: the one accented subjectivism, the other mechanism. Immanuel Kant sought to unite these traditions while admitting certain elements of Descartes's subjectivist view of knowledge and by accepting Newtonian mechanism in its entirety. He raised the question as to how scientific knowledge is possible at all, considering that science must be universal and necessary whereas human experience must be always contingent and concrete. His answer was in terms of the famous distinction between phenomena and noumena. He proposed that the phenomena, or the appearances of things, can be known scientifically, whereas the noumena, or things-in-themselves, are forever inaccessible to human reason. Once Kant's solution was accepted, natural philosophy as traditionally understood became impossible and natural science inherited the only task that was left, that, namely, of collecting data and analyzing phenomena as these present themselves in human experience.

To Descartes and Kant, therefore, the modern mind owes the distinction between philosophy and natural science; from them it also received certain fundamental principles that underlie, either explicitly or implicitly, most present-day philosophies of science. The first of these is that the clear and distinct idea is the criterion of truth; acceptance of this norm entails a view of science that is mainly mathematical in character. A second principle is that there can be no knowledge of things-in-themselves, i.e., of essences or natures; as a consequence of this, most philosophers of science profess a type of agnosticism concerning man's ability to know reality. A third principle—most influential with empiricists and positivists—is that all man's knowledge must begin in the senses and is ultimately incapable of transcending the sensible.

The foregoing constitute the remote origins of the 20th-century movement known as the philosophy of science. A further note may be added regarding Descartes's notion of philosophy itself, which he conceived as the study of all reality in the light of its ultimate causes. The simplicity of this definition, accepted by many thinkers since Descartes, hides the fact that it permits no distinction to be made between natural philosophy and metaphysics. Christian Wolff acknowledged this in his famous division of philosophy, wherein he classified cosmology and psychology (recognized by previous thinkers as branches of natural philosophy) as specializations within metaphysics. Thus, apart from the Kantian influences, the acceptance of a Cartesian notion of philosophy implicitly entailed the separation of philosophy from science. When Thomism was revived in the late 19th century, the definition of philosophy proposed by Descartes and elaborated by Wolff was tacitly accepted by most scholastics, and the divorce of natural philosophy from experimental science had become an established fact.

Proximate Origins. In view of the positivist and empiricist leanings of most contemporary philosophers of science, a sketch of the historical origins of the movement would be incomplete without a discussion of its more proximate origins in the teachings of Auguste Comte, the founder of positivism, and of John Stuart Mill, one of the foremost proponents of empiricism.

More fascinated than either Descartes or Kant with the successes of the new science, Comte formulated the positive spirit of his century into a theoretical principle. He conceived a new philosophy that, when added to the positive sciences, would yield a complete system of knowledge. Under the name of "the positive philosophy," this proposed to answer satisfactorily all questions that could be asked about man and the universe.

For Comte, knowledge is to be drawn from sense experience using

3

the methods of the new science. The objects of science are empirical or sensible facts and the laws of relationships that obtain between them. Since, in his view, laws themselves express only external relationships, they are incapable of furnishing explanations for phenomena in terms of intrinsic principles. Thus Comte, in effect, advocated a type of metaphysical agnosticism: human knowledge cannot attain to substances, causes, soul, or God; it is powerless either to assert or to deny their existence.

Mill, including psychology among the positive philosophies, perfected the positivism of Comte. He developed a logic that attempted to explain the entire intellectual life of man in terms of the association of sensations alone. As he saw it, a consistent positivist could invoke no other explanation. Thus one may speak of a "general idea," but this is nothing more than a name by which one evokes the memory of a series of sensations received from various objects. Similarly, when enunciating a judgment, man relies on a particular sense experience, either true or imagined, and merely enunciates an empirical fact in a more general way. Reasoning, depending as it does on judgment, must itself be empirical and based largely on induction—the process whereby, from one particular case that is empirically known, a person can infer another particular case. It is induction also that enables man to formulate general scientific laws.

The philosophical revolution affected by Descartes and Kant, and the elaboration of some of its consequents by Comte and Mill, thus effectively confirmed the separation of science from traditional philosophy. Not only this, but the expansion of positivism and empiricism into a complete theory of knowledge provided a new philosophy that was sympathetic to the scientific enterprise and at the same time could offer a type of criticism acceptable to scientists. Thus the ground was prepared for the beginnings of the philosophy of science movement.

The Philosophy of Science Movement

The chief stages through which philosophy of science movement has grown, from its start at the end of the 19th century to its current flourishing state in the 1960's, conveniently fall in a fourfold division: (1) empiriocriticism, (2) critique of science, (3) logical positivism, and (4) neoempiricism. The characteristic features of each stage is here noted briefly.

Empiriocriticism. The name "empiriocriticism" is commonly given to the thought of Ernst Mach and Richard Avenarius, both of whom were concerned toward the end of the 19th century with the foundations of science. Mach, in particular, was a scientist of note who wished to

4

develop an epistemology that could be used by scientists in their work of criticism.[1] Scrupulously studying the methods and conclusions to which classical mechanics had come, he wished to show its inherent limitations. He used positivist principles in his critique, however, and, convinced that there is no profound truth beyonde mpirical data, effectively denied the possibility of metaphysics.

The principal points of the philosophy of science elaborated by Mach may be summarized as follows. The object of any science is sensation and sensation alone; science does not attain to any object distinct from man's subjective impressions. Sensations are not disconnected but are organized into constant groupings that man designates as "things." Thus, contrary to a realist epistemology, Mach's empiricism held that sensations do not refer to "things" but that "things" are symbols of sensations. In Mach's view, therefore, the task of science is to analyze human sensations and their mutual interrelationships and to organize them into some type of synthesis. The aim of such a synthesis is not theoretical, i.e., it is not to inquire into the causes or meanings of phenomena or to supply explanations for them; rather it is purely practical. The end of science is to enable man to adapt himself, with a maximum economy of thought and effort, to the conditions producing the sensations he experiences.

Mach admitted hypotheses into his science as temporary and useful aids, viz, to organize experimental data and to suggest new experiments. In his view, one should never ask if they are true or false but only if they are useful. Similarly, laws for him are rules that can be used to replace a series of facts; whenever possible, they are to be expressed in mathematical formulas. On Mach's terms, it is impossible for man to know laws of nature in the sense of extramental regulators of phenomena.

Like his empiricist and positivist predecessors, Mach practiced the philosophy of science with a distinct anti-metaphysical bias. Yet he did admit a certain type of congruence or agreement between natural events and the expectation of them man would attain through scientific reasoning. He thought that this required more than chance as an explanation, and invoked a type of psychophysical parallelism as its underlying basis. Such an explanation obviously did not accord with his positivist principles, and left the way open for philosophies of science that would concede some validity to metaphysics.

Critique of Science. Somewhat like empiriocriticism and partly under its inspiration, the critique of science movement originated among

---

1. MACH'S most important writings include *Beiträge zur Analyse der Empfindungen* (Jena 1886) and *Erkenntnis und Irrtum : Skizzen zur Psychologie der Forschung* (Leipzig, 1905).

scientists who were concerned over the foundations and methods of their science. Many of the thinkers in the movement were French, and, if not Catholics, were at least sympathetic to Catholic culture. This possibly explains their more tolerant attitude toward metaphysics and the influence that they were later to have on the philosophy of science at the University of Louvain. Principal among them were Henri Poincaré and Pierre Duhem.

Poincaré's conventionalism may be said to epitomize the critique of science movement.[2] Through the influence of Antoine Cournot and Émile Boutroux, Poincaré was convinced that science has no absolute value, particularly in its work of prediction. He felt that any explanation being used at a given time to account for future phenomena must ultimately give way to a better explanation. While conceding that scientists speak of theories as true, he maintained that in actuality theories are not true but only convenient: they serve to simplify the work of scientists and provide them with an aesthetic picture of the universe. Poincaré, nonetheless, was opposed to the thorough-going empiricism of most of his predecessors, as well as to the extremes of rationalism and scientism.

In working out his philosophy of science, Poincaré proposed a distinction between sciences that are merely rational and those that are empirico-rational. The merely rational sciences, the paradigm of which is mathematics, are for him free constructions of the human mind; the role of experience is completely extrinsic to their development, merely suggesting possibilities to them and providing instances for their application. The objects of such sciences are beings of reason (entia rationis). The relationships that obtain among these objects are expressed by axioms; these are freely postulated and implicitly define the objects and their properties. Yet they are not completely arbitrary: they must avoid internal contradiction and be at least convenient, i.e., simple and adapted to the properties of the bodies with which they deal. The empirico-rational sciences, on the other hand, are concerned with the objects of experience, with entities in the external world. Experience provides single facts, which the mind uses to ascend to the universal order by constructing hypotheses. Such hypotheses, for Poincaré, are not merely arbitrary: they must agree both with experience and with experimental laws. Yet they are selected by "free convention," insofar as a great number of different possibilities may be excogitated to explain the same facts. For this reason, hypotheses should not be said to be true or false, but more or less "suited" to describing phenomena.

Duhem assimilated the teachings of Poincaré and on them erected

<hr />

2. The significant works in which POINCARÉ elaborated his philosophy of science include *Science et hypothèse* (Paris, 1902), *La valeur de la science* (Paris, 1905), *Science et méthode* (Paris, 1909), and *Dernières pensées* (Paris, 1913).

a philosophy of science that became acceptable to many Catholic scholars at the beginning of the 20th century. He distinguished two orders of knowledge, one of philosophy and the other of science. Philosophy, which for him was essentially metaphysics, seeks the explanation, causes, and essences of things, whereas the physical sciences seek none of these. Their function is essentially symbolic; they do not explain phenomena, they merely represent or symbolize them. The difference between the areas of philosophical and scientific discourse, as Duhem understood them, may be seen from the following passage, where he opposes laws of common sense to those of science:

> The laws that ordinary nonscientific experience allows us to formulate are general judgments whose meaning is immediate. In the presence of one of these judgments we may ask, "Is it true?" Often the answer is easy; in any case the answer is a definite yes or no. The law recognized as true is so for all time and for all men; it is fixed and absolute.
>
> Scientific laws based on the experiments of physics are symbolic relations whose meaning would remain unintelligible to anyone who did not know physical theories. Since they are symbolic, they are never true or false; like the experiments on which they rest, they are approximate. The degree of approximation of a law, though sufficient today, will become insufficient in the future through the progress of experimental methods; sufficient for the needs of the physicist, it would not satisfy somebody else, so that a law of physics is always provisional and relative. It is provisional also in that it does not connect realities but symbols, and that is because there are always cases where the symbol no longer corresponds to reality; the laws of physics cannot be maintained except by continual retouching and modification.[3]

Thus, for Duhem, the laws of common sense, like all philosophical expressions, are able to express truth in an absolute way, whereas scientific laws, and scientific reasoning generally, can provide only a provisional and symbolic knowledge of reality. It is not difficult to see why this teaching was acceptable to those who were intent on preserving the *philosophia perennis* against the inroads of modern science, for it placed such philosophy beyond question while according only a conjectural status to the so-called discoveries of modern science.

Logical Positivism. An outgrowth of empiriocriticism, and developed in large part by Moritz Schlick, one of Mach's successors as professor of the philosophy of inductive sciences at the University of Vienna, logical positivism was most influential in the United States in the early 20th century. By many, it would be identified with the philosophy of science movement, if for no other reason than that it seems best to exemplify the latter's spirit. Logical positivism was given great impetus

---

3. Cited by A. Danto and S. Morgenbesser, eds., *Philosophy of Science* (New York, 1960), p. 196, from Duhem's *The Aim and Structure of Physical Theory*, trans. P. Wiener (Princeton, 1954).

by a group of philosopher-scientists known as the Vienna Circle, the majority of whom emigrated to the United States because of the unfavorable political atmosphere in Vienna immediately prior to World War II.

Schlick's aim was not so much to develop a new system of philosophy as it was to inaugurate a scientific way of philosophizing. For him, philosophy is identified with the philosophy of nature, which is practically another term for the philosophy of science. He conceived the task of science to be that of obtaining knowledge of reality, and the task of philosophy to be that of interpreting scientific achievments correctly and of expounding their underlying meaning. As Schlick explains it:

> The entire task of natural science consists solely in the persistent and indefatigable examination of the correctness of its propositions which, in consequence, develop into more and more securely established hypotheses. In this way, the assumptions upon which these hypotheses are based, are simultaneously tested within the domain of natural science itself. There is, moreover, no other specifically philosophical vindication of the foundation,—such a vindication would not only be impossible, but superfluous as well. . .
>
> The task of the philosophy of science is nevertheless concerned with the hypotheses of natural science—but in quite another sense. Natural knowledge is formulated in propositions; and likewise all the laws of nature are expressed in propositional form. But the knowledge of its meanings is a prerequisite for testing the truth of a proposition. These two concepts are inseparable, and both occur within the domain of natural science. In spite of their inseparability, however, it is possible to distinguish here between two psychological attitudes: the one concerned with testing the truth of hypotheses, the other with the understanding of their meaning. The typically scientific methods assist in the discovery of truth while the effort of philosophy is directed to the elucidation of meaning. The task of a philosophy of nature is thus to interpret the meaning of the propositions of natural science; and therefore the philosophy of nature is not itself a science, but an activity which is directed to the consideration of the meaning of the laws of nature.[4]

The foregoing statement of Schlick may be said to have provided the positive inspiration for the philosophy of science movement. Previous thinkers had pointed out the necessity of a reflective consideration of the work of science, but most of them had fostered a negativist view of philosophy as this relates to science. Thus Poincaré and Duhem maintained, in effect, that science raises no philosophical questions, nor can it provide definitive answers to questions discussed by philosophers. In Schlick's formulation, however, philosophy was placed once again in closer relationship to science. It was taken into partnership, as it were, and given the task of interpreting the symbolism of science, of discovering the profounder meaning that underlies its laws and theories.

---

4. *Philosophy of Nature*, trans. A. von Zeppelin (New York, 1949), pp. 2-3.

Another thinker who exerted considerable influence among logical positivists is Hans Reichenbach, who advocated a relationship between science and philosophy similar to that proposed by Schlick. What was only implicit in Schlick's thought, however, viz, that philosophy itself is to be identified with the philosophy of science, came to be explicitly expressed by Reichenbach. Unable to conceive of any philosophical enterprise that did not base itself exclusively on the findings of science, Reichenbach consciously elaborated his "scientific philosophy." As he explains it:

> Since philosophy is dependent on science, we should make this dependence the conscious condition of our work: we should know that the nature of knowledge can be studied only through an analysis of science. The idea of a philosophical theory of knowledge that derives the general outlines of knowledge from the structure of the mind, or from an insight into the nature of being, should forever be abandoned. There is no ontology, no separate realm of philosophical knowledge that precedes science. Theory of knowledge is analysis of science. Philosophy does not contribute any content to knowledge; it merely studies the form of knowledge as exhibited in the work of the scientist and examines all claims to validity. In so doing, the philosopher will know that all he can strive for is a philosophy of the knowledge of his time.[5]

In Reichenbach's understanding, therefore, scientific philosophy evaluates the findings of modern science as of an ongoing enterprise; there is no finality in its results, but it serves to keep one abreast of scientific progress.

Neoempiricism. The strongest representation within the philosophy of science movement at the present time comes from neoempiricists. These thinkers preserve the mentality of logical positivism, but, because of the stigma attached to the label "logical positivist" after the aggressive polemics of the Vienna Circle, prefer to be known as tolerant or nondogmatic empiricists, or simply as neoempiricists. Representative of the neoempiricist movement is Ernest Nagel, currently professor of philosophy at Columbia University in New York. Working within the framework provided by Schlick and Reichenbach, Nagel has attempted a more systematic approach to the philosophy of science. The growth in literature associated with logical positivism had led, by 1960, to the application of the term "philosophy of science" to a heterogeneous collection of problems related in various ways to science. Textbooks of readings in the philosophy of science had also appeared. These discussed, among other things, problems relating to epistemology, such as the validity of sense perception; those relating to the genesis and development of scientific ideas, the nature of scientific laws and theories, etc.;

---

5. *Modern Philosophy of Science*, trans. and ed. M. Reichenbach (New York, 1959), p. 148. See also H. REICHENBACH, *The Rise of Scientific Philosophy* (Berkeley, 1951), *passim.*

and various technical problems relating to the axiomatization of systems, the justification of inductive procedures, and the confirmation of theories. Other topics ranged from the relationships between science and religion, science and culture, and science and society to ethical questions and value judgments associated with the scientific enterprise.

In reaction to this vaguely defined area of study, Nagel has proposed to limit "the philosophy of science to a group of related questions that arise in attempting to understand the intellectual products of scientific inquiry as embodied in explicitly formulated statements."[6] In Nagel's understanding, which is similar to Schlick's, the work of the scientist is to formulate laws and theories explicitly, whereas the work of the philosopher of science is to interpret their meaning. The area of inquiry for the philosopher of science has been defined more precisely by Nagel as follows:

> On such a delineation of the province of the philosophy of science, its problems can be handled by a unitary mode of analysis; and they fall, moreover, into a number of distinct but cognate sub-divisions: those addressed to the ways in which the conclusions of scientific inquiry are linked to the empirical evidence on which they may be based (e.g., problems relating to procedures of definition and measurement); those concerned with the logical principles involved in the assessment of the evidence and in the acceptance of the conclusions (e.g., problems relating to canons of probable inference); and those concentrating on the structure of the ideas imbedded in scientific conclusions as well as of the systems of statements to which the conclusions belong (e.g., problems relating to the character of scientific explanations or to the role of theories).[7]

Views of Catholic Philosophers

Unlike the proponents of a scientific philosophy, philosophers associated with the scholastic tradition who are interested in the philosophy of science have attempted to characterize that discipline in relation to the other recognized branches of philosophy. Thus some regard it as a branch of metaphysics, others as a development of epistemology, still others as a specialization within logic, and yet others as a part of the philosophy of nature. It will be convenient at this point to discuss these various positions in terms of their proponents, who may be grouped as follows: (1) the Louvain School, (2) the Gregorian Jesuits, (3) William Oliver Martin, (4) Jacques Maritain, and (5) Charles De Koninck.

Louvain School. Philosophers at the University of Louvain, under the inspiration of Cardinal Désiré Mercier, followed closely the development of the critique of science movement and even contributed to its literature. A trained psychologist, Mercier was a leading figure in

6. Preface to A. Danto and S. Morgenbesser, *op. cit.*, p. 13.
7. *Ibid.* For a fuller statement of NAGEL's own views, see his *The Structure of Science* (New York, 1961), particularly pp. VII-IX.

the neoscholastic revival, one of whose tasks was to renew scholastic philosophy by bringing it into line with modern science. Mercier himself repudiated the Wolffian division of philosophy then current in scholastic manuals, although some of his disciples later fell back into Wolff's error. Mercier did subscribe, however, to a Cartesian view of philosophy. This led him to distinguish modern science, which he saw as concerned exclusively with proximate causes, from philosophy, which he conceived as concerned with ultimate causes. While urging this distinction, he attempted to promote a close alliance between science and philosophy to assure unity in man's knowledge of nature.[8]

The Louvain thinker most concerned with the philosophy of science, himself a disciple of Mercier, was Fernand Renoirte. Renoirte criticized his predecessor, Désiré Nys, for promoting too close an alliance between philosophy and science and, in particular, for regarding natural philosophy or cosmology as a simple continuation of experimental science. The danger Renoirte saw in this view—and his thought here is reminiscent of that of Duhem—was that cosmology could thereby be reduced to the status of a scientific theory and would not have the certain and absolute character that should characterize philosophical thought. As he saw it, the study of the material universe poses three problems: the first is that of the description of the universe, the second that of the critique of science, and the third that of cosmology. The first two problems, for him, were the concern of the physicist and only the third that of the philosopher of nature. Natural philosophy "takes for its object of study this necessary and sufficient minimum of physics and asks not experience, but reason to state the conditions under which this minimum will not be contradictory." [9] How much of the philosophy of science would pertain to natural philosophy is not clear in Renoirte's account. Since he states, however, that "the impartial examination of physical facts and the determination of their value is the work not of the metaphysician but of the physicist in the critique of sciences," [10] it would seem that he advocates a complete separation of the philosophy of science from other branches of philosophy and makes it exclusively the concern of the scientist.

Similar to the teaching of the Louvain school is that of two Dutch professors of natural philosophy, Henry Van Laer and Andrew Van Melsen. Both make a sharp distinction between science and the philosophy of nature. According to Van Melsen:

> The philosophy of nature is concerned with the basic structure of matter and all material phenomena as such. It finds its starting point, as does science,

8. *Cours de philosophie : Logique* (Louvain, 1922), pp. 15-16, 28.
9. *Cosmology*, trans. J. F. Coffey (New York, 1950), p. 180.
10. *Ibid.*, p. 179.

in common experience, but investigates a different aspect of daily experience. The philosophy of nature is interested in the primary and fundamental aspect of this experience, whereas science, taking this aspect for granted, focuses attention on the more detailed aspects of daily experience.[11]

Making his position more explicit, Van Melsen argues that the philosopher of nature works with the same kinds of concepts as does the metaphysician, and thus he locates the philosophy of nature at the third degree of abstraction, the level traditionally assigned to metaphysical thought. Since he discusses many of the problems of the philosophy of science in his philosophy of nature, one may infer that the philosophy of science is for him essentially metaphysics.

Gregorian Jesuits. Under the influence of Peter Hoenen, a cosmologist who taught for many years at the Gregorian University of Rome, a number of Jesuits on that faculty have contributed to the literature on the philosophy of science. Among these may be mentioned Philip Soccorsi [12] and Philip Selvaggi. [13] In his *Filosofia delle Scienze*, Selvaggi maintains that the philosophy of science is identical with epistemology, which, in the customary European fashion, he regards as a special part of the science of gnoseology. Gnoseology treats of knowledge in general, whereas epistemology is concerned with the critique of scientific knowledge—in much the same way as the critique of science was conceived by Poincaré and Duhem. Selvaggi notes, however, that science constitutes the object of epistemology "in its formal part," i.e., insofar as science is itself a cognitive process, and not "in its material part," i.e., in the content of its affirmations concerning material reality.[14] The latter, he maintains, can also be the object of a philosophical consideration, but this pertains not to epistemology but to the philosophy of nature. Thus questions relating to atomism, mechanism, causality and indeterminism, space and time, the continuous and the discontinuous, vitalism, and evolutionism can be examined either by the scientist or by the philosopher of nature, but not directly by the epistemologist, who can study such problems only indirectly, and this insofar as he judges of the formal validity of statements made by the scientist or by the natural philosopher.

Selvaggi further explains that the philosophy of science has two major divisions: (1) a general part that studies the logical structure and

11. *The Philosophy of Nature* (Pittsburgh, 1953), p. 14.
12. Significant works by Father SOCCORSI on the philosophy of science include the three volumes of his series *Quaestiones scientificae cum philosophia coniunctae*, viz, *De Physica quantica* (Rome, 1956), *De vi cognitionis humanae in scientia physica* (Rome, 1958), and *De geometriis et spatiis non-Euclideis* (Rome, 1960).
13. Father SELVAGGI has likewise written a number of excellent works on the philosophy of science, including his *Filosofia delle Scienze* (Rome, 1953), *Cosmologia* (Rome, 1959), *Orientamenti della Fisica* (Rome, 1961), *Scienza e Methodologia* (Rome, 1962), and *Causalità e Indeterminismo* (Rome, 1964).
14. *Filosofia delle Scienze*, p. 21.

the methods common to all the sciences, and (2) a special part that analyzes the methods proper to individual sciences or to groups of sciences, e.g., mathematical, physical, biological, and human. The general part, as he conceives it, proceeds mainly a priori, from an abstract consideration of the human mind, to understand the mind's general cognitive processes and the ways these enter into scientific methods. The special part, on the other hand, proceeds in the light of these principles to a detailed analysis of scientific methodology, to ascertain what facts have been established in the gradual evolution of science, to explain their theoretical justification, and to determine the limits of scientific knowledge and the errors that may have been introduced into science through false philosophical conceptions. The special part of the philosophy of science, in Selvaggi's estimation, while the most difficult is also the most important part of the discipline.[15]

Since Selvaggi regards the philosophy of science as related at least materially to the philosophy of nature, it is important to understand how he conceives the philosophy of nature to be related in turn to metaphysics. This relationship is explained in his *Cosmologia*, a work whose introductory section is devoted to a characterization of natural philosophy. For Selvaggi, natural philosophy is neither pure physical science, which he locates at the first degree of abstraction, nor pure metaphysics, which he locates at the third degree; rather it is a mixed science *(scientia media)* intermediate between physics and metaphysics. It applies metaphysical principles to the objects of physics and treates of material, extended, and sensible being precisely under the aspect of being. In its consideration, the physical is "quasi material" and the metaphysical is "quasi formal." Thus he feels that the philosophy of nature can properly be called an applied metaphysics, "through the application of the formal to the material." [16]

In the same work, Selvaggi gives further consideration to the relation between the philosophy of nature and the philosophy of science. The philosophy of science, he maintains, considers science formally as it is the work of reason, i.e., as it is rational knowledge concerning physical entities, and on this account is a special part of logic and gnoseology. The philosophy of nature, on the other hand, does not consider science formally, but rather its object: quantity and natural bodies, space and time, physical and chemical forces, electrons, protons, photons, atoms, molecules, and so forth. Although thus different from each other, the philosophy of science and the philosophy of nature are intimately related and mutually complementary.[17]

15. *Ibid.*, p. 22.
16. *Cosmologia*, p. 9.
17. *Ibid.*, p. 11.

13

William Oliver Martin. A philosopher whose thought shows some kinship with that of Selvaggi, although deriving from a quite different intellectual tradition, is William Oliver Martin, professor of philosophy at the University of Rhode Island. In a passage of his *The Order and Integration of Knowledge*,[18] Martin gives the following characterization of the philosophy of science:

> More often the substitute for the philosophy of nature is something called "the philosophy of science." As usually found the name stands for no definite object of study but rather for bits of several: (1) Philosophy of science sometimes includes a "logical analysis of language," the aim being to find out what scientific concepts and propositions "mean." (2) Included are epistemological analyses of "scientific knowing." Epistemology is here conceived to be independent of, or a substitute for, metaphysics. (3) Philosophy of science includes also speculations on the subject matter of the various experimental sciences, the aim being to "stretch" the concepts of the sciences to make them metaphysical elements in postulational systems. The subject matter of the various experimental sciences do constitute part of the data of the philosophy of nature. But it is something quite different to consider "science" as a kind of knowledge. The subject matter now is a kind of knowledge, and the discipline considering it is the metaphysics of knowledge and not the philosophy of nature. The difference here is that represented by the distinction between first and second intentions. It is a sign of confusion to think of the philosophy of science as one homogeneous kind of knowledge when it is actually composed of fragments of other kinds. [19]

In another place, Martin explains further what he means by first and second intentions and makes explicit the second-intentional character of the philosophy of science. On this account he is led to identify the discipline with logic. Thus he states:

> The philosophy of history, logic, the philosophy of mathematics, and the philosophy of nature are synthetic sciences concerned with kinds of being. Logic as synthetic is the name for the "philosophy of logical forms." Each synthetic science is the result of the integration of the positive science and the ontological... The term referring to the positive sciences are taken in "first intention." That is, the philosophy of nature is literally about nature, not about "science." The "philosophy of science," a worthy study in itself, but one which unfortunately is often a substitute for the philosophy of nature, is actually a part of logic. It is concerned with "second intentions," the "philosophy of our knowledge about nature." [20]

In these two texts, both of which show signs of dissatisfaction with neoempiricism and its influence on American college curricula, Martin seems to identify the philosophy of science either with a metaphysics of knowledge, which is his term for epistemology, or with logic in the

18. Ann Arbor: 1957.
19. PP. 259-260.
20. P. 344.

14

accepted scholastic sense. While not identical with Selvaggi's teaching, it seems to be more related to this than to any other scholastic position.

Jacques Maritain. The Thomistic philosopher most often quoted on topics relating to the philosophy of science is Jacques Maritain. Altough Maritain has not written explicitly on the nature of the philosophy of science, his many writings on the relationship between the philosophy of nature and modern science have been analyzed by Yves Simon to yield what the latter has described as "Maritain's philosophy of the sciences." [21]

The most distinctive aspect of Maritain's analysis of the philosophy-science relationship is his rejection of the Wolffian doctrine that would make natural philosophy (or cosmology) a part of metaphysics and his return to the teaching of St. Thomas Aquinas, who held that the philosophy of nature is a discipline autonomous from metaphysics, located at the first degree of abstraction and not at the third, which is proper to metaphysics. Like earlier Thomists, Maritain also locates the positive sciences (as these have developed since the 17th century) within the first degree of abstraction. Impressed by the different methodologies and conclusions of the natural philosopher and the scientist, however, Maritain employs a distinction that he traces to the Thomistic commentator, John of St. Thomas, to effect a specific differentiation of disciplines within the first degree of abstraction. According to one formulation, Maritain sees a difference between ontological (or dianoetic) knowledge of nature, which in his view is characteristic of the philosophy of nature, and empiriological (or perinoetic) knowledge, which he finds typical of modern science. Ontological knowledge, in this understanding, penetrates through sensible appearances to attain to knowledge of the essence (and therefore is called *dia*-noetic), whereas empiriological knowledge never goes beyond the phenomena but remains always circumferential (and therefore is *peri*-noetic). In terms of this distinction, Maritain feels he can preserve the possibility of a valid philosophical knowledge of natures or essences, a possibility denied by many post-Kantian philosophers, and at the same time acknowledge the positivist character of modern science as this has been maintained by Comte and the empiricist tradition.

Granting Maritain's distinction, it would seem that the philosophy of science occupies a somewhat ambiguous position between the philosophy of nature and the positive sciences. Simon points this out when he makes reference to "the ambiguous literature which stands on the borderline between philosophy and positive science," [22] an obvious allusion to

---

21. "Maritain's Philosophy of the Sciences," *The Thomist* 5 (1943), pp. 85-102.
22. *Ibid.*, p. 91.

literature in the philosophy of science. Simon's complete statement is as follows:

> The philosophy of nature can be defined as a physical consideration whose conceptual instruments call for an ascending analysis, positive science as a physical consideration whose conceptual instruments call for a descending analysis. The very opposition of the two analyses provides an invaluable rule for the determination of the point of view prevailing in our studies about nature. Let us think of *the ambiguous literature which stands on the borderline between philosophy and positive science*. When a philosopher informed of positive science or a scientist interested in philosophy considers philosophical problems raised by the study of positive questions, the philosophical and the positive point of view appear successively in his expositions; generally the writer is not aware of the shift. The resulting confusion can easily be removed provided we carry out the analysis of a few key concepts. According as this analysis goes up or down, according as the concept demands to be explained in more and more characteristically ontological terms or in terms which refer more and more directly to definite experiences, we know whether we have to deal with a philosophical or a positive treatment.[23]

According to Simon's interpretation, then, the philosophy of science seems to function at the first degree of abstraction and to tend toward either polarity, that of natural philosophy or that of positive science, depending upon the type of analysis in which the philosopher of science engages.

A key difficulty in Maritain's explanation of the type of knowledge attained in the positive sciences is his tacit acceptance of the positivist view of such sciences, which rules out the possibility of the scientist's attaining any certain and causal knowledge of the real world (i.e., ontological knowledge). If Maritain's distinction is taken literally, his view of the relationship between science and philosophy seems on this account to be no different from that of Duhem. Possibly aware of this difficulty, Simon attempts to explain how Maritain would concede to the positive scientist the ability to attain knowledge of the real world without this being ontological knowledge. The citation is quite long, but it is worth giving in its entirety:

> Maritain would not agree with the superficial statement that the philosopher has never to worry about agreements or disagreements with the physicist, on the grounds the philosophy and physics are two separate domains of thought. His epistemological pluralism is by no means absolute. Let us give an idea of the distinctions which should be made and of the issue which should be surveyed in order to appreciate the bearing of physical theories with regard to the knowledge of the real.
> 1. The principles previously developed make it clear that a concept may be a genuine expression of the real without pertaining to the ontological type. A description of a non-ontological character is not thereby deprived of real bearing.

23. *Ibid.*, pp. 91-92, emphasis added.

Real, being, knowledge are so many analogical terms. An ontological description is more real than a non-ontological one, yet a non-ontological description may well be a description of the real.

2. Even within the first order of abstraction the mind often uses fictitious constructions in its approach to the real. Yet so long as we remain in the first order, the realistic spirit of science is not held in check. Except for possible failures, fictions never play more than a transitional role; they are used as mere means in view of achieving a representation of the real which cannot be brought about in a more direct fashion.

3. As soon as positive science assumes a mathematical form, something entirely novel takes place. The very nature of mathematical abstraction renders mathematical thought indifferent to the reality of its object. Consequently physico-mathematical science, in so far as it yields to the attraction of its mathematical form, tends to make no difference between *ens reale* and *ens rationis*.

4. Should this tendency prevail without check, it could be said truly that physical theories do not trace phenomena to their real causes and do not tell anything about the real world. Such is the conception of physics upheld by Pierre Duhem. For Maritain this interpretation, though not without basis, amounts to an over-simplification. In fact, the attraction exercised on physics by its mathematical form is not unchecked. If the form is mathematical, the matter remains physical, and accordingly there is in the very structure of the science a counteracting tendency to adhere to the real and to look for explanations by real causes. Actual science is probably a compromise between these two opposite and complementary tendencies. [24]

If Simon is correct in this account of Maritain's position, and if there is in modern science a "tendency to adhere to the real and to look for explanations by real causes," then the basic distinction employed by Maritain would seem, at best, to be itself an oversimplification and, at worst, to be a distinction without a difference.

Charles De Koninck. De Koninck was among those who recognized inconsistencies in Maritain's position and who wished also to take account of the current literature on the philosophy of science. Like Maritain, he urged a return to the Thomistic classification of the sciences, maintaining that the philosophy of nature and natural science are both situated within the first degree of abstraction. Unlike Maritain, however, he maintained that there is no specific distinction between the philosophy of nature and natural science. Although he would not simply identify the philosophy of science with the philosophy of nature, he seems to have regarded the philosophy of science as also a specialized discipline within the first degree of abstraction and thus as a part of the study of nature.

In a paper in which he summarized his mature views on "The Unity and Diversity of Natural Science," [25] De Koninck first described "two extreme positions" on this question, as follows:

24. *Ibid.*, pp. 100-101.
25. *The Philosophy of Physics*, ed. V. E. Smith (Jamaica, N.Y. 1961), pp. 5-24.

Some hold that if there is to be a natural philosophy it must remain confined to certain generalities, such as the conditions of absolute becoming, the definitions of motion, infinity, place, time, etc.; and that when we carry our investigation further, we then practice experimental science, as in seeking to know what the speed of light is. Others, again, believe that natural philosophy presupposes the experimental sciences, and is no more than a reflection on their method and on their present achievements and implications as compared to those of earlier science. Natural philosophy and philosophy of science would be much the same. [26]

The first position will be recognized as that of Maritain, whereas the second is that of Reichenbach and the school of scientific philosophy. De Koninck, surprisingly enough, was willing to recognize elements of truth in both positions. What he acknowledged as valid in Maritain's solution is its insistence on starting with generalities of which one can be certain when commencing one's observation of nature. Thus he commented:

Both of these conceptions are partly true, for there is no doubt that we must examine first of all the things we first name, and these are vague generalities. They are, in a sense, the most important, and to neglect them will eventually spell disaster. The doctrine of prime matter, for instance, is essential to save the unity of the human individual. For if we held that a man is no more than an accidental superstructure made up of electrical charges, a human person would be no more of an individual than an individual pile of bricks. [27]

His criticism of Maritain, on the other hand, is that a person does not cease to be a philosopher of nature when he proceeds to ask more and more specific questions about the reality he is studying. Thus he questions Maritain's solution in the following manner:

But is it the sole function of the natural philosopher to be stubborn about the validity of such problems, about their possibile and even definitive solutions? Does he cease to be a philosopher when he asks more concretely what a man is? When he asks what is the anatomy and physiology of the human brain? Or what are its chemical components? Why should the mind interrogating nature rest in vague generalities, no matter how important and how certain these may be? Is there anything unworthy about investigating man's organic constitution, or the activities of slugworms? It is of course true that no single individual can in our time ever hope to know the whole or even a single ramification of natural science, such as astronomy and botany, nor even list the unlimited number of questions men may eventually learn to ask about a relatively narrow domain of nature. Yet no matter how general or how particular, how certain or provisory, knowledge about nature will always be derived from, and must return to, experience, external or internal. In each and every case, if the knowledge is to be of nature, the descriptions and definitions, no matter of what kind, must

26. *Ibid.*, p. 16.
27. *Ibid.*

18

in the end include sensible matter. It does not seem possible therefore, to set a rigid frontier between philosophy of nature and science of nature. [28]

While thus differing from Maritain and insisting that there can be no rigid frontier between natural philosophy and modern science, De Koninck is no less insistent in his rejection of the view of the so-called "scientific philosophers," who would make all of the philosophy of nature consist in nothing more than a commentary on modern science. The defect De Koninck sees in this view is that it by-passes any consideration of the generalities of which man can be certain and which he must know at the outset if he is ever to attain more detailed knowledge of nature. As he himself explains it:

> The second opinion we described is likewise partly true. For if philosophy is to deserve its name, it will never confine itself to one narrow domain of nature or become indifferent to findings achieved by a particular method of research. A man may be a skillfull investigator, but he will never be master of his science until he knows just what it is that he knows, the status of his own mind with regard to his particular subject; and until he comes to realize, if only vaguely, how much there is that he does not know. *But the great shortcoming of this opinion, that philosophy of nature must be simply philosophy of science, is its inevitable failure to pay explicit attention to the vague generalities with which all thinking about reality must begin, and to which all later knowledge must be related.* To rest in vague generalities its unsatisfactory to the inquisitive mind, but to rest in "man is a swarm of atoms" is no less reprehensible, for the simple reason that intelligence must demand a connection between this statement and the knowledge we already have of man, as expressed in ordinary language; when we ask what man is, for example, or what he is made of and how. [29]

The last quotation is particularly significant because it reveals that De Koninck would not make a simple identification between the philosophy of nature and the philosophy of science. Undoubtedly he saw the philosophy of science as in some way contributing to the perfection of man's knowledge of nature, and thus as complementing the philosophy of nature. What he was opposed to, however, was a complete divorce of philosophy of science from philosophy of nature, because this would isolate specialized knowledge from general knowledge and render it totally unintelligible—i.e., as lacking contact with, and relevance to, what it proposed to explain in ever more specific detail.

A Proposed Definition

From the foregoing survey of views of Catholic philosophers regarding the philosophy of science, it may be possible now to formulate

28. *Ibid.*, pp. 16-17.
29. *Ibid.*, p. 17, emphasis added.

a definition that takes account of the essential features of philosophy of science as this has evolved within positivism and empiricism and that at the same time relates it to other branches of philosophy recognized within the Catholic tradition. De Koninck, it would seem, of all those discussed has come closest to realizing this dual objective, and thus what is said here may be regarded as a fuller statement and explication of his basic notions.

The philosophy of science is part of the general discipline known to St. Thomas Aquinas as *scientia naturalis*, which functions at the first degree of abstraction and is concerned with the study of nature. According to 20th-century usage, this general discipline may be conceived as having two parts, one concerned with generalities about nature, known as the philosophy of nature (or cosmology), and the other concerned with studies of nature in specific detail, usually associated with the positive sciences. As the positive sciences become increasingly formalistic, however, they tend to state their findings in terms of theories, equations, and constructs that require interpretation. The philosopher of nature who would leave the area of generality and attempt to know nature in its specific detail is presented with the problem of interpreting these formulations of modern science. As he does so, he perforce must become a philosopher of science. Therefore the philosophy of science is a specialization, just as is any specific branch of study within modern science, that is necessary for the integral perfection of *scientia naturalis*. As such, it serves to bridge the gap between generalized knowledge and knowledge of specific detail, and it is thus most useful for forging a unity within the disciplines at the first degree of abstraction.

It goes without saying that the philosophy of science presupposes knowledge of logic and of epistemology. Yet it would not seem to be formally identified with either of these disciplines. Every branch of philosophy and every branch of science must use logic in investigating its subject matter. Similarly, anyone who seeks knowledge of reality must successfully meet the objections of skeptics who deny the possibility of such knowledge. No science except logic, however, is concerned with second intentions precisely as such, and no science except epistemology is concerned with the validation of knowledge precisely as such. The philosophy of science is concerned, not with second intentions nor with knowledge in general, but with nature in all its specific detail; therefore it must be ultimately included among the sciences that deal with nature, the *scientiae naturales*.

If the philosophy of science is not logic or epistemology properly speaking, even less is it metaphysics or a branch of metaphysics, as this is understood in the Thomistic tradition. Those who are tempted to label it as metaphysical either base their contention on an erroneous

20

reading of Thomistic texts, as does Van Melsen,[30] or else they acquiesce to a usage accepted in some modern philosophical circles, where every philosophical consideration that transcends the empirical is referred to as metaphysical. It is to the merit of Maritain and De Koninck that they have called attention to the error of following the former procedure. Regarding the latter usage, on the other hand, one of the points stressed in this survey is the extent to which the philosophy of science derives from the empiricist and the positivist traditions, neither of which regards itself as metaphysical in intent or inspiration. To engage in metaphysical speculation is to do precisely what philosophers of science have been concerned *not* to do since the origins of the movement. To be a philosopher of science, in their understanding as in that of contemporary Thomists, is to philosophize about nature in terms of the concepts, constructs, and formulations of modern science. Best account is taken of both the scholastic tradition and that underlying the philosophy of science, it would seem, if philosophy of science be regarded as a study complementary to, and more specialized than, the philosophy of nature, while having the same concern, viz, knowledge of nature in all its general and specific detail.

30. *Op. cit.*, pp. 85-97

ESSAY II:

TEACHING THE PHILOSOPHY
OF SCIENCE

In the aftermath of Vatican II the Catholic philosopher faces a problem of monumental proportions. As the Church attempts to up-date her thought and bring it more into line with contemporary scholarship, increasing demands will be made on the individual who is acquainted with such scholarship and at the same time has an appreciation of the role of reason, or of philosophy, in shaping the Church's tradition. The problem is one, first of all, for the scholar of outstanding intellectual ability, of high integrity, and of supreme dedication, who can evaluate the merits of the old and the new in calm awareness of the Church's mandate to lead all men along the pathway of truth. This is a long-term project, one that cannot be influenced by popular pressures, by practical exigencies, or by concessions made to create the appearances of dialogue when there may be, in fact, no meeting of minds.[1]

Apart from such a long-term project, however, practical considerations dictate a more urgent confrontation with secular thought on the part of the Catholic philosopher. One such exigency arises because of the Church's heavy commitment in the United States to higher education. The philosophy teacher, like the teacher of the sciences and the humanities, must keep his subject-matter up to date if he would hold the interest of his students. The need for this has perhaps not been so much appreciated by those who have been teaching courses in scholastic philosophy, but the spirit of renewal that is sweeping the Church as a consequence of Vatican II has served to accentuate the need. Catholic students are no longer content with routine presentations of traditional doctrine; they wish to be faced with live problems and to be offered solutions that are

[1]For a start, see some of the items listed in the bibliography at the end of this volume.

both realistic and meaningful to their non-Catholic friends. By all indications students will continue to be importunate in this regard, and it behooves us as educators to make strenuous efforts, on a short-term basis, to accede to their demands.

The contemporary thought to which the Catholic philosopher must address himself, as a consequence, ranges through all the traditional divisions of philosophy. Surely in the area of natural theology, with the problems posed by atheism and the "God is dead" movement, there is need for a wholesale re-evaluation of traditional doctrine. This is no less true in the field of metaphysics generally, where existentialism, phenomenology, dialectical materialism, and analytical and linguistic philosophy invite serious study. Much the same could be said for psychology and ethics, where the need to make contact with the empirical disciplines, on the one hand, and to keep up with the changing mores of technological culture, on the other, present continuing challenges to the Catholic educator. These disciplines are mentioned solely to recognize the work to be done in these areas. It is not the intention of this paper to offer solutions to their problems or programs for dealing with them.

The exclusive concern of this paper is an area of contemporary thought that is most influential and, at the same time, most difficult to evaluate: modern science, and particularly physical science. No one would deny that the twentieth century, whether it be called the age of the atom, the age of space, or the age of automation, is a century dominated by physical science. Today's major psychological and ethical problems, as well as the basic metaphysical options, and even the movements within natural theology, are all traceable to an excessive concern with, or a complete rejection of, the methodology and conceptual structures of modern science. Similarly, many of the problems dealt with in the Constitutions of Vatican II arise within a scientific and technological civilization. Thus the up-dating of the Church's thinking would itself be unthinkable should one propose to ignore the physical sciences and the problems they present.

Philosophy of Science as a Pedagogical Problem

The difficulty of the undertaking, moreover, is accented by the fact that courses in natural philosophy or cosmology are on the decline in Catholic colleges. Part of the reason for this decline is that the traditional course in the philosophy of nature, usually taught at a level of great generality, is far removed from the needs of the average collegian. Part of the reason, too, is the shortage of teachers who feel competent to deal with the subject matter of natural philosophy, particularly in face of the many specific questions relating to modern science that are being raised by their students.[2]

Notwithstanding its difficulty, the overriding importance of a philosophy of the physical sciences in the present day forces the Catholic educator to consider it and to study how it is to be treated in the curriculum. As soon as he attempts this, however, he is faced with a question that does not seem to permit a simple answer. The question is this: Can the physical sciences be said to have a philosophy, or, put somewhat differently, is there any general agreement as to what that philosophy is? I will attempt first to answer this question and then to make a practical application of the answer in terms of some pedagogical alternatives it would seem to entail. The plan, then, is to treat first of science and its philosophy, and secondly of methods of teaching this philosophy in the Catholic college.

Two types of problems present themselves when educators discuss the philosophy of science. The first is a problem of pedagogy, on which there is already considerable agreement; the second is one of semantics, on which there is still quite basic disagreement. Let us make a remark about the first problem, and then turn quickly to the second as requiring fuller elaboration.

In most institutions in which the philosophy of science is taught, it is taught as a graduate discipline,[3] and the same is true of the

---

[2] Yet another reason is the wholesale reduction of credit hours that were formerly allotted by Catholic colleges to philosophy and theology. This has been necessary to bring their "college requirement" more into line with that of secular institutions. Cosmology is one of the first courses to be dropped in the process, usually because logic, psychology, metaphysics, natural theology and ethics are rightly regarded as more essential to a Catholic intellectual formation than is natural philosophy.

[3] It is not uncommon to have a Philosophy of Science Institute attached to one or other graduate faculty, as has been the case at the University of Minnesota and St. John's University, Jamaica, New York. In some institutions courses are taught by the graduate philosophy department, in others by the physics department, and occasionally they are sponsored jointly by two or more departments. Some of the larger secular universities offer courses in the philosophy of science to undergraduates, but these are usually survey courses having more the character of an introduction to philosophy than a systematic examination of problems in the philosophy of science.

history of science.[4] The reason for this pedagogical practice is that students are incapable of appreciating the problems that are discussed in these courses if they have not already had an undergraduate formation in science. Experience has shown that the student of science at the lower levels of education rarely exhibits a philosophical or historical turn of mind, particularly if he is a science major. More frequently than not he approaches his subject-matter as a technician, as someone learning the tools of a trade. He is disposed to accept uncritically the terminology and conceptual structure of such classical sciences as Newtonian mechanics.

Only when, in more advanced courses, the science major encounters the enigmas presented by relativity theory or by quantum mechanics is he liable to become concerned about the philosophical foundations on which the discipline has been erected. Even then, it may be noted, under the pressures of learning advanced mathematics, of taking specialized courses, or of being introduced to research techniques, his philosophical interests are liable to remain peripheral. As a consequence he cannot devote the time that is required to familiarize himself with the philosophical issues associated with science.[5]

This pedagogical problem is recognized by all educators, Catholic and non-Catholic alike, and serves partially to explain the shortage of satisfactory textbooks for teaching the philosophy of science at an undergraduate level. Most materials that are now available are adapted only to graduate students, and mainly to those who are acquainted with the terminology and methods of analytical philosophy and of mathematical logic.

Philosophy of Science in Secular Thought

The second difficulty, not unrelated to the first, is one of semantics. This arises as soon as one attempts to reply to the question: What is the philosophy of science? This question may be answered in a variety of ways, any one of which usually serves to identify the

[4] Thus Harvard University's Committee on the History of Science accepts only graduate students as candidates for degrees, although it offers survey courses to undergraduates.

[5] A surprising number of those who major in the history or philosophy of science turn to these disciplines in reaction to the way in which they have been taught science at the undergraduate or graduate level. Many then return to science teaching when they obtain their degrees.

ideological bias or basic philosophical commitment of the one answering. Since we are concerned here with the views of Catholics as these relate to those of non-Catholics, or with the intellectual tradition that is generally denominated as Catholic as opposed to that which is denominated as secular, it is desirable to sketch here how each of these traditions would define the philosophy of science.[6]

Beginning then with secular or non-Catholic thought, one finds no great unanimity on the nature of the discipline, although there is fairly good agreement on the type of problem it treats. At the risk of oversimplification, two currents may perhaps be distinguished, the first characterized as adopting a definite philosophical position and the second as being eclectic. The first may be referred to as scientific philosophy, the second as scientific criticism, or alternatively, the critique of science.

Scientific philosophy, generally an outgrowth of logical positivism or of neo-empiricism, expresses an a priori, if implicit, commitment to science. It constructs its philosophy in such a way as to respect the conclusions and utilize the methodology of the scientist. Perhaps no one has stated this commitment as clearly as Hans Reichenbach:

> Since philosophy is dependent on science, we should make this dependence the conscious condition of our work: we should know that the nature of knowledge can be studied only through analysis of science. . . . Philosophy does not contribute any content to knowledge; it merely studies the form of knowledge as exhibited in the work of the scientist.[7]

Because of its concern with problems of quantum and relativity theory, which theories are heavily immersed in formalism and mathematical systems, this philosophy makes extensive use of mathematical logic in its technical elaboration. Usually it is anti-metaphysical in bias, at least as represented in its empiricist and instrumentalist proponents.[8] Recently, however, a group of self-styled realists have joined the ranks of the scientific philosophers. These

---

[6] I have made an extensive survey of attempts at definition in an article, "Toward a Definition of the Philosophy of Science," to appear in *Mélanges De Koninck* (Quebec: Laval University Press).

[7] *Modern Philosophy of Science*, ed. and trans. Maria Reichenbach (New York: Humanities Press, 1959), p. 148.

[8] For example, Reichenbach, most of the Vienna Circle including Rudolph Carnap, and Ernest Nagel.

presumably express some commitment to a reality that transcends measurement and sense observation.[9]

The movement of scientific criticism, on the other hand, has been less a philosophy than an attempt to set science's own house in order. It has come largely from scientists themselves, most of whom have had no strong commitment to any existing philosophical tradition but have attempted to formulate their own philosophical views while criticizing and evaluating the results of science.[10] A worthwhile contribution of this movement is its demythologizing of science by accenting the conventionalist and operationalist character of many of its definitions and concepts.[11]

Notwithstanding the different emphases of these two secular or non-Catholic views of the philosophy of science, they agree generally that science is a primary enterprise concerned with the technical formulation of laws and theories based upon empirical data. Philosophy of science is a secondary enterprise concerned with the meaning or interpretation of these formulations.[12] The interpretation of the equations of the physicist, for example, is the work of the philosopher of science, whereas the writing of such equations is the work of the physicist. Philosophy of science, in this understanding, has a certain therapeutic function, since enigmas are seen to dissolve when equations, for example, are given a proper interpretation. Again, this view makes no sharp distinction between the scientist and the philosopher of science, since both must understand the formalism of science. Frequently the scientist is as adept as the philosopher at providing an acceptable interpretation.

Such a view of the philosophy of science is asystematic and problem-centered. Perhaps this serves to explain why many textbooks in the philosophy of science are anthologies, or selections of

[9] Mario Bunge, David Bohm, and disciples of Karl Popper such as Paul K. Feyerabend and Joseph Agassi may be enumerated in this group.

[10] Pioneers in the movement include Ernst Mach, Henri Poincaré, and P. W. Bridgman.

[11] The philosophies of conventionalism and operationalism, elaborated by Poincaré and Bridgman respectively, have been particularly influential in this regard, although both have severe limitations when erected into complete theories of knowledge.

[12] One of the first to state this view was Moritz Schlick, the founder of the Vienna Circle, in his *Philosophy of Nature*, trans. Amethe von Zeppelin (New York: Philosophical Library, 1949), pp. 2-3. Ernest Nagel has given it more precise formulation in his preface to *Philosophy of Science*, eds. Arthur Danto and Sidney Morgenbesser (New York: Meridian, 1960), pp. 12-13.

readings, on a variety of problems that interest the physical scientist.[13]

Philosophy of Science in Catholic Thought

Within Catholic circles, the philosophy of science is rarely interpreted as scientific philosophy, if only because of the fact that philosophy was cultivated as a discipline by Catholics long before the advent of modern science, and thus is not seen by them to stand in essential dependence upon the laws and theories of modern science. All agree, moreover, that a large component of what goes under the name of philosophy of science is epistemology.[14] This fortunately coincides with the generic view of non-Catholics that philosophy of science is concerned with the interpretation of the results of science. On the other hand, the types of answers given to epistemological questions by Catholics, which are generally along realist lines, diverge rather sharply from the answers given in the secular tradition, which are frequently empiricist or positivist or, at best, Kantian in their general orientation.

Apart from the general consensus regarding the epistemological character of much of the philosophy of science, a divergence is to be noted among Catholic scholars regarding the substantive or material discipline to which it pertains. Some thinkers regard it as a branch of metaphysics.[15] These are usually under the influence of a rationalist conception of philosophy that derives from Christian Wolff and has received a systematic elaboration in the scholastic manuals of the latter part of the nineteenth century. Others regard it as pertaining to the philosophy of nature, being a development of the specialized treatises that were part of natural

[13] Representative works are H. Feigl and M. Brodbeck (eds.), *Readings in the Philosophy of Science* (New York: Appleton-Century-Croft, 1953) ; P. Wiener (ed.), *Readings in the Philosophy of Science* (New York: Scribner, 1953); E. H. Madden (ed.), *The Structure of Scientific Thought: An Introduction to the Philosophy of Science* (Boston: Houghton Mifflin, 1960); and the anthology by A. Danto and S. Morgenbesser cited in the previous note.

[14] In Europe, the term "epistemology" is practically synonymous with "philosophy of science"; the more general study that would correspond to theory of knowledge is there known as "gnoscology." Here we take "epistemology" in the sense usually meant by Catholic educators in the U. S., viz., the branch of metaphysics concerned with the defense of man's ability to attain knowledge of reality.

[15] Among these may be mentioned F. Renoirte, A. Van Melsen, H. Koren, and F. Selvaggi.

29

philosophy in its Aristotelian understanding.[16] For such thinkers, the philosophy of science would be supplementary to the more generic parts of natural philosophy, and would serve to round out the student's specific knowledge of the universe in which he lives.

These semantic differences, as was mentioned earlier, are not without their pedagogical import. If one is not sure what the philosophy of science is, he will have difficulty knowing how to go about teaching it. If he opts for one definition as opposed to another, his treatment will consciously or unconsciously attempt to justify this definition throughout. If the Catholic teacher pursues an epistemological direction that rejects automatically most of what is written by his non-Catholic contemporaries, he may be open to the charge that he is not teaching a "real" philosophy of science, but something he has arbitrarily concocted to preserve his own ideological view.

These, then, are the difficulties the Catholic educator must face when discussing science and its philosophy. It is my opinion that they can be minimized by regarding the philosophy of science as an interpretative, or cognitional, or epistemological type of inquiry that has a stronger affinity to the philosophy of nature than it has to metaphysics.[17] Such an understanding would permit one who intends to teach the philosophy of science to by-pass the polemics that are usually indulged in by systematic metaphysicians, and to begin with problems that are concerned directly with the physical universe as known through experience and through the refined observational and experimental techniques of modern science. Orienting the Catholic student toward attaining a deeper understanding of the world of nature, the teacher would propose for study specific problems that are precisely those discussed in secular universities under the title of philosophy of science. While seeking solutions to these problems, moreover, he could evolve in the process a general philosophy of nature that has wider import and application than the specific problems with which he started might have given promise of providing.

In what follows, two ways of attaining this result are proposed: the first is more problem-oriented, whereas the second is more solu-

16 The more influential philosophers who have adopted this position include J. Maritain and C. De Koninck.

17 A recent justification of this view is to be found in V. E. Smith's *Science and Philosophy* (Milwaukee: Bruce Publishing Co., 1965).

tion-oriented, and each incorporates some features of the other. Which of the two is better adapted to meeting the problems of the Catholic educator in the present day is probably not easily decided, and may depend in large measure on the conditions that prevail locally throughout the nation. Perhaps the discussion that follows this paper will throw light on the various conditions that do exist, and the way in which they would influence adoption of one or the other alternative.

A Problem-Oriented Approach[18]

Following the general pattern of philosophy of science textbooks, the student would be supplied with a series of readings, prefacing each series with an introduction and concluding it with a summary analysis. The criterion for inclusion would be not that the essays are not otherwise available, but that a particular selection helps to raise a problem for discussion. Where the excerpts are from treatises readily available to the student, the larger work from which the excerpt is taken becomes a reference source for discussions that develop around the problem raised.

The course would be designed to be taught in a discussion or problem-centered fashion. The introduction to each series of selections would be written in such a way as to highlight the problem or problems involved. At the end of each group of selections, the strands of thought would be tied together in such a way as to bring out for the student the issues involved in competing points of view. No attempt would be made at a dogmatic resolution, and the teacher would be left with the task of eliciting from his students a response that would be generally consonant with Catholic teaching.

By way of content, the course would be divided into three parts, the first taking up the foundations of science, the second the principles of measurement in science, and the third the concept of emergence in science. Under foundations there would be an introductory chapter dealing with the competing viewpoints of mechanism, naturalism, and positivism. This would include a series of excerpts, drawn mostly from recent authors, discussing the respective methodologies of Plato and Aristotle, of Galileo and Newton,

[18]See Paul R. Durbin, *Philosophy of Science: An Introduction*, New York: McGraw-Hill Book Co., 1968.

31

and of the contemporary scientist.[19] The second chapter would then deal with the structure of matter, bringing into focus the problem of continuity and discontinuity, and providing readings from such temporally disparate authors as Aristotle and Heisenberg, and some intermediate proponents of corpuscular philosophy.[20] The chapter would conclude with discussions of the "dematerialization of matter" and of the reality of elementary particles as these are represented in recent literature.

The second part, dealing with principles of measurement in science, would be concerned with an examination of the concepts of space and time. The third chapter would deal with absolute space, as illustrated in the writings of Newton and his critics, while the fourth chapter would be devoted to the classical concept of time.[21] Chapter five would then survey the literature on relativity theory and the space-time continuum to show how more recent concepts are related to such classical notions.[22]

Part three, based on the general theme of emergence, would discuss such concepts as energy, activity, and causality in science.[23]

The text could be used in any one of three ways. It could serve as material for a course in natural philosophy along traditional lines, though with more than usual attention being paid to modern, even contemporary, problems in science. It could be taught also as a philosophy of science course in the way usually done on non-Catholic campuses. In this case, the selections from traditional authors would serve as a background against which to see recent problems. Finally, enough material would be included so that it might be used as an introduction to some key periods in the history of science. This approach is assuming increasing importance in the present day.

Obviously it is difficult to evaluate such a problem-centered approach without detailed knowledge of the selections incorporated and the use made of them in formulating the problematics. This

[19] Some of the authors whose writings might be utilized are W. Heisenberg, J. H. Randall, Jr., A. E. Taylor, W. A. Wallace, R. M. Blake, and E. Nagel.

[20] Representative authors here might be L. L. Whyte, M. Capek, and M. Jammer.

[21] Authors here could range from St. Augustine and E. Mach to M. B. Hesse and J. T. Fraser.

[22] The writings of J. J. C. Smart, A. Grünbaum, and G. J. Whitrow supply abundant materials for analysis in this regard.

[23] Two significant titles in this area are Mario Bunge, *Causality: The Place of the Causal Principle in Modern Science* (Cambridge, Mass.: Harvard Univ. Press, 1959), and Errol E. Harris, *The Foundations of Metaphysics in Science* (New York: Humanities Press, 1965).

type of course could be an excellent "stop-gap" measure. It has the advantage of being adaptable to the needs of a variety of students, and from it fruitful studies along more systematic lines could later develop.

However, the proposal also has its limitations. One is that some of the selections could prove difficult for students who are just beginning either philosophy or college-level science. The selections may be well adapted to science majors at the upper undergraduate level or to beginning graduate students in philosophy. Yet the solutions presented may not be completely satisfying even to these students. They, too, might be led in the direction of electicism or of skepticism, neither of which would be particularly helpful toward furthering the goals of Catholic education.

A Solution-Oriented Approach

In view of these limitations, and with the possibility in mind of working out a program that might be useful even at the lower levels of undergraduate education, I am emboldened to make another proposal.[24] The theme of this approach is realism in modern science, and, although it uses problem-centered techniques and the analysis of readings, it is more concerned to reach explicit conclusions consonant with Catholic philosophy as taught in other courses of the college curriculum.

The course would be made up of three parts. The first would be introductory and concerned largely with delineating the epistemological problems raised by modern science and its philosophers. The second would be analytical, and concerned with two problems that are of key importance in both the philosophy of science and the philosophy of nature. The third would be synthetic, and would propose solutions from which some central theses in the philosophy of nature could be drawn.

The first part would be essentially a thumbnail sketch of the Thomistic theory of knowledge with particular application to the

[24] This is based largely on series of lectures I have given over a period of five years at American University in an NSF sponsored Institute for the History and Philosophy of Science and Mathematics, at the Conference on Christian Humanism sponsored by Bishop Vincent S. Waters for several years at Asheville, North Carolina, and at various undergraduate institutions, such as St. John's College in Annapolis, Maryland. Three of these lectures have been published under the titles listed below in footnotes 27, 28, and 30.

concepts of natural science. It would first attempt to define what knowledge is, and establish the distinction between sense knowledge and intellectual knowledge.[25] Within the category of intellectual knowledge, it would then proceed to detail the types of concepts man can have, and to raise the question of the ontological reference of the various types.

For example, one might begin by discussing some concrete, physical, existing, singular entity such as "this lead ball." Associated with the ball, one could list a series of ideas or concepts that may be associated with the ball, or, alternatively, may be derived from it by the process of abstraction. Among these concepts should be some that are rational or purely logical (i.e., that exist only in the mind and cannot exist outside the mind) and others that are real or ontological (i.e., that exist in the mind but also exist somehow outside the mind). Among the real concepts some should pertain to the level of physical science, others to the level of mathematical science, and still others to the level of metaphysics—an implicit use of Thomistic teaching on the three degrees of abstraction. Examples of physical concepts would be "lead," "hot," and "heavy"; of mathematical concepts, "sphere" and "one"; and of metaphysical concepts, "thing" and "exists." Logical concepts, on the other hand, might include the "and" in the phrase "hot and heavy," the "if. . ., then. . ." in the phrase "if lead, then heavy," the "non" in "non-lead," and so on.

All of the foregoing concepts constitute ordinary knowledge of the lead ball, a subject that is studied in greater detail by the scientist. To illustrate typically scientific knowledge, along with the physical concepts one should now introduce some metrical or empirical concepts, together with some theoretical concepts that have been used to explain the metrical and the empirical in the history of science. Thus, in connection with "heavy" one would mention "35 gm" as a metrical or empirical concept, and the explanatory concepts of "pull of gravity" and "space-time geodesic" as theoretical. Similarly, associated with "hot" one might have "52° C" as metrical or empirical, and the explanatory concepts of "phlogiston" and "molecular motion" as theoretical. Again, with "lead" one might indicate subdivisions of its length and mass as metrical or empirical

---

[25] This section would be a much abbreviated presentation of the analysis in L. M. Régis, *Epistemology* (New York: Macmillan, 1959).

34

concepts, and "molecule of lead" or "atom of lead" as their theoretical elaborations.

At the completion of this introductory enumeration, the second or problematical part could be begun by raising the question whether the theoretical concepts of modern science have greater affinity with physical concepts or with logical concepts. That is, do they exist in the mind and also outside the mind, or do they exist in the mind but not outside the mind. To reach an answer, one might propose to analyze in detail, using historical as well as analytical techniques, the questions: "Is the pull of gravity real?" and "Are elementary particles real?"[26]

To discourage a naive realist or mechanist attitude of mind in the student, one might marshall considerable evidence to show that the first question, "Is the pull of gravity real?" is best answered in the negative. In other words, "pull of gravity" is more a logical construct than a physically existent entity.[27] Then, at the other extreme, to discourage a positivist or instrumentalist mentality, one might marshall similar evidence to show that the second question, "Are elementary particles real?" is best answered with a qualified affirmative.[28] I say "qualified affirmative," for it is important here to disabuse the student of a naive atomist mentality and at the same time to prepare him for more refined notions such as those of "virtual part," and, ultimately, of "primary matter." Elementary particles are "real" in some sense, but there is also logical construction involved in man's understanding of them. All of this, in my view, would be best done by using citations from historians and philosophers of science as well as statements of scientists themselves.[29]

The third, or synthetic, part would attempt to erect the results of the foregoing analyses into a coherent philosophy of nature built around the concepts of matter, nature, and motion. To introduce

26 These questions, incidentally, focus attention on the underlying theme's being that of realism in modern science.

27 The general line of argument is sketched in my "St. Thomas and the Pull of Gravity," in *Science and the Liberal Concept* ("McAuley Lecture": West Hartford, Conn.: St. Joseph College, 1963).

28 For details, see my articles, "The Reality of Elementary Particles," *Proceedings of the American Catholic Philosophical Association*, XXXVIII (1964), 154-66; and "Elementarity and Reality in Particle Physics," *Boston Studies in the Philosophy of Science*, III (1964-1966), R. S. Cohen and M. W. Wartofsky, eds. (New York: 1968), pp. 236-71.

29 Useful materials for this type of approach are contained in the monumental work, *The World of the Atom* (2 vols.), ed. Henry A. Boorse and Lloyd Motz (New York: Basic Books, Inc., 1966).

the student to the concept of substance, a section might be given on the measurement and definition of sensible qualities.[30] This could be followed by a discussion of substance or of substrate that would delineate the main features of the Aristotelian and Thomistic doctrine on primary matter.[31] The section on nature could begin within the context of the discussion on gravitational motion, and then be related to the previous work on substance and its principles.[32] Motion or change could be explained in detail as part of the definition of nature, and, associated with motion, the concepts of space and time. All of this material should be continually referred back to the analytical section to emphasize its explanatory value for science. In the process, an effort should be made to show how nuanced any philosophy of nature must be that attempts to avoid the extremes of ultra-realism, as exemplified in the classical views of mechanism and atomism, and logicism, as exemplified in the more recent views of logical positivism and instrumentalism.

Conclusion

These, then, are alternative proposals for a philosophy of science course that would substitute for the philosophy of nature, and at the same time would have immediate reference to problems of interest to the college student. The two approaches are by no means opposed, nor are they meant to exclude other possibilities. Work in the history of science, for example, suggests the possibility of a third approach that would be more professionally historical in orientation, and at the same time would justify a more realistic interpretation of modern science than is given by many contemporary philosophers.[33]

[30] This might cover some of the topics discussed in my "Measurement and Definition of Sensible Qualities," *New Scholasticism*, XXXIX (1965), 1-25.

[31] See the many excellent essays on this topic in *The Concept of Matter*, ed. Ernan McMullin (Notre Dame, Ind.: Univ. of Notre Dame Press, 1963), particularly pp. 169-315.

[32] This material is ably presented by J. A. Weisheipl, *Nature and Gravitation* (River Forest, Ill.: Albertus Magnus Lyceum, 1955).

[33] The writings of Gerald Holton and Leonard K. Nash, both scientists and both associated with the general education program at Harvard, illustrate this. *E.g.*, Gerald Holton and Duane Roller, *Foundations of Modern Physical Science* (Cambridge, Mass.: Addison-Wesley Publishing Co., 1958); L. K. Nash, "The Atomic-Molecular Theory," in *Harvard Case Histories in Experimental Science*, ed. J. B. Conant (Cambridge, Mass.: Harvard Univ. Press, 1957), I, pp. 215-321; and L. K. Nash, *The Nature of the Natural Sciences* (Boston: Little, Brown, & Co., 1963).

Catholic education should move closer toward teaching both science and its philosophy in the context of general education, with heavy emphasis on case histories and other techniques for unveiling cultural and sociological influences on the development of science. Preferably this should be done in one and the same course, rather than relegating these considerations to different departments, and, as usually results, to different compartmentations of knowledge.

The pedagogical alternatives discussed in this paper are predicated upon practical necessity. Catholic philosophers are far from having definitive answers to many of the questions being discussed by scientific philosophers. While awaiting the long-term effort that will be necessary to assure this, the courage must be shown to embark on programs that can offer stimulation to students and to teachers alike, and thus speed the day when such answers may become available.

ESSAY III:

BASIC CONCEPTS: NATURAL AND SCIENTIFIC

In the essay immediately preceding, two different methods for teaching the philosophy of science were outlined, the first problem-oriented and the second solution-oriented. Shortly after that essay was written, the promised textbook containing materials for utilizing the first method was published, viz, Paul R. Durbin, *Philosophy of Science: An Introduction,* New York: McGraw-Hill Book Company, 1968. The remaining essays in this book provide materials for utilizing the second method. As explained in the preceding essay, this second method presupposes that the student is acquainted with basic philosophical concepts. It is the function of the present essay to explain such concepts in an elementary fashion. Fuller details are to be found in the author's *The Elements of Philosophy,* New York: Alba House, 1977. The latter book is divided into sections, and the paragraphs within each section are numbered. For convenience of the reader in locating passages within it, parenthetical references of the type §12.2 have been inserted in the following exposition; the number before the decimal is that of the section, and that after it, of the paragraph within the section.

Knowledge and Truth

Knowledge (§38.1), for purposes of this essay, may be defined simply as the presence of an object in a subject. The object is the thing known, and the subject is the knower; thus the presence in the knower of something that is known constitutes knowledge. When a person knows an apple, the apple, apart from its existence outside the person, comes to have an existence within the person also. All knowledge, on this account, has both an objective and a subjective character: it is

39

knowledge of something, and to this degree is objective; at the same time it is knowledge possessed by
someone, and to this degree is subjective.

Knowledge so characterized is the result of a
vital operation, and as such is found only in a living
subject. When such a subject knows something outside
itself, although it remains what it is, it also becomes
something else (§23.1). Philosophers speak of this becoming as possessing the form of the thing known in an
immaterial or intentional way. To know an apple is to
possess the form of the apple, but not in the precise
way in which the form can be said to be in the apple.
The form is in the apple in a material or physical way;
in order for a person to possess apple in this way he
would have to have it within him materially or physically -- a feat he could accomplish by eating it.
Knowing apple is not the same as eating apple. Knowing
apple is to have an intentional form or likeness of
apple within one, all the while that the material or
physical form of the apple remains without. In this
sense the presence of the object in the subject is referred to as an "immaterial" presence, and the form of
the object known is said to be present in the knowing
subject in an immaterial or intentional way. Knowing
something destroys neither the knower nor the thing
known. The one knowing, remaining oneself, becomes the
thing known, and the thing known, likewise remaining
itself, takes on a new mode of being in the one who
knows it.

This description of knowledge is very general,
and can be made more specific by discussing the two
main types of knowledge, sense knowledge and intellectual knowledge. Sense knowledge is the simplest type,
and represents the knower's primary contact with the
external world through one or other of its organs.
These organs are usually referred to as senses, and are
further divided into two kinds: external or outer
senses, whose organs are on the periphery of the body;
and internal or inner senses, whose organs are located
in the central nervous system and the brain.

The term sensation is usually reserved for the
product of one of the outer senses; this results when
a sense of a living organism is properly activated and
produces its intentional form (§24.1). There are at
least five of these external senses, viz, sight, hearing, smell, taste, and touch, and each one puts the
knowing subject in contact with one or other quality of

the object that impinges on the sense (§24.3-4). Thus
sight receives the sensation of color, hearing of
sound, smell of odor, taste of flavor, and touch of
softness or temperature. A sensation, in this understanding, would be the simple awareness of green, of a
musical note, of sweetness, of heat, etc., without explicit reference to the particular object that would
be the bearer of these qualities.

The outer senses are not sufficient of and by
themselves to produce a complete representation of the
object sensed; their sensations must be combined in
some way to do this, and such activity is the work of
the internal or inner senses. There are at least four
internal senses, usually named the central sense, the
imagination, the cogitative or estimative sense, and
the memory (§24.6). The product of an internal sense
is called a perception, to distinguish it from a sensation: sensations are the elements out of which a perception is formed, and the latter is like an image produced in the central nervous system and the brain --
the composite representation, or percept, of the object
sensed.

Each of the inner senses has a different function
to perform with respect to this percept. The central
sense, for example, integrates diverse sense impressions into the percept as a unit of experience, makes
the knowing subject conscious of the individual sensations that enter into it, and effects comparisons among
them (§24.7). The imagination records the percept and
enables it to be recalled subsequently; its product is
spoken of as the phantasm, possibly because it is capable of re-presenting images with new, fanciful, and
even illusory elaborations (§24.8). The cogitative or
estimative sense apprehends the percept with an awareness of the value it has for the knowing organism, i.e.
whether it represents something good or bad, to be
sought after or avoided, and so forth (§24.9). The
memory, finally, preserves the percept with its func-
tional values as apprehended by the cogitative sense
and enables it to be situated in experience as something occurring at a particular time in the past (§24.
10). Through the inner senses, it should be noted, the
knower becomes aware not only of the objects of sense
experience but also of space, time, and motion, and in
general of the perceptual field in which he situates
these objects (§24.11-12).

The percept is a very important factor in human
knowing, and thus one must be precise in delineating

41

what it does and what it does not contain. Its essential characteristic is that it represents a singular concrete object as apprehended in past or present sense experience. Example of percepts would be 'this red apple,' 'this blade of grass,' and 'this bouncing ball.' The percept contains more than the individual sensation, since it itself is the composite of various sensations. At the same time it is not the same as the concept. Concepts, as will be explained presently, are abstract and universal, whereas percepts are singular and concrete. The latter can be stored up in memory, however, and cumulatively they represent the knower's total experience of the external world, the raw data or basic fund of information on which his intellect must draw for its various thought processes.

Intellectual knowledge (§25.1) serves to differentiate man from the lower animals, and is the source from which his language, literature, culture, science, and other distinctively human accomplishments derive. The simplest way to characterize intellectual knowledge is to say that it is concerned with meaning or content, that it grasps ideas or concepts which transcend the level of sensation and perception. Whereas the percept puts the knower in contact with 'this apple,' the power of intellect enables him to extract from such a percept its intelligible content -- the meaning of 'apple' in general, 'appleness,' if you will, which can be translated into different languages using appropriate terms to make that meaning be understood in them. The percept, it should be noted, is a rich source from which a great variety of concepts can be formed, as will be explained in the following section. Thus from the percept of an apple one can grasp the concept of 'apple,' and with it also the idea of 'red,' of 'sweet,' of 'soft,' and of 'warm.' Similarly one knows 'grass,' and with grass 'green,' 'blade,' 'fragrant,' etc. Each one of these concepts has an aspect of universality associated with it, in the sense that the one who formulates the concept is able to apply it to the next object he meets in experience, and say of it, for example, 'that also is an apple' or 'this is another blade of grass.' The concept, as extracted from the percept, is abstract; as applicable to other perceived objects, in unlimited number, it is also universal, and thus is the root source of the generalizations that one is subsequently able to make.

The diagram on the facing page summarizes what has been stated thus far, and shows in a schematic way the interrelationships between sensations, percepts, and concepts as these are produced by the external senses, the internal senses, and the intellect respectively.

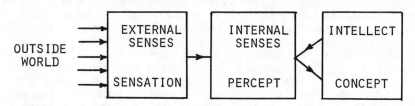

The schema should not be interpreted mechanically, as though the knowing process consisted in impressions made on the knower in the way a seal may be impressed on wax. Knowing is a vital operation, and in the human being, for example, there is a continuous interplay between the intellect, the internal senses, and the external senses. Moreover, one need not understand the diagram genetically, as though simple sensations always precede the percept, and so on. It may happen, for instance, that the knower first apprehends the object he perceives and then isolates in his perception the various sensations that go to make it up. But the diagram does serve to focus on the various elements involved in human knowing, and particularly makes clear how intellectual knowledge is related to sense knowledge and is ultimately based upon it.

Knowledge has been defined generally as the presence of an object in a subject, and this definition can now be seen to be verified at each stage of the process diagrammed. Sensation is knowing at the basic level, since it consists in the reception of a form in an external sense that corresponds to an object outside the knower: thus 'green' is sensed in the eye when the eye is presented with a green object such as grass. Perception is likewise an instance of sense knowledge, although more elaborated, since it consists in the presence within the internal senses of an image or likeness of the object perceived: thus 'this blade of grass' is known when the senses grasp such an object with all its singular attributes. Conceptualization is also knowledge, now at the intellectual level, since it consists in the presence within the intellect of an idea or concept that expresses the whatness or essential content of the thing that is apprehended: 'grass' as instantiated in this blade of grass, but as applicable to any other grass the knower may subsequently encounter.

The definition of knowledge thus explained also
provides a foundation for understanding what is meant
by truth (§39.1). Its basic definition is the following: truth is the conformity between the object as it
exists outside the knower and the form that corresponds
to this object in the knowing subject, or, put more
simply, it is the conformity of object to subject. The
possibility of attaining truth rests on the proper
functioning of the senses and presumes that these are
healthy and free from organic defects, such as color
blindness. What a normal person calls 'green,' however, is the color green as this exists in green objects such as grass. Likewise when a person apprehends
'grass' in the sense of knowing what grass means, as
instantiated in the object before him, then he has the
basic information for making truthful statements about
grass in his subsequent discourse.

A fuller understanding of the notion of truth may
be gained by expanding on what has already been said
about intellectual knowledge. The intellect's basic
activity is apprehending concepts that inform it of the
meaning or whatness of the objects it encounters in experience (§3.1); it also has two other activities,
namely, judging, or combining concepts to form meaningful statements (§4.1), and reasoning, or discoursing
from two or more statements to conclusions that are
entailed by them (§5.1). Most of the literature on the
philosophy of science is concerned with how to proceed
correctly in these various operations of the intellect.
For purposes here it may suffice to note that truth is
most properly attained in the second operation of the
intellect, namely, in judgment, in formulating a proposition such as 'grass is green.' In a sense, one could
say that the knower either grasps 'grass,' 'green,' and
other concepts, or he does not; viewed in this way,
conceptualization is a "go" or "no-go" operation that
provides the materials on which a truthful judgment can
be made, without itself enunciating a truth. When one
states, on the other hand, 'grass is green,' he puts
together two concepts, and his composition either corresponds to the way in which things are outside his
mind, in which case he states a truth, or it does not
so correspond, and then he utters a falsehood. The
possibility of truth and falsity is therefore lodged
in the way in which the intellect forms its concepts,
i.e., by grasping various intelligible aspects of the
objects presented to it in sense experience. When it
reconstitutes these intelligible aspects or meanings in
ways that correspond to the state of affairs outside

44

the mind, it attains truth; when it does not, it fails
to attain true knowledge, and any statement based on
its erroneous composition of concepts must therefore be
regarded as false. Falsity is the absence of conformity between object and subject, whereas truth is the
presence of such conformity.

Types of Concepts

It has been stated above that the intellect is
able to form a wide variety of concepts, and it is now
time to explain their more important types. One way of
doing so is in terms of the process by which the intellect forms its concepts, usually referred to as abstraction, and represented by the broken line connecting
the 'intellect' box with the 'internal senses' box in
the diagram on p. 43 (§7.4, §25.2). To abstract is to
pull out, or to extract, one or other intelligible content or meaning that can be seen to be contained in a
percept, while leaving aside everything else that may
be present in it. As might be suspected, there are
various degrees of abstractness, depending on how much
the intellect leaves aside the concrete and individual
aspects contained in the percepts it considers. Three
orders or degrees of abstraction are commonly enumerated, and these suffice to distinguish concepts into
three types, namely, natural or physical concepts,
mathematical concepts, and metaphysical concepts, each
of which will now be explained.

Consider the percepts represented by such expressions as 'this yellow sulphur' and 'this lead ball,'
and then the concepts that may be formed from them.
Sulphur and lead are natural or physical objects that
exist outside the mind, and so the concepts we form to
understand them may be spoken of as natural or physical
concepts. Examples would be 'sulphur,' 'yellow,' or
'element,' related to the sulphur, or 'lead,' 'heavy,'
or 'hot,' related to the lead. What one does when he
forms concepts such as these is leave aside all of the
individual characteristics associated with the 'this'
of the percept, and grasp a meaning that is common to
all classes of objects that would share these characteristics. The concepts formed, it should be noted,
all imply some reference to sensible matter, i.e., to
material things that fall under the senses, but they
abstract from, or leave aside, individual or singular
characteristics. The resulting type of abstraction from
matter is referred to as physical abstraction, and it is
used in all of the natural sciences as well as in ordinary knowledge.

45

Mathematical concepts are more abstract than physical concepts, for the simple reason that more matter is left aside when the former are grasped by the intellect than the latter (§13.4, §63.3). Consider, for example, the perceptual basis represented by the expressions 'this lead ball' and 'these five crystals of sulphur,' and then the concepts of 'sphere' and 'five' that may be abstracted from this ball and from that number of crystals. 'Sphere' and 'five' are mathematical concepts; they do not refer to any individual sphere or five, but to all classes of objects that share the respective quantitative shape or number. Neither do they contain any reference to sensible matter, in the sense that 'sphere' does not connote that the object is made of lead or of wood, but merely that it is composed of continuous quantity, an imaginable matter made of pure extension, if you will, but not one that has the sensible qualities usually associated with lead or wood. Similarly the concept 'five' contains no reference to the sensible objects from which it is abstracted, and so it too is composed of units that are only imaginable. Because of its greater abstractness, one could say that 'sphere' is a more intelligible concept than 'ball,' in the sense that it leaves aside all the imperfections usually associated with sensible matter such as lead, and can be conceptualized as perfectly fulfilling the definition that every point on its surface is at exactly the same distance from its center. In this way of looking at things, mathematical concepts are more intelligible than physical concepts insofar as they are more removed from sensible matter, which is a source of contingency and even imperfection when compared to pure quantitative extension.

Metaphysical concepts, finally, have more in common with mathematical than they do with physical concepts, since they are the most abstract of all, so much so that they are usually spoken of as being separated from matter entirely, i.e., as not including any reference whatever to sensible or even to imaginable matter (§30.1-3). Examples of such concepts would be 'being,' 'substance,' and 'existent.' Such concepts express an intelligible content of sulphur and lead, since both of the latter are beings and substances, and both have existence in the extramental sense. Metaphysical concepts, so characterized, are very general, moreover, and can apply across the entire range of beings, even to things that are incorporeal and immaterial, should such exist. Little need be said about them here, since philosophy of science is concerned mainly with physical and mathematical concepts, but they do serve our pur-

46

poses by illustrating how concepts of various types can be distinguished on the basis of their abstractness or degree of separation from the matter that is directly perceived in sense experience.

All three types of concepts, it should be stressed, are the product of intellectual activity, and as such they exist in the intellect or in the mind. The objects they represent, however, exist outside the knower or outside the mind. Granted that the mode of existence of the object outside the mind is different from the intentional existence of its formal representation or concept in the mind, there is still a correspondence or equivalence between them. It is on this basis that all of the concepts discussed so far can be regarded as *real* concepts. They are real in the sense that they exist in the mind, but their content also exists in some way outside the mind. This point is of extreme importance for developing a realist philosophy of science. For our purposes, therefore, real when applied to intellectual knowledge will henceforth always have a twofold reference: it will refer to something that, as known, exists in the intellect, and that, as extramental, also exists outside the intellect.

Having defined knowledge as the presence of an object in a subject, and real concepts as representations in the mind of forms that exist outside the mind, the question arises whether there can be any concepts that are not real in this sense. The common answer to this is affirmative, because it is possible for the intellect to formulate concepts that have no direct extramental reference but that serve a useful purpose in putting order into the concepts that do. This second broad class of concepts are spoken of as *logical* concepts. One could say that such concepts designate beings or entities that exist in the mind, and for this reason they can be referred to as "beings of reason" (*entia rationis*). They may also be thought of as having an intentional character, since they have an intentional mode of existence that is similar to that of real concepts. To differentiate them from the latter, however, they are called "second intentions" and real concepts are spoken of as "first intentions." A second intention, in this way of speaking, is based on a first intention, or builds on a first intention, usually by manifesting some way in which it is related to other concepts (§2.2, §6).

Some examples may suffice to clarify this difference between real concepts, which stand for or represent

47

entities that exist outside the mind, and logical concepts, which designate entities whose only existence is in the mind. Consider the statement 'sulphur is yellow' and compare it with the statements 'sulphur is a *subject*' and 'yellow is a *predicate*.' We have already given reasons for holding that 'sulphur' and 'yellow' are real concepts; now we point to *'subject'* and *'predicate'* as being examples of logical concepts. To say 'sulphur is a *subject*' is to say nothing about sulphur as it exists extramentally, but it is to say something about how it is related to the concept 'yellow' when the mind forms the proposition 'sulphur is yellow.' The term *'subject*,' therefore, represents a logical concept. Another example: suppose one wishes to take the statement, 'all sulphur is yellow,' and reverse the order of the subject and predicate while still preserving the truth of the statement. He can do so by converting the *'all* sulphur is yellow' into the statement, *'some* yellow is sulphur.' The *all* and the *some* he then uses are logical concepts: the mind makes them up so as to quantify or modify its real concepts and preserve a true relationship between them when their position in a proposition is changed.

Again: consider the statements 'man is an animal' and 'man is a *species*,' meaning by *species* a class that contains only numerically distinct individuals; or 'animal is a sentient organism' and 'animal is a *genus*,' meaning by *genus* a class that contains things different in kind as well as numerically distinct from each other. Here *genus* and *species* are logical concepts, for although men and animals exist extramentally, *genus* and *species* have essentially the same character as *subject* and *predicate*: they tell us how such concepts as 'man' and 'animal' are related to other concepts, without telling us anything about a man or an animal in its extramental existence (§8).

More sophisticated examples can be taken from any logic book, most of whose technical terms stand for logical concepts. We shall have occasion to refer later to concepts of this type that explain how propositions, rather than concepts or terms, stand in relation to one another (§65.4). For example, one can consider the complex statement, 'this is lead *and* this is heavy.' The *and* here is a logical concept that connects the two propositions making up the complex statement. One concern of logicians is how to define the truth and falsity of a compound proposition of this type in terms of the truth and falsity of the components that make it up. Such a compound proposition can alternatively be written

48

in the form *'p and q,'* where *p* stands for the first component, *q* the second, and *and* the relation that obtains between them. Logicians define important characteristics of this relation, called conjunction, that are independent of the contents of the propositions *p* and *q*, and are a function only of their truth and falsity. Another complex proposition that assumes importance in what follows is the statement: *'if* this is lead, *then* this is heavy; *and* this is lead; *therefore* this is heavy.' Here the italicized terms *'if,'* *'then,'* *'and,'* *'therefore,'* as previously, all designate logical concepts. One can again use a variable, *'p,'* to stand for the statement 'this is lead,' and another variable *'q,'* to stand for the statement 'this is heavy.' Then he can reformulate the complex statement just given as:

if p, then q; and p; therefore q.

This is a logical statement, all of whose terms stand for logical concepts, and whose verification pertains to the science of logic.

The various types of concepts discussed to this point may now be tabulated as in the diagram on the following page. All of the entries to the left of the vertical double line pertain to the perceptual order, and therefore they designate extramental objects perceived by the senses, as schematized in the two boxes to the left of the diagram on p. 43; all of the entries to the right of the double line, on the other hand, represent concepts, and thus they refer to the contents of the 'intellect' box on the right of the same diagram. Concepts between the vertical double line and the vertical single line are real concepts, whereas those to the right of the vertical single line are logical concepts. Real concepts are further subdivided into physical, mathematical, and metaphysical, as indicated, with the progression from top to bottom being in the order of greater abstraction from matter.

Scientific Concepts

Practically everything that has been stated thus far pertains to ordinary experience and thus does not require any special knowledge of science to be understood. The concepts employed in science, of course, are partly those of ordinary experience, but in addition to these there are other more technical concepts that now require explanation. Two classes of such con-

49

TYPES OF CONCEPTS		
OUTSIDE MIND	INSIDE MIND	
	REAL CONCEPTS	LOGICAL CONCEPTS
this yellow sulphur ⏎ this lead ball	PHYSICAL ⏎ sulphur yellow element ⏎ lead heavy hot ⏎ MATHEMATICAL ⏎ sphere five ⏎ METAPHYSICAL ⏎ being substance existent	*subject* *predicate* ⏎ *all* *some* ⏎ *genus* *species* ⏎ *p and q* ⏎ *if p, then q; and p; therefore q*

cepts are metrical concepts and theoretical concepts.
These are of special importance since scientists make
extensive use of measurements, and for these must employ metrical concepts, and also tend to theorize when
putting order into their measurements, and for such
speculation make use of theoretical concepts.

A metrical concept, as the name implies, is one
that expresses the result of a measuring operation or
measurement, a process that will be examined in detail
in Essay 5 below (§67.3). For the time being it suffices to note that a metrical concept combines the content of a mathematical concept with that of a physical
concept, since it designates how a number is applied to
a quantifiable aspect of a physical object. This quantifiable aspect is initially something observable and
so falls in one way or another under the senses. Usually objects of ordinary experience are selected, on

the basis of convention, to furnish units to which numbers can subsequently be applied so as to obtain a
measurement. The meter bar, for example, has been so
selected to determine the unit of length. Were one to
inquire about the size of the lead ball already referred to, he could use a calipers to measure its diameter
and come up with the result, say, of '7.2 centimeters.'
The measurement '7.2 cm.' is what we shall understand
by a metrical concept. It contains a number, sometimes
further specified by the limits of accuracy to which it
has been ascertained, such as '7.2 ± 0.1,' plus a unit,
in this case the centimeter, or hundredth of a meter.
Similarly one could weight the lead ball to determine
its gravity or weight, and obtain the result '524 gm.'
This again is a metrical concept, combining the number
524 with the unit of weight, the gram. Alternatively,
to further specify how hot the lead ball might be, one
could measure its temperature and get the result, '70
degrees Celsius,' which again is a metrical concept.

   One great advantage of metrical concepts is that
they enable one to associate mathematical concepts and
operations with physical phenomena, and thus make the
latter more tractable for purposes of calculation.
Viewed in another way, they seem to confer greater in-
telligibility and greater objectivity on the physical
concepts for which they are more or less obvious counterparts. They do this, moreover, without being less
real than physical concepts, even though they involve a
component that is more abstract. If the lead ball is
actually 7.2 cm. in diameter, for example, then the
'7.2 cm.' qualifies as a real concept -- according to
our definition of the real. Again, to make the statement, 'the lead ball is 7.2 cm. in diameter,' is to
make a true statement, or to attain truth, whereas to
say 'the lead ball is 5.0 cm. in diameter' is to utter
a falsehood. Thus metrical concepts provide a basis
for determining the truth about reality in ways that
are not essentially different from the physical concepts already discussed.

   Another advantage of metrical concepts is that
they can serve to extend the domain of the physical into the areas of the very small and the very large.
Once a unit has been specified on the basis of sense
observation, it is possible to assign a number to it
that might correspond to a reality that is not directly
perceptible by the senses but is nonetheless measurable.
For example, suppose that one had determined that a
monochromatic yellow light ray has a wavelength that is

very small compared to the meter, but that could be
measured in terms of a unit that is 10^{-10} meter long,
or one ten billionth of a meter, called the Angstrom
unit (written Å). By a method of indirect measurement,
say, one might determine that the wavelength of this
particular light ray is 5745 Å. The unit, and the
wavelength so measured, are certainly invisible, and
yet this does not make them unreal or make statements
concerning them untrue. The same could be said about
the domain of the very large, such as is treated, for
example, in astronomy. One might measure a length or
distance that is exorbitantly great in terms of direct
sense experience by using the light-year, i.e., the
distance light will travel in one year. One cannot see
a light-year in the same way as one can see a meter
bar, and yet he can speak meaningfully and truthfully
about distances measured in terms of it, the same as he
can of lengths measured by the Angstrom unit.

Theoretical concepts, from the viewpoint of a
realist philosophy of science, are more problematical
than metrical concepts, but they provide very powerful
tools for the investigation of reality and so are de-
serving of careful attention. Just as metrical concepts combine elements of the physical and the mathematical, so theoretical concepts combine elements of the
physical and the logical, and frequently of the mathematical as well. The intriguing problem that presents
itself in connection with theoretical concepts is
whether they represent something that exists outside
the mind, and so can be regarded as real, or merely
represent a 'being of reason' (an *ens rationis*) and so
have only a fictional existence, i.e., in the mind
alone and not extramentally. While one is seeking an
answer to this question it is convenient to think of
theoretical concepts, from the realist point of view,
as designating entities that are "candidates for existence." The problem is resolved when one is able to
disengage the physical content (or the physical-mathem-
matical content) of the theoretical concept from the
logical apparatus in which it is embedded -- usually
some type of hypothetical reasoning. If the concept
cannot be so disengaged it remains problematical, and
can be thought of as a hypothetical concept that may or
may not have reference to an actually existing entity
(§67.6-7).

Because of the role hypothetical reasoning plays
in adjudicating the ontological (or real) status of
theoretical entities, it is important for us to examine

52

the nature and validity of hypothetical arguments. As
has already been explained, these can be expressed in
the logical form, *'if p, then q; and p; therefore q.'*
At this point, because of our concern with questions of
truth, it is convenient to introduce another logical
relation, that of negation, and show how it can be incorporated in various ways into the above complex expression. Assume that the proposition *p* stands for
'this is lead' or, alternatively, 'it is the case that
this is lead': then the negation of this proposition,
written *non-p*, stands for 'this is not lead' or 'it is
not the case that this is lead.' This terminology
presupposed, logicians are able to show that there are
only two universally valid forms of hypothetical argument (§7.10), as follows:

if p, then q; and p; therefore q (1)

if p, then q; and non-q; therefore non-p (2)

These may be illustrated with the following simple examples: (1) if it is raining, then the ground is wet;
and it is raining; therefore the ground is wet. (2)
if it is raining, then the ground is wet; and the
ground is not wet; therefore it is not raining. In
both cases *p* may be referred to as the antecedent of
the argument and *q* as the consequent. An argument of
form (1) determines the truth of the consequent by establishing the truth of the antecedent, whereas an argument of form (2) determines the falsity of the antecedent by establishing the falsity of the consequent.
For our later purposes it is important to note that
form (2) can be used to falsify a hypothesis or antecedent in terms of the known falsity of the consequent,
but form (1) cannot be used to verify a hypothesis or
antecedent, since it assumes the truth of the antecedent in order to verify the consequent. Hence form
(2) lends itself to the process of falsifying an hypothesis, known as falsification, but form (1) cannot be
used for the process known as verifying an hypothesis,
or verification, although it has other uses, as will
be explained presently.

Apart from the two valid forms of hypothetical
argument just explained, there are two invalid forms
that involve fallacies or fallacious reasoning, and
these should now be explained. The fallacies are the
following:

if p, then q; and non-p; therefore non-q (3)

53

$$if\ p,\ then\ q;\ and\ q;\ therefore\ p \qquad (4)$$

Examples of these are the following: (3) if it is raining, then the ground is wet; and it is not raining;
therefore the ground is not wet. (4) if it is raining,
then the ground is wet; and the ground is wet; therefore it is raining. Form (3) expresses the fallacy
known as "denying the antecedent" and form (4) expresses the fallacy known as "affirming the consequent." The reasoning in both cases is fallacious, as
can be seen by evaluating it in terms of the conditions
that are necessary to have a true argument. As stated,
for example, the condition 'if it is raining' is *sufficient* to explain the consequent 'the ground is wet,'
but it is not *necessary* to explain it, since the
ground could be made wet by another cause, for example,
sprinkling the lawn. A conditional statement, however,
merely states that the antecedent is sufficient to explain the consequent, without asserting that it is
necessary to do so. For forms (3) and (4) to be true,
one would have to show that p was *both sufficient and
necessary* to imply q, and the argument would then be
expressible in the stronger form, *'if and only if p,
then q.'* If one could make this stronger statement,
logicians are able to show that form (4) would then
become equivalent to form (1), and one would be able
to verify hypotheses as well as falsify them. The
usual way in which conditions that are necessary as
well as sufficient can be known is through identification of a proper cause-effect relationship, such that
a unique cause is seen as required to explain a particular effect. This is why causality is so important
in scientific explanation, a point stressed frequently
in subsequent essays.

Now, as it turns out, the overwhelming majority
of scientific arguments do not use any of the four
forms given above. Instead they use a form similar to
(4), which may be written as follows:

$$if\ p,\ then\ q;\ and\ q;\ therefore\ possibly\ p \qquad (5)$$

This form is generally used when the entity or situation designated by p is not directly observable or
measurable, whereas some other state of affairs that p
would be sufficient to explain, namely q, is directly
observable or measurable. In such an event one can
use observation and measurement to identify possible
realities that otherwise are unobservable and unmeas-
urable. The fact that a hypothesis entails a proposi-

54

tion whose truth is testable by measurement or experiment seems to lend support to one's accepting the truth of the hypothesis, at least as a real possibility. Moreover, should one be able to formulate a hypothesis that has a large number of testable consequents, and should each of these consequents in turn be verified, then one would be inclined to accept the truth of the hypothesis as more than possible, and even as probable (§67.1). Such a situation would suggest a type of argument that may be formulated differently from (5), which could be written:

$$if \; p, \; then \; q_1, \; q_2, \; q_3 \; \cdots \; q_n; \; and \; q_1, \; q_2,$$

$$q_3 \; \cdots \; q_n; \; therefore \; probably \; p \qquad (6)$$

Here the p, as previously, indicates the hypothesis, and the various q's, numbered from 1 to n, designate a series of consequents that are testable or measurable. When all of these, upon test, have been verified experimentally, and especially when the numbered consequents pertain to different domains of experience, the hypothesis would appear to be not merely a real possibility but to be, in fact, probably true.

Finally, if an argument of form (6) is combined with that of form (2), which enables one to reject or falsify hypotheses that do not yield verified consequents, then a methodology would be set out whereby one could eliminate false hypotheses and at the same time retain those that are more and more confirmed and therefore have greater and greater chance of being true. There is no simple way in which such probability can be calculated in terms of the number of confirming instances (n), but the considered judgment of the scientific community accords many propositions that are so confirmed a degree of verisimilitude approaching truth, and these are commonly regarded as constituting the body of scientific knowledge.

To return now to theoretical concepts, such concepts initially have the status of theoretical concepts, or concepts formulated or constructed as part of a hypothesis. They frequently function also as explanatory concepts, since they serve to explain why certain statements, usually employing observable or metrical concepts, are true or are otherwise thought to be valid generalizations. The theoretical concepts that are of particular interest for a realist philosophy of science are those that designate theoretical

55

entities, which we have already referred to as candidates for existence. Some examples may now make clear the sense in which such entities are candidates of this type, and how the question of their existential status is finally resolved.

Theoretical Entities

The observable features of things, such as yellow, heavy, and hot, have aroused curiosity for centuries, so that it is not surprising that the history of science is replete with explanatory concepts that have been proposed to account for them. It is not unusual, moreover, that such explanatory concepts have associated with them hidden or unseen entities, and thus the problem arises whether these entities are mere fictions created by the mind, or whether they exist, or at least have counterparts that exist, outside the mind. For instance, to explain why some objects of experience are hotter than others, it was early hypothesized that the hotter objects might contain more of an invisible substance known as phlogiston, which had some peculiar properties such as negative weight, than objects containing less heat. Later, on the basis of experiments performed with combustible substances, the hypothesis was offered that a quite different substance, also invisible but with a positive weight, called oxygen, could explain most of the phenomena that phlogiston had previously been invoked to explain. Again, rather than propose that heat itself is caused by the presence of a substance whose essence it is to be hot, such as phlogiston, it was further proposed that heat might be caused by the motion of the minute particles of which material substances are composed, called molecules. This last proposal, referred to as kinetic theory or the molecular theory of heat, is accepted in the present day as the best explanation of ordinary phenomena involving the generation of heat and the presence of varying degrees of heat in the objects of experience.

The theoretical concepts 'phlogiston,' 'oxygen,' and 'molecule' all designate entities whose existence is not immediately apparent but which, because of their explanatory force, were regarded by those who first proposed them as candidates for existence. With the progress of science, however, 'phlogiston' has come to be regarded as a concept that designated a fictive entity, a being of reason (*ens rationis*) if you will, and is no longer thought of as a real substance. On

56

the other hand, 'oxygen' and 'molecule' have enjoyed a better fate: they are still mentioned in science text-books, and most scientists regard them as being just as real as the objects of ordinary experience. Hence 'phlogiston,' which was first proposed as part of a logical schema of the *'if p, then q'* type, has been relegated to the same domain as the logical concepts with which it was first associated, whereas 'oxygen' and 'molecule' have seemingly passed out of the logical domain and are now entertained as real concepts, as having extramental counterparts to the same degree as sulphur and lead.

Similar examples may be drawn from the field of astronomy. At one time, in order to explain the seem-ingly erratic movement of the planets against the back-ground of the fixed stars, it was hypothesized that planets were carried along by an elaborate series of rotating circles or mechanisms referred to as 'eccen-trics' and 'epicycles' (see Essay 8). Astronomers ar-gued about the ontological status of these rotating mechanisms, some proposing that they were merely con-venient fictions that enabled one to calculate the pos-itions of the planets, others regarding them as real and speculating about the materials of which they might be composed and how they could propel planets along in their orbits. Later, after detailed observations of the planet Mars had been made, it was argued that plan-ets move in paths that are elliptical, and that their motions could be explained on the supposition that planets are massive objects like earth urged along by the 'force of gravity' and 'inertia.' Again, to ex-plain irregularities in the motion of the planet Uran-us, it was hypothesized that these were caused by the gravitational attraction of a planet too far out in the solar system to be seen, called 'Neptune.' Alterna-tively, to explain irregularities in the motion of the planet Mercury, it was postulated that these were caus-ed by a hidden planet, called 'Vulcan,' too close to the sun to be observed, but nonetheless a candidate for real existence.

Here, as in the previous cases, some of these theoretical entities have survived the passage of time and are still thought to have real existence as well as explanatory value, whereas others have been discarded as constructs that at one time were useful for predict-ing phenomena but no longer have extramental existence. So now one finds no mention of 'eccentrics,' 'epicyc-les,' and 'Vulcan' in astronomy textbooks, whereas 'force of gravity,' 'inertia,' and 'Neptune' are still very much a part of the science of our day.

Many of the essays in this book, and especially those in Part III, analyze in detail the line of reasoning that enables one to disengage a theoretical concept from the hypothetical schema in which it was first entrenched and to see it as designating a really existent entity. Usually such disengagement requires the process known as demonstration (§12), described in Essay 7, which is equivalent to developing a valid '*if and only if*' type of argument that makes joint use of forms (1) and (4) of hypothetical reasoning described above. Somewhat easier to see is the type of reasoning that enables one to reject hypothetical entities as merely fictive and as not enjoying extramental existence. This usually employs form (2) of the hypothetical argument, for the rejected entities all imply testable consequences that are found not to be true, and thus they too are "falsified" and seen not to exist.

Apart from these two possibilities for theoretical entities, viz, that they either are accepted into the domain of the real along with more directly observable and measurable objects or are rejected from this domain and relegated to that of the logical, there is a final possibility: the entity may remain merely a candidate for existence, retaining a problematic status somewhere between the real and the logical, but not yet accepted with certainty by the scientific community. 'Quarks' and 'black holes' are entities of this latter type, and one can readily understand why they provoke great interest and discussion among scientists and philosophers of science alike. For our purposes it may suffice to mention one epistemological value of such problematic entities that is elaborated on in Essay 10, namely, their use in modeling the real and thus as supplying analogical insights into the structure of matter and the universe (§67.7).

This modeling value of theoretical concepts may be explained by the use of a homely example, that of the 'mermaid.' According to the usual account, mermaids were thought to exist because sailors, after long months at sea and when observing under adverse conditions of distance and at dusk, saw beings nursing their young at the breast, with long hair and fish-like tails that came into view when they dove beneath the surface. In order to explain these appearances, the sailors constructed an explanatory concept by putting together two concepts of which they had previous experience, namely, 'fish' and 'woman,' and arrived at the construct 'mermaid.' Thus 'mermaid' became a candidate for existence, but not in a complete and absolute sense, since the sailors were sure that they had observed something, though they were not sure of what it was. Their problem focused on the nature rather than on the existence of what they had seen, and hence their construct was formulated to explain the entity's nature rather than its existence. Their problem was solved, it is commonly acknowledged, with the identification of a manatee-like mammal called the dugong, which, when viewed under conditions approximating those of sailors at sea, were found to explain the phenomena they had observed.

A somewhat similar situation exists with the theoretical entities known as elementary particles and discussed in Essay 9, an example of which would be the 'electron.' The 'electron' is a very useful concept for explaining electrical and magnetic phenomena, to say nothing of light and colors such as the yellow associated with sulphur. As a theoretical entity it enjoys a status much like that of the 'molecule,' for it is generally accepted among scientists as having extramental existence. When trying to discover more about the nature of electrons, however, investigators have encountered puzzling phenomena, including some in which electrons apparently behave like waves and others in which they behave like particles. To explain these phenomena, therefore, they formulate a construct that combines features of both, and so give rise to the theoretical concept, 'wave-particle.' One can go on from there, obviously, and formulate a proposition such as: 'the electron is a wave-particle.' And 'wave-particle' turns out to be a very useful construct, for it suggests a large number of mathematical calculations and predictions that can render an account of the metrical aspects of electronic phenomena, most of which can be tested experimentally and verified according to form (6) of the hypothetical reasoning explained above. Yet despite such extensive verification, 'wave-particle' remains a problematic concept in that it is still enmeshed in the logical apparatus of the form (6) type of reasoning. Its status is only probable, even though that of electron might be quite certain. However, granted that 'wave-particle' does not tell the whole truth about electron, it nonetheless furnishes an insight into what an electron might be, as is explained more fully in Essay 10. It is in this sense that 'wave-particle' can be thought of as modeling 'electron' in much the same way as 'mermaid' functioned as a prelim-

59

inary model (admittedly poor) of 'dugong.'

Theoretical constructs of this type are useful
for investigating the domain of the very large as well
as that of the very small. For example, it is generally acknowledged that planets and stars are massive objects in the heavens, that they have weight or gravity.
Although 'weight' and 'gravity' are concepts that are
well understood, however, the cause of gravity has
turned out to be much more problematic. As explained
in Essay 8, Newton spoke of 'gravitational attraction'
and speculated as to whether or not the 'pull of gravity' is real without committing himself to a definitive
answer. Some two and a half centuries later, after
having studied gravitational phenomena more extensively,
Einstein proposed a quite different explanatory concept.
He did so by taking two apparently well known concepts,
'space' and 'time,' and making from these the theoretical construct, 'space-time.' This suggested mathematical calculations and predictions, much like those generated from the construct 'wave-particle,' which have
subsequently been verified, and thus give 'space-time'
a probable status analogous to that of 'wave-particle.'
One need not hold that 'space-time' is fully real, however, for indeed the concepts gets its meaning and in-
telligibility only in the context of form (6) type of
reasoning. Yet it is generally acknowledged that such
a construct furnishes some insight into the reality
behind gravity and gravitational phenomena, much as did
Newton's earlier construct of 'pull of gravity,' though
admittedly in a different way.

To bring together all that has been stated about
types of concepts used in scientific as well as in ordinary discourse, we have drawn up the table on the
facing page. This is similar to that on p. 50, in that
it includes many of the entries in the previous table,
with the more scientific concepts now added. The various columns are numbered, and one can see that physical concepts have been expanded to include columns [2],
[3], and [4], listing observable, metrical, and theoretical concepts respectively. In the case of theoretical concepts [4], arrows have been added to each of the
concepts suggesting that they are now generally regarded as real (thus: ←molecule), or as beings of reason
similar to logical concepts (thus: phlogiston→), or as
entities with a problematic status whose ontological
reference is still undecided (thus: ←wave-particle→).
It is the concepts listed in column [4] that generate
most of the literature in the philosophy of science,
and that will be discussed more fully in the essays

60

TYPES OF CONCEPTS

OUTSIDE MIND Extramental Reality	INSIDE MIND but also exists in some way outside mind REAL CONCEPTS			INSIDE MIND but not outside mind LOGICAL CONCEPTS
[1] Perceptual Order	PHYSICAL CONCEPTS [2] Observable	[3] Metrical	[4] Theoretical	[5]
this yellow sulphur	sulphur yellow element	5745 Å	←molecule ←electron ←wave— particle→	*p* *non-p* *p and q* *if p, then q;* *and p;* *therefore q*
this lead ball	lead heavy hot	7.2 cm. 524 gm. 70° C.	←pull of gravity→ phlogiston→	*if p, then q;* *and non-q;* *therefore non-p*
this planet Mars	planet movement oval path	ellipse	eccentrics→ epicycles→ ←space→ time→	*if p, then* $q_1, q_2 . . . q_n;$ *and* $q_1, q_2 . . . q_n;$ *therefore* *probably p*
this sea mammal	woman fish dugong		mermaid→	
	MATHEMATICAL CONCEPTS	sphere five set		*zero* *null-set*

that follow.

Metaphysical Concepts

This suffices for a general introduction to the problem of conceptual knowledge and the natural and scientific concepts with which we shall be most concerned. For completeness, however, and to prepare the way for the discussion of problems of ultimate explanation that will be broached in Part V, a final word may be said about metaphysical concepts. Such concepts, as explained earlier, differ from physical and mathematical concepts in that they are most abstract, leaving aside all reference to matter, so that they can be regarded as separated from matter entirely (§30.2). In this class of concepts two are of perennial philosophical interest, namely, the concepts of 'God' and of 'soul.' The full discussion of these concepts pertain to other courses in philosophy, but they can be related to the foregoing discussion by regarding them after the fashion of theoretical entities or hypothetical concepts, as we shall now explain.

By the use of negation, one can construct a meaningful conceptual framework based on ordinary experience, involving such concepts as 'incorporeal' (non-corporeal), 'immaterial' (non-material), 'immutable' (non-mutable), and so on. Similarly, by extending our concepts of power and knowledge, we can formulate notions such as 'omnipotent' (all-powerful), 'omniscient' (all-knowing), etc. (§44). These concepts permit the development of terminology sometimes referred to as "God-talk" that provides the basis for theological discourse. From the viewpoint adopted in this essay, however, the concept of 'God' may be seen as a hypothetical concept that makes reference to a theoretical entity, in the sense that God is not directly observable or measurable, and yet can be thought of as a 'candidate for existence.' The traditional proofs for the existence of God, viewed in this context, then become ways of disengaging the concept of 'God' from the logical schemata in which it can be enmeshed, and showing that God exists not only in the mind but outside the mind also (§43). The process of demonstration is applicable here, just as it is in demonstrating the existence of elementary particles (see Essay 7). Further problems associated with this process are discussed in Essays 14 through 16, at the end of the volume.

Similarly, the concept of 'soul' gets one involved in notions such as 'invisible,' 'intangible,' 'immortal,' and so on (§22, §29). The way in which this concept may be related to the study of man is discussed briefly in Essay 11. Again, in the context of this essay, the human soul may be viewed as a theoretical entity whose extramental existence requires demonstration. The techniques of demonstrating the existence of God and of soul are, of course, quite different from those employed in the natural sciences. Yet both are concepts that are not completely unrelated to the work of the scientist, as suggested in the essays that make up Parts IV and V of this book. In fact, the logical and methodological problems that arise when scientists consider the "hidden entities" that serve to explain the world of nature turn out to be essentially the very problems whose solution can bring them to the threshold of metaphysics itself.

PART II

METHODOLOGY IN SCIENCE

THREE VIEWS OF
SCIENTIFIC METHOD

I T is frequently said of St. Thomas Aquinas that the man has been lost behind the voluminous quantity of his writing. Commenting further on this literary output of the Common Doctor, one could say that his valuable contributions to the development of physical science have been lost in the great mass of his writing on theology and philosophy. In this vein, it might not be amiss to bring out of the shadows cast by Aquinas' more famous works a few specimens of his thought on the subject of scientific knowledge, contributions that, had they been those of a lesser genius, might have been appreciated the more by assessors of the medieval scientific tradition.

To those who are friends and admirers of St. Thomas, no apology is needed for treating the question of his basic theory of physical knowledge. But even should the reader make no commitment whatsoever to Thomism, it could well be profitable to reconsider some of the perennial problems of the universe in the light of Aquinas' conception of physical science. Such a consideration need not be anachronistic. As Burtt has pointed out in his *Metaphysical Foundations of Modern Science,* every age has its unconscious presuppositions, and these can sometimes be brought to light by setting off current views against those of an earlier period, when prevailing notions were not so commonly entertained.[1] And if every age has its hidden presuppositions, it is also true that every age has its problems—not unconnected, possibly, with these same suppositions. We in America are now very much preoccupied with the study of the physical universe: on the surface, great progress is being made in science and technology, but at the heart of the matter, when scientists ask how much is really known about the world in which we live, there is a gnawing doubt that makes itself increasingly felt about our ability ever to reach any definitive answers. It is on such a problem of the validity of scientific knowledge that Thomas Aquinas may have something worthwhile to offer to the modern mind, and this proposal will therefore be the burden of our study.

St. Thomas Aquinas (1225-1274)

The intellectual atmosphere that Aquinas breathed at the University of Paris in the mid-thirteenth century was not sympathetic to natural science; in fact, it was markedly hostile to the influx of Aristotelian and Arabian thought into Western Europe—an influx that brought with it much of the scientific learning of the ancient world. This attitude of hostility at Paris, however, was not apparent at the other great center of studies in medieval Christendom, Oxford University. There the discovery of Aristotle's logical works, and particularly the translation of the *Posterior Analytics* (with commentary) by Robert Grosseteste, Bishop of Lincoln (1175-1253), had stimulated great interest in a type of mathematical physics which accented studies in optical science.[2] This had resulted in what Baeumker has called a " metaphysics of light," a philosophy immediately put to the service of theology to develop the

---

[1] E. A. Burtt, (London: 1932), pp. 15-17.

[2] A. C. Crombie, *Robert Grosseteste and the Origins of Experimental Science,* (Oxford: 1953), pp. 91-134.

Christian Platonism of the Oxford school.[3] What is of more importance, however, in this scientific revival at Oxford was its insistence on the role of mathematics in physical proof. In this school a pure mathematical structure was commonly conceived as objectively existing in things, before their physical properties, and giving the only adequate explanation of observed reality. Possibly through Roger Bacon, the influence of Grosseteste's work was gradually felt on the continent, and provoked a decided reaction from the pen of St. Albert the Great (1206-1280), the teacher of St. Thomas Aquinas. Albert himself, unique among the Paris Masters, had been sympathetic to the influx of Aristotelian thought, had done extensive observational and experimental work in biology, meteorology and alchemy, and had reconstructed a physical theory from Aristotle's *Physics* that was opposed to the mathematical realism of the Oxford school.[4] The young Aquinas then built upon Albert's foundations, and elaborated this theory that was primarily physical, but at the same time allowed for a legitimate use of mathematics in obtaining strict physical explanation or proof.[5]

For Aquinas, as for Albert, mathematical structure is not imposed on reality by the mind, but rather is abstracted from reality by a mental process that leaves aside all the irregularities of matter and the flux of movement and time. More basic than this mathematical structure is the physical nature of the reality studied, which is determined to express itself in a certain figure—by which, for example, we can easily recognize a horse, and distinguish it from a cow. The quantitative characteristics that are thus expressive of a type are not themselves mathematical entities, but rather are physical ones,

[3] C. Baeumker, "Der Platonismus im Mittelalter," in Studien und Charakteristiken zur Geschichte der Philosophie insbesondere des Mittelalters, *Beiträge zur Geschichte der Philosophie des Mittelalters*, Bd. 25, 1-2, Münster-i-W.: 1927, p. 160 ff.

[4] J. A. Weisheipl, O. P., "Albertus Magnus and the Oxford Platonists," *Proceedings of the American Catholic Philosophical Association*, Vol. 32 (1958), pp. 124-139.

[5] J. A. Weisheipl, O. P., *The Development of Physical Theory in the Middle Ages*, (London: 1959), pp. 27-62.

although originative sources of the idealized static structure studied by the mathematician. Thus, in Aquinas' view, the insight afforded by mathematics is not deeper—or more " divine," as the Platonists would have it—but actually is more superficial than a physical insight. As a consequence, explanation through mathematics does not explain the physical nature, but it does accurately describe that nature, and it can help in discovering a physical explanation or proof.[6]

The help that mathematics gives to the physicist was conceived by Aquinas as being of two kinds, one which functions at the level of hypothesis to suggest *possible* physical explanations, the other which functions conjointly with physical reasoning to give *conclusive* explanation or proof.[7] An example of the first would be the Thomistic evaluation of Ptolemy's explanation of the motion of the heavens through eccentrics and epicycles. Viewed mathematically, Aquinas noted, the observed appearances of the stars result " either from the motion of the object seen or from the motion of the observer, . . . it makes no difference which is moving." [8] But as a physical explanation he showed considerable reserve towards the Ptolemaic hypotheses, noting that while they do account for the stellar appearances, " we must not say that they are thereby proved to be facts, because perhaps it would be possible to explain the apparent movements of the stars by some other method which men have not yet thought out." [9] His whole treatment of astronomical and meteorological problems, in fact, seems aimed at correcting a naive mathematicism among medieval Aristotelians, for he points out that Aristotle, in dealing with the heavenly spheres, had mistaken a suppositional theory for established fact.[10] He himself is at pains to elaborate the reasons why we cannot have certain judgments about the heavenly bodies; [11] yet, he observes, it is not stupid or neces-

[6] Cf. *In I de Caelo*, lect. 1, n. 2, and lect. 3, n. 6; *In II Phys.*, lect. 3; *Summa Theologiae*, I, q. 1, a. 1, ad 2.

[7] Cf. *Summa Theologiae*, I, q. 32, a. 1, ad 2; *In II Phys.*, lect. 3, n. 9.

[8] *In II de Caelo*, lect. II, n. 2, and lect. 12, n. 4.

[9] *Ibid.*, lect. 17, n. 2.   [10] *Ibid.*   [11] *Ibid.*, lect. 4, n. 3.

sarily precipitate to venture an explanation, for he holds that a theory or supposition that does not conflict with the facts is far better than no explanation at all.[12]

In addition to this first, or hypothetical use of mathematics in seeking a possible explanation, Aquinas also conceived of mathematics as functioning directly in physical argument to furnish a conclusive explanation or proof.[13] This too can best be illustrated by an example.[14] In discussing the shape of the earth, he notes that the latter can be proved to be a sphere merely by an analysis of measurements made on its surface—essentially a mathematical proof.[15] But he regards as more conclusive for the physicist a proof which arises not simply from a mathematical description of the earth's surface, but which leads to a knowledge of the *physical causes* that make the earth to be a sphere. Thus he observes, " all gravitating bodies . . . approach the earth at the same angle, that is, at a right angle . . . and not in parallel lines." [16] This universal mode of gravitation " is what makes the earth to be spherical by nature," he says, because the spherical shape alone can satisfy the uniform tendency of all parts to a common center of gravity.[17] " If the earth were naturally flat, as some have said," he continues, " then bodies would not gravitate everywhere towards the earth at the same angle." [18] It should be noted in this proof that the physical cause Aquinas assigns need not make the earth a perfect sphere—" irregularities such as mountains and valleys arise," he concedes, although " not of notable dimensions compared with those of the earth," and he attributes them to " some other incidental cause." [19] Thus pure or perfect mathematical shape, for Aquinas, does not exist in physical reality: it is only the human mind, abstracting

[12] *Ibid.*, lect. 7, nn. 4-5; *In I Meteorologicorum*, lect. 11, n. 1.

[13] *In I Post. Anal.*, lect. 25, nn. 5-6.

[14] For other examples, together with some applications to modern science, see my " Some Demonstrations in the Science of Nature," *The Thomist Reader 1957* (Washington, D. C.: 1957), pp. 90-118.

[15] *In II de Caelo*, lect. 28, n. 4.

[16] *Ibid.*, n. 1. [18] *Ibid.*

[17] *Ibid* . [19] *Ibid.*

71

from material irregularities such as mountains and valleys, that can conceive of the earth as a perfect sphere.[20] But the earth does have a natural or physical shape which is approximately spherical, and this shape can reveal to the inquiring mind the physical reason which makes the earth to have this shape in the first place.[21]

Space does not permit even a sketch of the historical consequences of this theory of physical proof developed by Albert and Aquinas. It is indisputable, however, that this theory made clear, at a critical period of medieval thought, the distinction between hypothetical explanation and proven fact, while allowing for a legitimate use of mathematics in both types of reasoning. To this one might add that some recently edited texts can be used to argue to the existence of a " Dominican school " in optical science, beginning with encyclopedic collections of data by Thomas of Cantimpré, Vincent of Beauvais and Albert the Great, developing through the theoretical speculations of Thomas Aquinas, John of Paris and Peter of Alvernia, and culminating in the brilliant experimental researches and physico-mathematical theories of Theodoric of Freiburg.[22] The historical import is not insignificant: in less than a century, this line of thought, quite independent of the Oxford school, furnished the first correct fundamental theory of the rainbow—and this more than three hundred years before the publication of Descartes' *Discours de la Méthode* and *Les Météores*, where basically the same explanation of the rainbow is cited as one of the brilliant achievements of the new Cartesian methodology.[23]

[20] *In II Phys.*, lect. 3, nn. 4-6.
[21] *Summa Theologiae*, p. I, q. 1, a. 1, ad 2; *In I de Caelo*, lect. 3, n. 6.
[22] See my *The Scientific Methodology of Theodoric of Freiburg*, Studia Friburgensia No. 26 (Fribourg: 1959), pp. 132-249. Newly edited texts are contained in Appendix III, pp. 305-376.
[23] The full title of Descartes' work on methodology reads: "Discours de la Méthode pour bien conduire sa raison, et chercher la vérité dans les sciences. Plus la Dioptrique, les Météores, et la Géométrie, qui sont des essais de cette Méthode," (Leyde: 1637). The explicit statement from *Les Météores* is contained in Descartes' *Oeuvres*, ed. C. Adam and P. Tannery (Paris: 1897-1910), Vol. VI, p. 231.

While not belittling the importance of Descartes' influence on modern thought, we may turn now to one of his contemporaries, Galileo Galilei, to whom the accolade is commonly given for having procured the " downfall of Aristotle " and the beginning of a new era in science. Some might quibble on the phrase " downfall of Aristotle " and urge that this was more a downfall of a caricature of Aristotle drawn by third-rate scholastics,[24] but without gainsaying the point, the effect was pretty much as popularly conceived. One of Galileo's admirers, Fr. Paolo Sarpi, registered a not uncommon reaction when he said: " To give us the science of motion God and Nature have joined hands and created the intellect of Galileo." [25] In our own day, the popular image is that of an indefatigable experimenter climbing the leaning tower of Pisa to put the Aristotelians to rout with his measurements of falling bodies.[26] Recent studies point more significantly to the Renaissance reaction to Galileo's *Message of the Stars.* Thus Koyré summarizes:

Mountains on the moon, new ' planets ' in the sky, new fixed stars in tremendous numbers, things that no human eye had ever seen, and no human mind conceived before. And not only this . . . also the description of an astonishing invention . . . the first scientific instrument, the telescope, which made all these discoveries and enabled Galileo to transcend the limitation imposed by nature— or by God—on human senses and human knowledge.[27]

The experimental work of Galileo might easily—though falsely—be interpreted as the beginning of modern scientific method, with its accent on postulational procedures subsequently verified by experimental proof. Actually Galileo's method was more closely patterned on that of the late Aristo-

---

[24] Cf. G. de Santillana, *The Crime of Galileo* (Chicago: 1955), pp. 24, 56, 69.

[25] Cited by Burtt, *op. cit.*, p. 74.

[26] But see L. Cooper, Aristotle, *Galileo & the Tower of Pisa* (Ithaca: 1935); also E. A. Moody, "Galileo and Avempace: The Dynamics of the Leaning Tower Experiment," *Journal of the History of Ideas*, 12 (1951), pp. 163-193, 375-422.

[27] A. Koyré, *From the Closed World to the Infinite Universe*, (New York: 1957), p. 90.

telians of the Paduan school,[28] and its most significant aspect was not its insistence on experiment, but rather on the fact that "the book of nature" is written *only* in the language of mathematics.[29] "This book is written in the mathematical language," wrote Galileo, "and the symbols are triangles, circles, and other geometrical figures, without whose help it is impossible to comprehend a single word of it; without which one wanders in vain through a dark labyrinth."[30] Galileo was quite convinced of the absolute truth of the heliocentric theory, maintaining that it was not merely a possible explanation, a "saving of the appearances," as Osiander had indicated in his preface to Copernicus' work,[31] but rather that it expressed a certain truth with which one could even contest traditional interpretations of Sacred Scripture. "Although [a theory that saves the appearances] satisfies an astronomer merely arithmetical," he said, "it does not afford satisfaction or content to the astronomer philosophical."[32] His own metaphysical option, according to Burtt, was for a much refined Platonism that was actually a strict mathematical realism [33]— one could almost call it a revival of the Pythagorean doctrine of twenty centuries previous.[34] Experiments had no probative value for Galileo; they were meant to appeal to the popular mind—those who knew mathematics really had no need of them. But the popular mind also needed convincing, and here Galileo's genius for stirring up trouble came to the fore. His wit and sarcasm in controversy are well known, and on hearing

[28] Cf. J. H. Randall, Jr., "The Development of Scientific Method in the School at Padua," *Journal of the History of Ideas,* 1 (1940), pp. 177-206; P. R. Wiener, "The Tradition Behind Galileo's Methodology," *Osiris,* 1 (1936), p. 733 ff.

[29] See, for example, J. Collins, *A History of Modern European Philosophy,* (Milwaukee: 1954), pp. 79-81.

[30] Galileo, *Il Saggiatore* (Florence: 1842), p. 171.

[31] For a detailed examination of the relations between Copernicus and Galileo, see P. Conway, O.P., "Aristotle, Copernicus and Galileo," *The New Scholasticism* 23 (1949), pp. 38-61, 129-146.

[32] Galileo, *Dialogue on the Great World Systems,* Third Day, ed. G. de Santillana, pp. 349-350.

[33] Burtt, *op. cit.,* pp. 82, 84; cf. A. Koyré, "Galileo and Plato," *Journal of the History of Ideas,* 4 (1943), pp. 400-428.

[34] Cf. G. de Santillana, *The Crime of Galileo,* p. 69.

this brief excerpt from a letter, one can imagine the hot arguments he provoked. He writes:

Oh, my dear Kepler, how I wish that we could have one hearty laugh together! Here at Padua is the principal professor of philosophy, whom I have repeatedly and urgently requested to look at the moon and planets through my telescope, which he pertinaciously refuses to do. Why are you not here? What shouts of laughter we should have at this glorious folly! And to hear the professor of philosophy at Pisa laboring before the Grand Duke with logical arguments, as if with magical incantations, to charm the new planets out of the sky! [35]

In sober fact, Galileo Galilei never did prove that the earth went around the sun, and not vice versa. Conclusive proof of the type Aquinas would have sanctioned, such as is found now, for instance, in our astronomy textbooks, had to wait two more centuries for the contributions of Foucault and Bessel.[36] Galileo's real " crime " had nothing to do with revealed religion: it consisted merely in this, that he saw proof too easily, and thus obscured (in his own mind, at least) the distinction between hypothetical explanation and proven fact already well known to Aquinas. Yet there was much that was good in his work—he had offered new evidence that should have been taken into account by the philosophers of his day. As de Santillana remarks, " Had there been in Rome, at the time of the first crisis of 1616, a youthful Aquinas . . . instead of an aged Bellarmine," history might have been written differently.[37] But " there was no Aquinas," [38] and well known is the unfortunate stand taken by those who were in Rome, to bring about what history will always regard as a tragic ending in a most unsatisfactory case.

[35] Letter to Kepler, 1610; cited by Burtt, *op. cit.*, p. 77.
[36] Cf. A. C. Crombie, " Galileo's 'Dialogues Concerning the Two Principal Systems of the World,'" *Dominican Studies,* 3 (1950), pp. 105-138.
[37] *The Crime of Galileo,* p. ix.
[38] *Ibid.*

ALBERT EINSTEIN (1879-1955)

Crombie has suggested that the great genius of Albert Einstein, working three centuries after Galileo to elaborate the theory of relativity, consisted in his breaking away from the spell under which the great Italian had put mathematical physics from its inception. " Einstein was able to advance the theory of relativity," Crombie writes, " because he acted on the principle that the object of physical science is to ' save the appearances ' by mathematical abstractions postulated *for no other purpose* than to ' save the appearances.' " [39] Einstein seems to have had little hope of penetrating to the reality behind his equations, and there can be little doubt that recent revolutions in physics, traceable in large measure to Einstein, show a decided break with the Galilean concept of proof. In fact, with Einstein ends the naive optimism of a classical physics that saw the book of nature written in the language of mathematics.[40] Proficiency in mathematics, it is true, enabled this modern scientist to achieve brilliant successes in theoretical physics, but the more he worked, the more he doubted the exact correspondence of pure mathematics to physical reality. " As far as the laws of mathematics refer to reality," he says, " they are not certain; and as far as they are certain, they do not refer to reality." [41] In fact, Einstein would go even further; for him, fundamental principles cannot be " abstracted " from sensory experience—they are " free inventions of the human intellect." [42] Far from subscribing to the strict mathematical realism of Galileo, he oscillates between positivism and idealism, while ever leaving a provisional cast to his conclusions.[43] " Our notions of physical reality can never

[39] A. C. Crombie, *Augustine to Galileo*, (London: 1952), p. 328 (italics added).

[40] In writing this, we are aware that Niels Bohr and the Copenhagen school are even more radical in their renunciation of classical physics than Einstein, but the latter's position is sufficiently representative for our purposes.

[41] *Geometrie und Erfahrung*, cited in *Albert Einstein, Philosopher-Scientist*, Library of Living Philosophers, Vol. VII, (Evanston: 1949), p. 380.

[42] *Herbert Spencer Lecture*, 1933 cited *ibid.*, p. 273.

[43] Cf. P. G. Frank, " Einstein, Mach and Logical Positivism," *ibid.*, pp. 269-286;

be final," he states. " We must always be ready to change those notions . . . in order to do justice to perceived facts in the most logically perfect way." [44]

Compared to the physical views of Aquinas and Galileo, those of Einstein stand in proper relief. Seven centuries ago, Aquinas saw the possibility of a mathematical physics that could provide both provisional explanation and conclusive proof, although he had no illusions about the difficulties involved in unveiling the ultimate secrets of the physical universe.[45] Three centuries ago, flushed with his dramatic conquest over the popular mind, Galileo saw proof too easily in the mathematics he had learned to read in the book of nature; in his view, conclusive proof was quickly had—all one need do was study his new science of motion, and the Ptolemaic-Copernican controversy would perforce come to an end. In our own day, Einstein went to the other extreme, for where Galileo saw proof as too easy, he saw it as too difficult—hence an essential relativism in his physical theory which permits no final answers about the physical universe. Aquinas would look for the evidence of Bessel and Foucault to decide the Copernican controversy; Galileo would say that the mathematical simplicity of his laws had already decided it; Einstein would say that his general theory of relativity had made it forever undecidable.[46]

The Problem

This brings us to the problem that is vexing modern science, to the solution of which the physical theory of Aquinas might be able to register a contribution. In the popular mind, science

V. F. Lenzen, " Einstein's Theory of Knowledge," *ibid.*, pp. 355-384; H. Margenau, " Einstein's Conception of Reality," *ibid.*, pp. 243-268.

[44] " Clerk Maxwell's Influence on the Idea of Physical Reality," cited *ibid.*, p. 248.

[45] Cf. *In I Meteorologicorum*, lect. 1, n. 9.

[46] " The struggle, so violent in the early days of science, between the views of Ptolemy and Copernicus would then be quite meaningless. Either CS [coordinate system] could be used with equal justification. The two sentences, 'the sun is at rest and the earth moves,' or 'the sun moves and the earth is at rest,' would simply mean two different conventions concerning two different CS."—A. Einstein and L. Infeld, *The Evolution of Physics*, (New York: 1942), p. 224.

is making great strides forward, finding out new truths every-day that undermine traditional philosophies and even religious beliefs, supplying definitive answers to questions that have plagued men's minds since the dawn of civilization. But within the scientific fraternity itself, there is no such optimism—at least not so far as the question of conclusive proof is concerned. "*Proof*," writes Eddington, "is an idol before whom the pure mathematician tortures himself. In physics we are generally content to sacrifice before the lesser shrine of *plausibility*." [47] Relativity and quantum theories are now the standards against which scientific achievement is measured. One is not surprised that some now hold that whether the earth goes around the sun or vice versa depends strictly on one's point of view, and cannot be proved one way or another. Not long ago, a metho-dologist told the writer that it was merely a *theory* that the earth is round! Today the whole world is talking of "mole-cules" and "atoms" and "electrons" and "cosmic rays"; even high-school children can tell us of "evolving galaxies" and the "expanding universe." Has science proved that such things exist? Or are they merely "free inventions of the human mind"? Is the hard core of scientific fact softer than we think? Or is it possibly even an empty shell?

Einstein, we may presume, would want to disabuse the modern mind of its confidence in the permanent achievements of science. Galileo, no doubt, would be tremendously surprised at the state of affairs that has arisen in the science that he fathered, but one may surmise that he would still champion the absolute power of mathematics to give certain truth. Aquinas, we can be sure, would temper the optimism of Galileo, but—realist that he was—he would also temper the pessimism of Einstein by bridging the gap between science and common sense. While denying that mathematics is the skeleton key that opens *all* the doors of knowledge, he would say that it has a proper role to play in physical research, that it can lead to conclusive physical proof, that some final answers can be given about the world in which we live.

[47] A. S. Eddington, *The Nature of the Physical World*, (New York, 1928), p. 337.

Three divergent answers to a perennial question about the physical universe. Which is correct? While recognizing that the latter question would be regarded as unanswerable (if not meaningless, in Wittgenstein's sense) by some philosophers of science, and while conceding that the extreme polarity between the positions of Galileo and Einstein is more by way of suggestion than by way of explicit commitment in the writings of these scientists, we should like to propose a somewhat novel evaluation of the three possible alternatives. It is this, namely, that Aquinas' answer—the teaching of the analytical school to the contrary—is still the one implicitly subscribed to by the practicing scientist, and that the essential contribution of Einstein is to cancel out the excessive mathematical realism of Galileo, while still leaving open the possibility of a type of physical certainty and proof as conceived by Thomas Aquinas.

A Thomistic Proposal

The justification for this view may perhaps be seen if we analyze the scientific evidence commonly adduced to prove (1) that the earth rotates on its axis, and (2) that its shape is approximately that of an oblate spheroid. In the interests of rigor, and to facilitate discussion of the central issue, we shall frame both arguments in the form of a syllogism, then answer an objection that is commonly encountered against each argument, and with that draw some inferences about the current status of physical proof in modern science.

The first argument may be stated as follows:

A body on which a freely swinging pendulum deviates at the rate of one revolution per twenty four hours at the poles, decreasing according to the sine of the latitude to zero deviation at the equator *is* rotating on its polar axis once every twenty-four hours.

But the earth *is* a body on which a freely swinging pendulum deviates at the rate of one revolution per twenty-four hours at the poles, decreasing according to the sine of the latitude to zero deviation at the equator.

Therefore the earth *is* rotating on its polar axis once every twenty-four hours.

The second argument then reads:

A body on which a freely swinging pendulum of fixed length has periods of oscillation which increase slightly with increasing latitude from the equator to both poles *is* an oblate spheroid slightly flattened at the poles.

But the earth *is* a body on which a freely swinging pendulum of fixed length has periods of oscillation which increase slightly with increasing latitude from the equator to both poles.

Therefore the earth *is* an oblate spheroid slightly flattened at the poles (and here we add parenthetically—although this does not follow logically—the flattening being caused by the centrifugal force of its daily rotation).

Here, then, are two demonstrations which conclude to some predication about the earth, namely, (1) that it is an oblate spheroid, and (2) that it rotates on its axis of symmetry once every twenty-four hours, both arguments using as the middle term some aspect of the behavior of a pendulum on the earth's surface, which is discovered to be *caused* by the shape and rotation of the earth itself.

Some will object against the second argument—the one concluding to the shape of the earth—that this was regarded as valid in the pre-Einstein period, when it was thought that Euclidean geometry was uniquely applicable to the physical universe. But in the present day, when non-Euclidean geometries have proved to be remarkably fruitful in explaining physical phenomena, one cannot say *for sure* that the earth is a sphere or an oblate spheroid; in another geometry it might be another mathematical figure, and thus the argument no longer truly demonstrates.

To this objection we answer that, if relativity theory has shown anything, it has shown that the geometry used by the physicist to describe the shape of the earth is basically immaterial. For dimensions as small as those of the earth, it is of no physical importance whatsoever whether the geometry is Euclidean, or Riemannian, or Lobatchewskian. But the very objection reveals one thing that is quite important, namely, that the objector is a mathematical realist who conceives pure mathematical form as objectively existing in, and determining, the universe to a particular geometry. As has been shown earlier, this is not the Thomistic concept: physical quantity is much too irregular, it is much too perturbed by physical factors—such as matter and motion and time, and their means of measurement—to yield pure geometrical form, except through a process of mathematical abstraction. Thus, when the physicist says that the earth is an oblate spheroid, just as he prescinds from the mountains and valleys and other physical irregularities, so he prescinds from the slight differences associated with alternative *pure* geometries, to say something that is physically meaningful about the shape of the earth.

The first argument also seems to be vulnerable—this time to an objection drawn from the general theory of relativity. We have argued that it is possible to *demonstrate* that the earth is actually rotating on its axis once every twenty-four hours. Now Einstein, and before him the great German physicist, Ernst Mach—who undoubtedly gave inspiration to Einstein's new theories—have held that it is impossible to detect an *absolute* rotation in the universe. Thus they would argue that the cause assigned above for the deviation of the pendulum on the earth's surface (or for the bulge at the equator) need not be the rotation of the earth: the same effect can be correlated mathematically with the apparent motion of the " fixed " stars, and thus one cannot be absolutely sure that the earth's rotation is causing the pendulum phenomena or the bulge at the center, since these *might be* caused by other forces connected with the diurnal motion of the stars.[48]

A Thomistic answer to this difficulty is suggested by that of the English astronomer and commentator on general relativity theory, Sir A. S. Eddington, who writes in this connection:

I doubt whether anyone will persuade himself that the stars have anything to do with the phenomenon. We do not believe that if the heavenly bodies were all annihilated it would upset the gyrocompass. In any case, precise calculation shows that the centrifugal

---

[48] For a fuller statement of this position, see H. Reichenbach, *Modern Philosophy of Science,* (New York: 1959), p. 12.

force could not be produced by the motion of the stars, so far as they are known.[49]

As for the search for some unknown force that *might* explain the phenomenon, Eddington becomes more caustic:

As we go further into space to look for a cause, the centrifugal force becomes greater and greater, so that the more we defer the debt the heavier the payment demanded in the end. Our present theory is like the debtor who does not mind how big an obligation accumulates, satisfied that he can always put off the payment. It chases the cause away to infinity, content that the laws of nature . . . are satisfied all the way.[50]

In this matter, Thomas Aquinas, we may be reasonably sure, would be content with a physical explanation of the motion of the pendulum or of the bulge at the equator in terms of known causes, and would be quite unhappy with an explanation, or a methodology, that would remove a hypothetical cause to infinity. As to the mathematical correlation with the fixed stars mentioned by Mach and Einstein, this would not disturb him: he would say, as has already been pointed out, that *mathematically* it makes no difference whether either one, the earth or the fixed stars, is conceived as moving. But once he saw the physical evidence available today to show that the plane of oscillation of a pendulum is independent of the motion of its support and is determined uniquely by its point of suspension, the center of gravity of its bob and the center of gravity of the local region, or once he convinced himself that there are centrifugal forces connected with every rotation that *we* initiate, he would look no further for a causal explanation in the remote depths of space to account for the deviation of a pendulum on the earth's surface, or for the observed bulge in the earth's contour at the equator. He would conclude, as do most modern scientists, that these are caused by the rotation of the earth, and that the earth therefore is actually spinning on its axis.[51]

[49] *Space, Time and Gravitation* (Cambridge: 1920), p. 153.
[50] *Ibid.*
[51] This argument can be stated more technically by referring the motion of the pendulum to the local inertial axes of the Copernican coordinate system. Thus

This conclusion, it should be noted, does not commit the Thomist to the Newtonian conception of a subsistent absolute space (or absolute time) in which such spinning motion is executed. The notion of absolute space is again an extreme of mathematical realism which attributes static, extra-mental existence to an extension that has been abstracted by the mind from bodies in motion. Space, for St. Thomas, does not exist apart from *bodies* that are extended and in motion; itself based on the relation of distance between bodies, it is rather a relative thing, not an absolute. More properly it is a mathematical concept that abstracts from matter and motion, and as such is conceived statically by us. This need not, therefore, be interpreted to mean that it also exists statically outside the mind as an independent subsistent reality.[52]

A similar observation might be made about the existence of privileged frames of reference or inertial systems which correspond, in the language of relativity, to the absolute space of Newton. Motions within the solar system—or in any local region, for that matter—can be investigated without referring them, in a larger context, to the motions of other systems. The difficulty arises only when space (or the space-time continuum) is hypostasized to be a subsistent background, sometimes conceived physically as an " aether," against which the frames of reference of various systems are actually moving. Operating with such a supposition, the question can be raised as to which system is " really " at rest, or what is the privileged frame of reference in terms of which " absolute " motion and rest in the universe can be detected. It is to the merit of Einstein that his theories of relativity make clear how such a question, if raised, is unanswerable in terms of the data available to the physicist

our analysis accords with the view of Whittaker, recently taken up by Polanyi: " Sir Edmund Whittaker (' Obituary Notice on Einstein,' *Biogr. Mem. Roy. Soc.*, 1955, p. 48) points out that, contrary to widespread opinion, the physical significance of Copernicanism is not impaired by relativity. For the Copernican axes are inertial, while the Ptolemaic are not, and the earth rotates with respect to the local inertial axes."—M. Polanyi, *Personal Knowledge*, (Chicago: 1958), p. 147, fn. 1.

[53] Cf. J. A. Weisheipl, O. P. " Space and Gravitation," *The New Scholasticism*, 29 (1955), pp. 175-223.

in any system. The Thomistic position would rather seem to be that the question should not be asked in the first place, because of the uncritical supposition on which it is based.

Physical Proof

It is interesting that the view of St. Thomas that has been urged in this paper, namely, that there can be some "final answers" in physical science, is once again finding support from scientists. Heisenberg, for example, who seemed to shake traditional thought to its foundations when he enunciated his "principle of uncertainty," has written in a recent work:

With respect to the finality of the results, we must remind the reader that in the realm of the exact sciences there have always been *final solutions* for certain limited domains of experience. Thus, for instance, the questions posed by Newton's concept of mechanics found an answer *valid for all time* in Newton's law and in its mathematical consequences. . . . In the exact sciences the word 'final' obviously means that there are always self-contained, mathematically representable, systems of concepts and laws applicable to certain realms of experience, in which realms *they are always valid for the entire cosmos and cannot be changed or improved.* Obviously, however, we cannot expect these concepts and laws to be suitable for the subsequent description of new realms of experience.[53]

With this, we think St. Thomas would heartily agree. In a very real sense, in physical research one never knows what the morrow will bring, but the scientist can know that if he does his work well, and does not read into his results more than the evidence warrants, he can gain *new* knowledge without thereby destroying the science he has previously acquired.

This view, we would maintain, is the one implicitly held by the practicing scientist.[54] Yet there remains the difficulty,

[53] W. Heisenberg, *The Physicist's Conception of Nature*, (London: 1958—translation by A. J. Pomerans of *Das Naturbils der heutigen Physik*, Hamburg: 1955), pp. 26-27 (italics added).

[54] It has also been stated explicitly by Oppenheimer, in his third Reich lecture, as reported by Hall: "In its [science's] progress since 1800 the later discoveries have always embraced the earlier: Newton was not proved wrong by Einstein, nor Lavoisier by Rutherford. The formulation of a scientific proposition may be

continually raised by logical empiricists, that such a position—no matter how commonly it may be accepted—is still naive and *a priori*, that it does not make sufficient allowance for future discoveries, and in effect represents a nineteenth-century attitude of mind which is unprepared for revolutionary developments that may further advance scientific thought. They would argue that to maintain *anything* as certain or final is to close the mind to new knowledge, that the very *possibility* of someone's making a new discovery forces the scientist to be hesitant about ever saying the "last word," or to despair even of proposing a "final answer" in the area of his investigations.

Aquinas' concept of physical proof, surprisingly enough, is not vulnerable to this objection, and in fact might even be said to have anticipated difficulties of this type that await anyone who would claim too facile a "final explanation" of physical phenomena. For one thing, St. Thomas insisted that the logical procedure that most characterizes physical science is not *a priori*, but is rather *a posteriori*, based on a patient study of the world of nature, not starting with any preconceived knowledge of essences, but rather arguing from effect to cause solely on the basis of observed facts.[55] In this matter, he was insistent that a basic and irreconcilable difference exists between the canons for physical proof and those for mathematical proof. He was aware that the mathematician could have *absolute* certitude, and that the very abstractness and necessity of his subject matter permit him to proceed *a priori* and with the most exacting standards of proof. The certitude he ascribed to physical science, on the other hand, was somewhat circum-

modified, and limitations to its applicability recognized, without affecting its propriety in the context to which it was originally found appropriate. We do not need sledge-hammers to crack nuts; we do not need the Principle of Indeterminacy in calculating the future position of the moon: 'the old knowledge, as the very means of coming upon the new, must in its old realm be left intact; only when we have left that realm can it be transcended' (J. R. Oppenheimer)."—A. R. Hall, *The Scientific Revolution, 1500-1800: The Formation of the Modern Scientific Attitude,* (Boston: 1954), p. xiii.

[55] Cf. *In II de Anima*, lect. 3, n. 245; for a full treatment, see M. A. Glutz, C. P., *The Manner of Demonstrating in Natural Philosophy,* (River Forest, Ill.: 1956), pp. 84-102.

scribed: he referred to it as a "*supositional* certitude," and gave detailed instructions for attaining it when working with the contingent or non-necessary matter of the physical world.[56] His methodological precisions need not concern us here, but certainly one of its suppositions was entirely consistent with Heisenberg's *proviso*, namely, that results are valid *only* for the realm of experience from which they are derived. Thomas, as a matter of fact, would go even further than Heisenberg, and maintain that, even within this realm, final explanations can only be expected, and are only valid, for events that happen "regularly or for the most part," for these alone are sufficient to manifest some type of dependence on the antecedents which produce them, and thus induce a causal necessity into the proof.[57]

Implicit in Aquinas' treatment is also allowance for the acquisition of new knowledge, either by way of refinement within an existing realm of experience, or by revolutionary extension to completely new realms, and both without jeopardizing explanations that have already been conclusively established in science. An example of the first type is the proof already discussed for the sphericity of the earth. Thomas argues that the earth is approximately a sphere because this shape is caused by the uniform action of the gravitational forces of its components; at the same time, he admits that other causes are at work that further modify this shape from that of a perfect sphere. In his day, science had not advanced sufficiently to detect the earth's rotation or the resultant bulge at the equator; yet this advance in knowledge does not nullify his reasoning or his basic explanation. Modern science holds that the earth is an oblate spheroid, and assigns this modification of the spherical shape to rotational forces which are *superadded* to the gravitational forces, but which do not *replace* them. And both Aquinas and the modern scientist would pre-

[56] *In II Post Anal.*, lect. 7, nn. 2-3; *In II Phys.*, lect. 15, nn. 2, 5 and 6.

[57] The details of such a methodology, as applied to the late medieval theory of the rainbow, will be found in my *The Scientific Methodology of Theodoric of Freiburg*, pp. 237-245.

sumably be open-minded to the discovery of further irregularities in the observed shape of the earth's surface, which might be traceable to yet unknown causes still awaiting our investigation, but would not force us to re-open our minds again to the possibility that the earth is flat.

With regard to revolutionary knowledge applicable to completely new realms of experience, we can only surmise how Aquinas would proceed because of the very rudimentary state of science in his day. A not too far-fetched example may perhaps be taken from his generalization, derived from empirical data, that material objects tend in a straight line towards a center of gravity, elaborated mathematically by Newton, over four centuries later, into the law of universal gravitational attraction. It is possible, on the basis of this generalization, to say that *all matter* is ponderable or massive, a statement not inconsistent with the definition frequently found in science textbooks to the effect that matter is whatever has mass and occupies space. Yet such a definition does not close the physicist's mind to other possibilities: in theoretical cosmology, for instance, he will speculate about " anti-gravitation " as accounting for the recession of galaxies, while in fundamental particle theory he will speak of " anti-matter " (or anti-terrestial matter) as having properties radically different from the matter we observe macroscopically. The very fact that he assigns new terms to such entities is evidence that he regards the phenomena on which their existence is based as constituting, in Heisenberg's phrase, a " new realm of experience," about which he can freely speculate, and for which he can even seek hyper-generalizations, without relinquishing a single theorem in classical mechanics. And St. Thomas' willingness to countenance such a procedure is at least implicit in his recognition that celestial matter might be radically different from terrestial matter, while allowing for some common features and a diversity in the laws applicable to each—although there is no doubt that he was mistaken on many details clarified by subsequent investigators.

It would thus seem that the essentially philosophical suggestion of Einstein, taken up by logical positivists, to the effect that " our notions of physical reality can never be final," performs too radical a surgery on the corpus of scientific knowledge. Some surgery was undoubtedly necessary after nineteenth-century excesses in mechanism had pushed to further extremes the mathematical realism sponsored by Galileo in the seventeenth century. But scientific agnosticism is also an extreme, and it can do more harm in the long run than an over-acclerated mathematical or mechanist development, for it eliminates the very possibility of organic growth within science itself. Heisenberg's reaction is thus an encouraging one: it stresses the continuity of science, the assimilation of the new to the old, while insisting on a rigorous methodology that would not over-assert the objective value of mathematical theorizing in recent science. To those who appreciate the essential contribution of Albert and Thomas to medieval science, the parallel between their correctives to the mathematicism of Grosseteste and Heisenberg's emendations to the idealism of Einstein is as interesting as it is unexpected.

Einstein does have a message for the modern mind, and it is this, namely, that the mathematical realism of a Galileo, or the space-time absolutism of a Newton, are antiquated notions that can no longer function fruitfully for the modern scientist. We propose that the same cannot be said for the theory of physical proof proposed seven centuries ago by St. Thomas Aquinas.

ESSAY V:

MEASURING AND DEFINING
SENSIBLE QUALITIES

I T HAS BEEN fashionable for philosophers of science, since the time of Galileo, to question the objective reality of sensible qualities.[1] During the same period scholastic philosophers have insisted on the reality of such qualities but, generally unappreciative of the role of measurement and quantitative techniques in advancing knowledge of their nature, have contented themselves with maintaining either the ontological priority of quantity over quality, or the basic irreducibility of the qualitative to the quantitative.[2]

Similarly, under the influence of Hume and Comte, the concept of causality has been attacked by philosophers of science. Here too scholastic philosophers have risen to a defense, but generally concentrate on the efficient cause to the exclusion of final, formal, or material causality. Recently and somewhat unexpectedly, however, scientists have themselves become interested in causality, in all its forms, as useful for resolving enigmas arising in quantum mechanics.[3]

This development, as well as the perennial interest in qualita-

[1] Typical statements of such philosophers, including an excerpt from Galileo's *Il Saggiatore*, are given by A. Danto and S. Morgenbesser in their anthology, *Philosophy of Science* (New York, 1960) pp. 1-173.

[2] There have been a few notable exceptions, especially P. Hoenen, who has treated the subject of the measurement of sensible qualities extensively in his *Cosmologia*, 4th ed. (Rome, 1949) pp. 184-203, 369-379, 518-527. For a summary and critique of his teaching, together with that of other manualists, see M. Heath, " Can Qualities Be Measured?," *The Thomist*, XVIII (1955) 31-60.

[3] Noteworthy studies are M. Bunge, *Causality* (Cambridge, Mass., 1959); D. Bohm, *Causality and Chance in Modern Physics* (New York, 1957); V. F. Lenzen, *Causality in Natural Science* (Springfield, Ill., 1954).

tive knowledge, invites a Thomistic study of the measurement and definition of sensible qualities. Basic to the measurement of such qualities is a full understanding of reality in both its quantitative and qualitative aspects, such as Aquinas himself sought. Likewise the correct definition of these qualities requires a causal analysis employing all four causes in the traditional Thomistic mode. Such analysis, particularly when supplemented by the measuring techniques of modern science, can strengthen the foundations of moderate realism and render it more acceptable to the modern mind. It may be further suggestive of analogous studies of the structure of matter that can reconcile recent thought in quantum mechanics with traditional concepts of material substance.

MEASUREMENT OF SENSIBLE QUALITIES

Measurement, according to St. Thomas Aquinas, is the process by which the quantity of a thing is made known.[4] It is applied directly to physical bodies when their discrete quantity is ascertained, e. g., by counting the number of objects in a room, or when their continuous quantity is measured, e. g., by using a scale to determine individual lengths. In current practice the term measurement is sometimes applied to counting, but is more usually reserved for determinations of dimensive or continuous quantity.

The elements involved in a direct measurement of quantity can best be delineated in the process of length determination. Such measurement obviously presupposes a unit, and this is the first requirement. The unit may be one naturally occurring, like the individual counted as discrete quantity, or one fixed by convention. The choice of the latter type of unit, not completely arbitrary, is dictated by its suitability as a minimum dimension into which lengths can be divided.

[4] *In I Sent.*, d. 8, q. 4, a. 2, ad 3. See also *In VIII Phys.*, 20, n. 2; *In X Meta.*, l. 2; *De virt. card.*, a. 3.

The unit used, secondly, must be homogeneous with the thing measured.[5] For example, if length is to be determined, the unit must be a length. Similarly the thing measured must be uniformly structured and continuous to permit the application of the same unit to each of its parts.[6]

A third requirement is that the unit of measurement and the object measured be invariant throughout the measuring process.[7] This ideal is never completely realized for any physical object, since all bodies continually undergo change. Because of such variation, plus the infinite variety of contingent circumstances accompanying any measuring process, every measurement is at best an approximation. Yet a practical invariance is not only detectable, but more or less guaranteed by the nature of both the object measured and the standard used. For example, a person's body temperature, although varying over a small range, is held constant by natural causes. Similarly the unit of time is determined by the rotation of the earth and the gram by the weight of one cubic centimeter of water, both maintained constant through the regularity of nature's operation.

A final requirement is that measurement involve a judgment of comparison between object measured and measuring unit.[8] Such a judgment is an intellectual operation, although it presupposes a physical one. Operationalism's attempt to reduce every measurement uniquely to the manipulation of instruments thus disregards an essential requirement of the measuring process.[9] Instruments cannot measure; ultimately they require mind, which, because of its reflexive character as a " self-reading

[5] *In I Anal. Post.*, 36, n. 11.

[6] This poses no difficulty in measurements of dimensive quantity, since all parts of such quantity are homogeneous. It does, however, present a problem in the case of indirect qualitative measurements. See *infra*, n. 16.

[7] Cf. *Summa Theol.*, I-II, 91, 3, arg. 3 et ad 3; 97, 1 ad 2.

[8] Cf. *Summa Theol.*, I, 79, 9 ad 4.

[9] For other serious difficulties with operationalism, see the article by C. Hempel, " Operationism, Observation, and Theoretical Terms," in Danto and Morgenbesser, *op. cit.*, pp. 101-120.

instrument," can effect the judgment of comparison and make the measurement.[10]

The foregoing are requirements for direct measurements of quantity or bodily extension. Entities other than extended bodies, such as the qualities of such bodies, can also be measured insofar as they possess a quantitative aspect. To effect such measurement, however, some adaptations of the above elements are necessary, and these will now be taken under consideration.

METHODS OF QUALITATIVE MEASUREMENT

Physical qualities can be classified into two general categories, with different measuring procedures appropriate to each. The first category comprises qualities that produce alteration or qualitative change in other bodies, or are themselves the result of such alteration. These are known as sensible qualities, or more accurately as *qualitates passibiles*.[11] They in turn are subdivided on the basis of their proximity to sense experience. Some are directly sensible, such as heat, color, sound, odor, and taste, all of which can be sensed immediately by external organs. Others are not directly sensible but can be known through sensible effects. Electricity, magnetism, chemical affinity, etc., belong in this subdivision. Such qualities, because not directly manifest to sense experience, were known to medievals as " occult qualities." [12] A designation perhaps more acceptable to modern scientists would be " reductively sensible qualities," since their existence, known through experiment, is ultimately attained by reduction to sense experience.

A second category of sensible quality includes qualities that do not directly produce alteration but are able to effect mechani-

[10] A full development of this theme is given by V. Smith, " Toward a Philosophy of Physical Instruments," *The Thomist*, X (1947) 307-333. .

[11] *In VII Phys.*, 4, nn. 1-3; *In II Phys.*, 3, n. 5; *In I de Gen.*, 2, n. 4; *Summa Theol.*, I, 67, 3; 77, 3; 78, 3 c. et ad 2, etc.

[12] See, for example, J. McAllister, *The Letter of St. Thomas Aquinas ' De Occultis Operibus Naturae '* (Washington, D. C., 1939).

cal motion, or else are resistive to such motion. The medievals knew these as motive or resistive potencies, or powers, or virtues; an example of motive potency would be gravity, while inertia would be an instance of resistive potency.[13]

Qualities pertaining to both categories mentioned, because present in quantified bodies and intimately associated with quantity, can be said to be quantified. Their quantity can be measured in two different ways, giving rise to the two measurements usually associated with physical quality, viz., extensive and intensive measurements. Physical qualities receive extensive quantification from the extension of the body in which they are present; thus there is a greater amount of heat in a large body than in a small body, assuming both to be at the same temperature.[14] They receive intensive quantification, on the other hand, from the degree of intensity of a particular quality in the body.[15] If two bodies are at different temperatures, for example, there is a more intense heat in the body at the higher temperature, or it is the hotter, and this regardless of the size of either. Measurement of the extensive aspect of physical qualities, being effectively the same as the quantitative measurement of length, area, and volume, is less difficult and of lesser interest than the measurement of intensive qualities, which will receive greater attention on that account.

Two possibilities suggest themselves for the latter measurement. The simplest is to arrange objects with a given quality in the order of increasing intensity and then number them sequentially. For example, if bodies be arranged according to increasing hotness as discernible to touch, and these bodies be numbered, the higher number will indicate the greater degree of heat. This is the closest one can come to a direct intensive measurement of qualities. Such a measure offers difficulties, however, in view

[13] Cf. *In III de Caelo*, 7, n. 9.
[14] *De virt. in comm.*, a. 11 ad 10.
[15] *Ibid., Summa Theol.*, I, 42, 1 ad 1.

93

of the subjectivity of sensation and the arbitrariness of assigning numbers depending on the number of objects that happen to be compared.

The other and more interesting possibility is that of determining the intensity of a quality from an effect, or from a cause, or from a quantitative mode the quality introduces in the subject in which it is. An effect would be the change it produces in another body, a cause would be the agent that produces the intensity in the subject body, and a quantitative mode would be some concomitant variation between the intensity of the quality and a quantitative aspect of the body in which it is present. These possibilities suggest a variety of methods which require individual examination.

If the quality is an active one, i. e., if it produces alterations in other bodies, it can be measured by the effect it produces in such bodies. This is usually done through special types of bodies known as instruments. Thus heat intensity is measured by a thermometer containing a substance that expands noticeably when contacting a hot object. Similarly the intensity of sound is measured by vibrations produced in a microphone, light intensity by electric current generated in a photocell. In each case the intensity of an active quality in one subject is measured by the quantity of the effect it produces in a receiving subject, thenceforth known as the measuring instrument.

Active qualities, it may be noted, can sometimes be measured independently of external alterations of the type just mentioned. If they induce pronounced quantitative changes in the subject in which they are present, they can be measured directly through measurement of the subject body. In this way the temperature of mercury in an immersion thermometer is measured simply by reading the length of its own expansion. Similarly the wavelength of sound in a resonating chamber of variable length is measured directly, using a standing wave technique to ascertain the length of the vibrating column. Such a method of

94

concomitant variation, however, while of theoretical interest, is of limited applicability, being restricted to bodies that are quantitatively sensitive to the presence of the qualities being discussed.

If a quality is not particularly active, i. e., does not produce pronounced effects in itself or in another body, its intensity can alternatively be measured through some type of causality required to produce it in the subject body. In this way one measures the intensity of light on a reflecting surface by the number of foot-candles emitted by the source illuminating the surface. A variation on this technique is that of using an instrumental cause to measure some modality of the principal cause that actively produces the quality. An example would be using a prism or ruled grating selectively to refract and measure the wavelength of colored light incident on a surface, and in this way indirectly to measure the ability of the surface to reflect light of a particular color.

All of these methods are indirect ways of measuring qualitative intensity through a cause-effect relationship. All involve techniques whereby a precise quantity is assigned to the quality being measured and, on this account, are considerably more accurate and objective than direct ordinal measures of qualitative intensities. As a consequence these constitute the type of qualitative measurement most widely used in the physical sciences.

UNITS OF QUALITATIVE MEASUREMENT

The unit employed in this type of qualitative measurement, different from that of direct intensity measurement, is also quite different from the quantitative unit. That involved in direct qualitative measurements, as already observed, depends on the number of bodies compared and, as such, is an ordinal number of arbitrary character. In indirect qualitative measurements, on the other hand, while the unit can be established quite precisely, it normally lacks the additive property of the quantitative unit. For example, the difference between any two lengths is properly a length, but the difference between two degrees is not itself a special degree of heat. Thus, while the difference between a length of 100 cm. and one of 80 cm. is a length of 20 cm., the difference between water at 100° C. and water at 80° C. is not water at 20° C. The unit of length, in this sense, is homogeneous while the degree of heat is not. Being qualitatively heterogeneous, it does not have the simple additive dimensionality of the unit of length.[16]

Nonetheless, one may speak of a type of qualitative dimensionality in the unit of indirect qualitative measurement. Such " dimensions " are the concern of theorists working in dimensional analysis. Their studies show that certain simple relationships hold between all metrical units, qualitative as well as quantitative, when some are chosen as fundamental and others as secondary and derived. Usually qualitative units are treated as secondary units, and these then analyzed in terms of quantities of a more fundamental character. On the basis of such an analytical procedure, it is a simple matter to prove mathematically that every secondary unit can be expressed as the product of various powers of fundamental or primary units. The primary units most frequently employed in such analysis are those of mass, length, and time, all of which show additive properties.[17]

[16] Still there is a type of " proportional homogeneity " even in units of qualitative intensity. If this were not the case, it would be impossible to preserve a primary requirement of measurement (see *supra*, n. 6). John of St. Thomas mentions this difficulty in his *Cursus Philosophicus* (ed. Reiser), II, 382a20-22, and then resolves it using the distinction between " proportional " and " like " homogeneity. Heath translates the significant passage in *art. cit.*, pp. 44-45.

[17] Other primary units are sometimes added to these, such as a fundamental unit for electric charge or internal heat energy, with resulting simplification of the dimensional analysis required to solve particular problems. Most theorists, however, agree that such additional units are not absolutely necessary, and can be eliminated by a proper choice of unit

How such qualitative dimensions can be expressed in terms of the primary units of mass, length, and time is shown in Table I. This lists the powers to which the respective units for these quantities should be raised so that their cumulative product expresses the proper dimension of the quality being measured. The only requirement laid on the corresponding exponents is that they be constants; thus, as is shown by the entries indicated, they can assume zero, negative, and fractional values.

The first and simplest qualitative unit in Table I is that of

Measurement	Exponent of unit for		
of	Mass	Length	Time
	(M)	(L)	(T)
1. Heat temperature	0	1	0
2. Heat capacity	0	1	-2
3. Specific heat	0	0	0
4. Sound velocity	0	1	-1
5. Sound frequency	0	0	-1
6. Fluid density	1	-3	0
7. Fluid viscosity	1	-1	-1
8. Electric charge	1/2	3/2	-1
9. Electric potential	1/2	1/2	-1
10. Energy	1	2	-2

Table I—Units of Qualitative Dimensionality

temperature, typically expressed by the degree Centigrade. Intensity of heat, being measured through the expansion of mercury in a thermometer, as already mentioned, reduces quantitatively to a length measurement. Thus the qualitative dimension of degree Centigrade is the same as the quantitative dimension of length, namely, the unit L.

The second dimensional unit shown is the calorie, or measure of the quantity of heat in a body, which itself differs from temperature in being dependent on the amount and kind of

for measuring such things as dialectric constant or thermal capacity, even though this may complicate dimensional calculations in certain cases.

matter in the body heated. A calorie is defined by the physicist as the amount of heat required to raise the temperature of one gram of pure water one degree Centigrade. As such, it has the dimensionality of energy per unit mass per degree temperature, which can be shown to yield the more complex dimensional unit LT^{-2}.[18]

Not all qualitative measurements need have a dimensional unit associated with them, as can be seen from the third entry in the Table, that of specific heat. Here all of the exponents are zero, indicating that this dimension is a pure ratio. Specific heat, by definition, is the ratio between the thermal capacity of a substance and the thermal capacity of water. Thermal or heat capacity, in turn, is a characteristic of particular physical substances, being the number of calories required to raise the temperature of one gram of a substance one degree Centigrade. Thus, although heat capacity has the dimension already mentioned, LT^{-2}, when two heat capacities are placed in simple ratio, these dimensions cancel out and the result is a pure number. Mathematically, however, one can still say that specific heat is expressible as a function of the primary units of mass, length, and time, if one intends by this the trivial case where all exponents are zero.

Similar observations can be made for the remaining qualitative units in the Table. All are reducible to some combination of the simpler quantitative units shown, when these are raised to appropriate powers. Why this is so presents an interesting problem in the philosophy of science, whose solution, we believe, is intimately connected with the causal process at work in qualitative measurements.

Dimensional analysts usually by-pass this problem, being

[18] Since energy, or force times distance, has the dimensional unit ML^2T^{-2} (item 10 in Table I), when one divides this by mass (M) and length (L), the latter being the dimensional unit of temperature, the resulting dimensional unit is LT^{-2}.

inclined to regard the choice of fundamental units as arbitrary, or made merely on the basis of convenience in maintaining standards of measurement. When one considers, however, that they invariably assign mass, length, and time as primary quantities, a philosophical explanation of their choice can be given in causal terms. If, as already explained, every indirect measurement of qualitative intensity involves cause-effect relationships, registered as changes effected in instruments, then the most basic quantitative modalities available for such measurements are mass, length, and time. Instruments are nothing more than physical bodies of determinate size and mass, which, when acted upon by an intensive quality, move over definite distances in measurable periods of time. Therefore, the measurement of any qualitative effect by an indirect process automatically entails quantitative determinations of mass and mechanical motion. The latter is measured in terms of length and time, and therefore, the simplest units available reduce, on a straightforward basis, to those of mass, length, and time.[19]

These units, it may be further observed, are closely related to the accident of quantity, which itself is the proximate ontological subject of sensible quality. This partially explains why quantitative knowledge of qualities can be revelatory of the true natures of such qualities in the order of being. That length is directly related to quantity requires no explanation. Similarly time, being a measure of movement along a distance or length, needs no justification of its quantitative character. The status of mass as an accident rooted in quantity, however, might not be immediately evident and thus will bear exposition.

THE NATURE OF MASS

St. Thomas Aquinas has no treatment of this topic, but he does express views on weight which are helpful for reconstruc-

[19] St. Thomas discusses the measurement of such entitles in *In X Meta.*, n. 1941 and following.

ting his likely analysis of mass. Weight, for him, is an active quality which accounts for the inclination or tendency of a body towards a center of gravity.[20] He regarded it as measurable and mentioned the grain as a suitable unit.[21] Ultimately, for Aquinas, weight measurements involve comparisons between gravitational tendencies of two different bodies and thus reduce to pure ratios. This notion, interestingly enough, is preserved in modern science in the concept of specific gravity, and ultimately in that of atomic weight, both of which are ratios without dimensionality, analogous to the unit of specific heat already mentioned.[22]

Modern science carries its analysis much further than this, measuring weight through an effect, viz., the acceleration it produces in a falling body. The work of Galileo, Newton, and later scientists has greatly influenced the choice of a proper dimensional unit for this measurement. Large numbers of experiments with accelerating bodies show that acceleration depends on the locality in which a measurement is performed. To allow for this,

[20] *Ibid.*, n. 1942. Aquinas' notion of gravity is somewhat similar to that later expressed by Copernicus: " I myself think that gravity or heaviness is nothing except a certain natural appetency implanted in the parts [of the universe] by the divine providence of the universal artisan, in order that they should unite in their oneness and wholeness, coming together in the form of a globe."—*On the Revolutions of the Celestial Spheres*, Book I. Translation from S. Cummins and R. Linscott (eds.), *The Philosophers of Science* (New York, 1947) p. 62.

[21] In English units, 7000 average grains taken from the middle of ears of wheat are equivalent to one pound avoirdupois; thus there are 15.43 grains in one gram (c.g.s. system). St. Thomas also mentions the talent as too large for accurate measurements. The latter, deriving from the Greek τάλαντον (= balance), weighs about 59 pounds and is equivalent to 40,000 grains. Since the medievals used whole numbers and not decimals or fractions for numerical measurements, one can see why Aquinas regarded the grain as a more practical unit.

[22] The specific gravity of any natural substance is defined as the ratio between the weight of a given volume of that substance and that of an equal volume of water, while the atomic or molecular weight of a substance is the average weight of an atom or molecule of that substance relative to the average weight of the oxygen atom taken at 16.000 units.

the unit of weight is taken to be the dyne (in the c.g.s. system), a composite of the body's gravitational tendency and the acceleration characteristic of the place in which its rate of fall is measured. When this value is divided by acceleration, the quantity obtained, which measures the gravitational tendency of the body irrespective of the place at which a particular weight measurement is made, is called the mass of the body. Its dimensionality is that of the gram, represented by the letter M in Table I. Weight, to be consistent with this, becomes the product of mass by acceleration and has the dimensional unit of the dyne, MLT^{-2}.

Although mass is a quality, it is directly associated with the matter of which an individual body is composed and, in this sense, is quantitative and extensive. It also has an intensive aspect but does not manifest the heterogenous character of other intensive units, showing additive properties instead. Ultimately it would seem to be that modality of an individual quantified substance which measures its natural tendency to a center of gravity independent of its particular place in the universe. It can also be regarded as a measure of the same body's resistance to mechanical motion. The measurement of tendency to the center of gravity is frequently called gravitational mass, whereas the measure of resistance to mechanical motion is referred to as inertial mass. These are known through experiment to have identical values.[23]

Weight and mass can also be said to have a specific aspect, i. e., one common to many individual bodies of the same species, insofar as they measure the active and passive natures of such bodies as productive of, or resistant to, mechanical motion. Different elements and chemical compounds, for example, have the characteristic masses indicated by their atomic or molecular

[23] This represents a Thomistic view of the mass concept. For a historical summary and critique of other views, see M. Jammer, *Concepts of Mass* (Cambridge, Mass., 1961).

weights. These values, as already mentioned, are essentially relative and given by pure numbers. Since, in St. Thomas' view, nature itself is a relative concept,[24] one gains from this concept an insight into why these characteristics naturally associated with a species, such as specific heat, specific gravity, and atomic and molecular weight, ultimately lack dimensional units. They do not measure absolute entities, but rather interrelated aspects of bodies pertaining to a particular order of nature that can be known only in their natural context. The same notion of nature, it may be added, also has explanatory value relative to the numerical equality of gravitational and inertial mass. Both are indirect measurements of the same physical nature, viz., in the case of gravitational mass the nature of a particular body as an active principle of its motion and in the case of inertial mass the same nature as resistant and passive.

The measurement of sensible qualities, therefore, when reduced through causal analysis to its ontological foundations, reveals interesting connections between qualitative accidents, those more radically associated with quantity, and the specific natures of inorganic substances.[25] It is also extremely useful for arriving at greater knowledge of the natures or definitions of sensible qualities themselves, as will now be explained.

DEFINITIONS OF SENSIBLE QUALITIES

Sensible qualities, constituting as they do a species of predicamental accidents, are defined differently from substances. Substances are defined through intrinsic principles, while acci-

---

[24] *In II Phys.*, 1, n. 5. For a discussion of this point, which is not without its subtleties, see J. Weisheipl, *Nature and Gravitation* (River Forest, Ill., 1955) pp. 22 ff.

[25] This procedure, it should be noted, is quite different from that of mechanistic reductionism. It in no way implies that qualities *are* quantities, but merely that the former may be measured, by their effects, through quantitative modalities they introduce into more easily measured parameters.

dents are defined through reference to something extrinsic to the accident itself, namely, the subject or substance in which it is found.[26] To put this differently, the matter or material cause of a substance is part of the substance, while the matter or material cause of an accident is not part of the accident but rather its appropriate subject.[27] The formal cause of an accident, similarly, is the precise effect or modality which the accident introduces into this appropriate subject or substance by its presence. In order to investigate this, it is convenient first to consider the subject without the accident (assuming this is not a proper accident in the strict sense of *proprium*), then determine the proper extrinsic agent or efficient cause that produces the accident in the subject, and from this ascertain precisely what new effect or modality exists in the subject as a result of the accident's presence. The resulting method is one of defining an accident through its proper effect, " effect " being taken here in the sense of primary formal effect and not that produced directly by an efficient cause.

To define accidental being, then, one does not begin by considering the accident statically, in a state of existence, but rather by considering it dynamically, as it comes to be, in order to isolate its proper causes.[28] When this is done, and when a causal analysis is made not of the sensible quality but of the process of its production, the identification of all four causes, viz., efficient and final as well as formal and material, becomes much simpler than in the static case. For example, if sound is being investigated, the final cause of the production of sound is its generation in some subject, and ultimately its sensation in a hear-

[26] *In II de Anima*, 1, n. 213. For a discussion of this methodology, see my *The Role of Demonstration in Moral Theology* (Washington, D. C., 1962) pp 169 ff.

[27] Cf. *Summa Theol.*, I-II, 55, 4.

[28] This is analogous to the way in which substance is defined in natural philosophy, where its coming-to-be (substantial change) is used to argue to its proper intrinsic principles: matter, form, and privation.

ing subject, while the efficient cause is the agent that produces this sound where it was previously not present. Similarly the material cause is the medium or substance capable of supporting sound, while the formal cause, the precise quality being defined, is the modality which sound introduces, as its formal effect, in the medium in which it comes to exist. Once sound has been generated, on the other hand, to ascertain its further finality is considerably more difficult than to trace the causal sequence of its generating process.

St. Thomas Aquinas, following Aristotle, employs such a method when analyzing the nature of sound.[29] He makes appropriate distinctions between sound as it is fully actual, i. e., as sensed in the ear, sound as it exists in media capable of supporting it, and sound as it comes from agents that produce it. Pointing out that sound as fully actual is the end point of the process of generation, he enumerates everything required to produce this result, concentrating particularly on efficient and material causes involved in the process. He notes, for instance, that sound is not produced directly by alteration, but can be initiated by mechanical or local motion, if the proper sounding agent is available.[30] Thus he distinguishes two efficient causes: the first, or remote, agent which moves mechanically, like the striker or hammer that hits a gong to make it sound; and the second, or proximate, agent which produces sound in a medium. The latter agent—in the example, the gong—must be capable of sounding, it must have a *potentiam sonandi,* and this potency must be reduced to act before an active cause of sound is available.[31] St. Thomas observes that a bell has this potency, while a sponge does not. Good resonators, for him, should be made of bronze or other resilient material, and have a smooth and preferably concave surface, so as to reinforce reverberations in the

[29] *In II de Anima,* 16.
[30] See also *In VII Phys.,* 4, n. 2.
[31] *In II de Anima,* 16, nn. 440-441.

medium.[32] Similarly, the striker should move quickly and with force, striking at regular intervals to produce a continuing sound. He also cites the analogous case of the plucked string to observe that the greater its tension, the higher the frequency of its vibratory movement.[33]

Thus for Aquinas there must be a twofold efficient causality of sound: a driver moving mechanically and a resonator capable of producing sound in a suitable medium. The medium is the material cause, or appropriate subject, in which sound comes to exist. He names air and water as suitable media, since they have no background sound or motion of their own that would impede the generation of another sound.[34] Also, they are naturally suited to transmitting homogeneous and continuous vibrations with rapidity and regularity. When these become actual, it is further possible to distinguish differences in them. Sounds we hear as shrill and acute are accompanied by a rapid and high frequency movement of the medium, while those that are deep or low in register have a slow but regular movement.[35]

For a rudimentary analysis made seven centuries ago, this account of the origins of sound is fairly complete. Yet one can improve on it by incorporating material from modern science into the Thomistic method of definition. For instance, our present knowledge of the microstructure of fluid media necessitates that we revise St. Thomas' notion that the medium must itself be motionless. Molecules of air are actually in a type of continual movement now associated with heat phenomena.[36] Such movement, however, is the random, irregular movement

---

[32] *Ibid.*, nn. 442-443.

[33] *Ibid.*, nn. 464, 460.

[34] *Ibid.*, n. 445.

[35] *Ibid.*, nn. 462-464.

[36] This assumes that molecules are not mere constructs, but that their existence is demonstrable by *a posteriori* demonstration. For an indication of the methodology by which this can be done, see my " Some Demonstrations in the Science of Nature," *The Thomist Reader 1957* (Washington, D. C., 1957) pp. 90-118, particularly pp. 103-110.

of individual molecules, whereas the motion associated with the propagation of sound is a regular vibratory movement of relatively large masses of molecules.

Refinements of this type enable us to define sound and acoustical phenomena in a way that distinguishes these from heat and thermal phenomena. The final cause of sound's generation is what is heard in the ear, while the efficient cause is twofold: a driving source that strikes a resonator or maintains it in regular vibration, and a potential resonator or acoustical transducer which, when actuated, becomes the active cause of sound in a medium. The material cause is such a medium capable of supporting sound as an accident, i. e., a body whose parts can undergo regular vibratory motion under the action of an acoustical transducer. In the normal case, this is a fluid such as air or water, although metals, crystals and other solid objects can also transport sound. The formal cause of sound, completing the analysis, is the act corresponding to this potency or susceptibility in the medium. In other words, the precise formal effect which we recognize as sound in a medium is the regular vibratory motion of the medium, at greater or lesser amplitude, with differences of frequency and wavelength dictated by the characteristics of the medium and the driving source. When this motion actually exists in the medium, we say that sound is present there.[37]

Heat and Color

The same procedure can be used to define heat through the four causes of its generation. As in the case of sound, the final cause is its perception by the appropriate sense organ, in

[37] In its primary acceptation, sound is taken as the quality perceptible by the sense of hearing, and thus the term is applied most properly to vibrations in the audible region. Once the peculiar quantitative modality that is the formal effect of sound has been ascertained, however, the term is not restricted to audible phenomena, and even vibrations in the subsonic and ultrasonic regions are thenceforth referred to as sound.

this case the sense of touch.[38] The efficient cause again is two-fold. The first mover, analogous to the striker or driver that intitiates vibratory motion, is electromagnetic radiation or some type of mechanical mover such as generates friction. The latter's motion is not heat, although it can make the potentially heatable subject become an active source of heat, much as the gong or resonating chamber can become an active source of sound when mechanically actuated. There is a difference in this regard, however, because the active source of heat can be one of two types: either a body that itself becomes hot and then heats other bodies on contact, or a body that radiates energy capable of heating a distant body. Acoustical phenomena, on the other hand, are only actively transmitted by contact.

The material cause, or subject in which heat properly exists, is a physical body whose microstructure is such that its parts are susceptible to random motion. The peculiar motion associated with heat is not only more irregular than that associated with sound, but also of smaller amplitude. Rather than being a bulk movement of large volumes of the medium, it is essentially a random molecular movement. This may be either a translational motion of entire molecules or vibratory and rotary motions within molecules themselves on the part of their constituent atoms.[39] A body having parts susceptible to one or other random motion of this type is the material cause of heat, while its formal cause is the actuation of this particular susceptibility.

The sensible quality of color is more difficult to analyze causally. To simplify the discussion, we shall restrict our com-

[38] This too is the ordinary use of the term hot, which is then extended to regions where heat is so intense that it would destroy an organ of touch, but can be perceived by instruments or by another sense, e. g., that of sight.

[39] Temperature differences in heat are then a function of velocity distributions of individual molecules, while thermal capacity or specific heat is associated with the internal degrees of freedom within molecules dependent on the particular state of the substance, whether this be gaseous, liquid or solid.

ments to color seen by the eye in opaque surfaces.[40] Such color is directly sensible to sight, just as sound is sensed by the ear and heat by touch. The efficient cause that renders color existent and visible is again twofold. The remote agent is electromagnetic radiation or the collision of atoms and molecules in a thermal or other energetic state ultimately reducible to mechanical motion. The proximate active cause of color is a light source, which is a type of transducer converting heat energy into radiant energy. Such a source, or radiator, is a substance whose atoms are excitable, i. e., whose electrons can be moved to a state of higher energy, from which they can return to their normal or ground state and emit, in the process, rays of particular wavelength or frequency referred to as colored light. These rays are not themselves colored, but have the ability to make visibly colored any object containing this color at least virtually.

The material cause, or proper subject in which color is found, is a surface or volume capable of selectively scattering and reflecting some particular wavelength distribution to the eye. This capacity of a surface to absorb and selectively scatter incident radiation is not completely understood, but is usually explained by various kinds and degrees of unfulfilled valencies in the molecular structure of the body. Such unfulfilled valencies, when subjected to radiation, reduce the relative speed or frequency of one or more pairs of vibrating electrons. This modification of electronic vibration in turn imparts to the entire molecule a special vibratory motion or chemical resonance, which explains its selective refraction of light and, therefore, its color manifestation.

The formal cause of color, in line with this explanation, is

[40] For a complete causal analysis of radiant color, with particular emphasis on the rainbow, see my analysis of the *De iride* of Theodoric of Freiberg, a 14th century Dominican, in *The Scientific Methodology of Theodoric of Freiberg* (Fribourg, 1959) particularly pp. 131-248.

the actualization of such a capacity or ability in the molecules of the body being illuminated. When this potency is actualized, the body is actually colored, and is so seen by the eye. In view of the special relationship between color manifestation and the incident light illuminating a body, one cannot strictly specify the color of an object without reference to the light under which it is viewed. Similarly, if one questions whether colors exist in darkness or in the interiors of objects, answers can only be given in terms of the distinctions just indicated between the formal and material cause of color. Thus, as explicitly taught by medievals such as Theodoric of Freiberg, colors do not formally exist in darkness nor in the interior of bodies, because they there lack the light by which they become actually visible.[41] They are present materially, however, when the structure of matter is such that it is capable of reflecting colored rays to the eye, should they be illuminated by a proper light source.

This completes our definition, through causal analysis, of the sensible qualities most studied in physical science, viz., sound, heat, and color. The results, summarized in Table II, reveal the extent to which the measurement of sensible qualities yields knowledge of their natures when subsumed into Aquinas' methodological procedure for defining accidental being. They also suggest a concluding observation concerning current problems in the philosophy of science.

PHILOSOPHICAL POSTSCRIPT

Qualitative knowledge presents a perennial problem to philosophers of science in the positivist tradition. Their difficulties are akin to those of other philosophers who have attempted to

[41] This teaching is contained in Theodoric's opusculum, *De coloribus*, which is edited in the work cited in the previous note, pp. 364-376, with my commentary on pp. 163-173. Theodoric here proceeds considerably beyond the work of his predecessors: Avicenna, Averroes, Vincent of Beauvais, O. P., St. Albert the Great, O. P., and St. Thomas Aquinas, O. P., all of which is summarized on pp. 132-152.

Cause	Sound	Heat	Color
1. Final	heard in the ear	sensed by touch	seen by the eye
	produced by	produced by	produced by
2. Efficient a. Remote	mechanical motion	mechanical motion or radiation	mechanical motion or radiation
	driving	energizing	energizing
b. Proximate	an acoustical transducer	a thermal radiator	excitable atoms
(potency)	capable of,	capable of,	capable of,
(act)	then actually,	then actually,	then actually, emitting colored light
	educing from	educing from	on
3. Material (potency)	a medium with parts susceptible to regular vibratory motion	a medium with parts susceptible to random molecular motion of one or more degrees of freedom	a surface or volume capable of electronic resonance and selective refraction of colored light
4. Formal (act)	a vibration of particular amplitude and frequency.	a particular velocity distribution in the given degrees of freedom.	the actual refraction of a particular spectral distribution.

Table II—Causal Definitions of Sensible Qualities

reduce all scientific explanation of reality to some one ontological class, viz., to primary qualities in the case of Galileo, to sense data in the case of G. E. Moore, to pointer-readings in the case of Eddington. The foregoing analysis shows how unrealistic this preoccupation can be, and how necessary is an epistemological outlook that recognizes the existence of " ontological depth " in the universe, with its accompanying stratification of being.[42]

For example, even in the order of sensible qualities there exists a type of ontological hierarchy. This can be illustrated by using the alternative expression for material cause and inquiring into the proper subject of sound, heat, and color.[43] The proper subject of sound, as we have seen, is a medium or entity with parts susceptible to regular vibratory motion. This requirement automatically limits the existence of sound to subjects large enough to include macroscopic domains of molecules that can support such motion. Similarly the proper subject of heat is an entity with parts susceptible to random motion in one or more degrees of freedom; under this requirement heat can exist only in aggregates of atomic particles and not in the individual atom as such. Again, the proper subject of color is an entity whose electronic parts are capable of a special type of resonance. It is therefore fruitless to seek color in an entity that does not possess such electronic parts, as, for example, the electron itself.

The relevance of this to current problems in the philosophy of science is easily seen. If one cannot speak of a " red electron " or a " hot atom " or a " shrill molecule," on the basis of the very definition of these sensible qualities, then one should be even more wary of assigning conventional attributes to entities at the level of the so-called fundamental particles. The ontological hierarchy

---

[42] An interesting refutation of the positivist position in terms of a doctrine of " ontological depth " is R. Harré's *Theories and Things*, Newman History and Philosophy of Science Series No. 9 (London, 1961).

[43] This terminology seems to be preferred by St. Thomas. See *In I de Gen.*, 2, n. 4.

of which we have spoken demands certain minimum quantitative dimensions for the existence of sensible qualities, with color preceding heat and heat preceding sound in terms of minimum requirement. Beyond these minima, even though quantified matter be itself present, it cannot be endowed with these particular qualitative attributes. This illustrates well the Thomist's traditional assertion of the ontological priority of quantity over quality, without denying their mutual interdependence under appropriate aspects of material and formal causality.

Quantitative dimensionality, in this understanding, becomes the material cause of sensible quality.[44] One could push such a type of inquiry further, and ask for the material cause of quantitative dimensions themselves. If quantity is prerequisite to, and in a certain respect serves to explain, the presence of sensible quality, is there something ontologically prior to quantity which is prerequisite to, and serves to explain, such realities as mass, length, and mechanical motion? No less a quantum physicist than Werner Heisenberg raises this question and answers it in the affirmative. He regards such a prior ontological subject as necessary, and identifies it, surprisingly enough, with the *materia prima* of Aristotle and St. Thomas.[45] Such a concept, for him, offers the only realist solution to the enigmas posed by the principles of uncertainty and complementarity, which prohibit us not only from applying conventional attributes, including the terms of classical mechanics, to elementary particles, but even of speaking of their proper parts as though such particles could be divided into " smaller bits." [46] Quality is explained, as through a material cause, by quantity, and the latter in turn is explained, on the same basis, by a

[44] Cf. *Summa Theol.*, I, 78, 3, ad 2.
[45] W. Heisenberg, *Physics and Philosophy* (New York, 1958) pp. 70, 119, 160 and 166.
[46] *Ibid.*, p. 73.

material principle of substance that itself exists only *in potentia.*[47]

Such explanation through material causality, it goes without saying, does not banish its correlate, formal causality, from the universe, nor does it dispense with a single aspect of efficient and final causality. But it does serve to highlight the assistance modern science can give, through its techniques of indirect measurement, to an increased understanding of the ontological structure of the real.

[47] *Ibid.*, pp. 41, 53, 180-186.

CAUSE AND EFFECT:
TEMPORAL RELATIONSHIPS

Iт would be difficult to find views more markedly opposed regarding the temporal relation between cause and effect than those propounded respectively by Hume and Aristotle. For Hume, cause and effect must be temporally distinct; in fact, almost by definition the cause is an event anterior in time to the effect, another event. The key problem of causation in Hume's formulation is thus one of making precise the way in which these two temporally distinct events are connected, and he decides this by opting for psychological projections into reality rather than conceding the existence of necessary connections in nature. Aristotle, on the other hand, accepts the fact of productivity or causal efficacy in nature, and so defines cause as to have it actually causing only when it is producing an effect, and thus at best instantiated when cause and effect are simultaneous. While not rejecting the possibility of antecedent causation, in the sense of denying outright that the cause might somehow temporally precede the effect, Aristotle treats this possibility as troublesome and as contributing little or nothing toward the understanding of basic causal processes.[1]

Contemporary thinkers who address the problem of causal relations generally favor Hume's analysis, although some periodically manifest interest in Aristotle's exposition as an important and viable alternative. Few, however, find among the many philosophers who came between Aristotle and Hume any worthwhile contributor to the development of this problematic. Some might note, for example, Nicholas of Autrecourt as a medieval precursor of Hume, but this merely keeps the discussion fluctuating between the same two poles. This essay aims to call attention to a differ-

---

[1] For the basic texts and a discussion of the problematic and its history, see J. S. Wilkie, "The Problem of the Temporal Relation of Cause and Effect," *British Journal for the Philosophy of Science* (1950), pp. 211–29.

ent and intermediate view, not hitherto noted, that was proposed in the High Middle Ages by Thomas Aquinas. It argues that Aquinas made a significant advance beyond Aristotle in his analysis of antecedent causation, and thereby made possible the certification of some elements in Hume's analysis, without subscribing to its more extreme results. In so doing, moreover, Aquinas adumbrated some problems in contemporary analytic discussions of the causal relationships between events, and consequently may shed light on their solution.

<h1 style="text-align:center">I</h1>

Aquinas' contributions to natural philosophy and to the methodology of science are not so well known as is his work in metaphysics, but they proved considerable nonetheless. A number of his distinctive teachings in these fields, in fact, had important consequences for the origin of modern science.[2] For purposes of subsequent exposition, we shall here restrict ourselves to one such teaching that runs through his physical writings and that gives rise to a peculiar methodological problem. This is the theme that the *scientiae naturales* are concerned uniquely with changeable being, or with being in process, which process pertains to the sensible or phenomenal order, and on this account is readily available for empirical observation and analysis. The processes that are thus studied by the natural philosopher, however, unfortunately have a contingent aspect to them, in the sense that they are not absolutely necessitated but could be otherwise than they are. If this is the case, then the possibility of attaining true demonstrative knowledge of natural processes would seem to be compromised, and the *scientiae naturales* might have to forfeit their claim to being sciences *simpliciter* in the sense of the *Posterior Analytics*. Aquinas was quite aware of this seeming incompatibility of contingent process and necessary demonstration, and nonetheless maintained that both features serve to characterize the *scientiae naturales*. In maintaining this, moreover, he was led to develop

<hr />

[2] A brief sketch of these contributions is given in my article on Aquinas in the *Dictionary of Scientific Biography*, Vol. 1. (New York: Charles Scribner's Sons, 1970), pp. 196–200.

a distinctive theory of proof for the natural sciences, which may be his greatest single innovation as a scientific methodologist.[3]

As regards the scientist's primary concern with the analysis of process, perhaps the following brief indications may serve to establish this general Thomistic thesis, itself quite Aristotelian in character. The first two books of the *Physics*, in Aquinas' view, are seminal for all of natural philosophy, for they serve to delineate respectively the principles of changeable being and the principles of natural science.[4] Consequent on the determination of these principles, the remaining six books of the *Physics* are devoted to a study of the general properties of process or change.[5] And the subsequent books in the Aristotelian corpus, *De caelo, De generatione et corruptione, Meteorologica*, etc., investigate in detail the various types of process found in the physical universe, viz., local motion, alteration, and growth. From these latter treatises, as is well known, were developed the modern sciences of physics, chemistry, biology, etc., which first separated themselves from the main body of philosophy and then underwent independent development. But even the last six books of the *Physics*, still generally regarded as philosophical in character, concentrate on process as their most formal concern. Thus the third book, which for Aquinas contains the first strict demonstration in natural science, establishes that change is properly found in the thing undergoing change and not in whatever initiates it, and that infinitude, insofar as it is studied by the natural scientist, is formally connected with process insofar as the latter is lodged in some way in the sensible continuum.[6] Demonstrations in Book IV show that every process takes place in time, in Book V that process is possible

---

[3] This theme is developed at some length throughout my two-volume study, *Causality and Scientific Explanation* (Ann Arbor: University of Michigan Press, 1972–74) ; see Vol. 1, pp. 71–80, 102, 104, 143, and Vol. 2, pp. 247, 250, 293, and 354.

[4] *In II Physicorum*, lect. 1, n. 1.

[5] *In III Physicorum*, lect. 1, n. 1.

[6] There has been no satisfactory full-scale study of the various demonstrations that are to be found in Aristotle's physical works; for a preliminary outline, indication of sources, etc., see my "Some Demonstrations in the Science of Nature," *The Thomist Reader 1957* (Washington, D.C.: The Thomist Press, 1957), pp. 90–118.

strictly speaking only in categories of being that allow contrariety (location, quality, and quantity), and in Book VI that everything that undergoes a process of these kinds must be a divisible or quantified body. The last two books, finally, propose to demonstrate the existence of a First Unmoved Mover, and do so, not through a metaphysical analysis of potency and act, but rather through an analysis of the requirements for initiating change in a body that has the capability of successive movement in time.[7]

The concern with spatial and temporal succession that runs through the *Physics* and the subsequent *scientiae naturales* suggests that Aquinas will also address himself to the problem of the successive and temporal relationships between cause and effect, and this does in fact prove to be the case. The principal loci for this treatment are his commentary on the second book of the *Physics,* toward the end, where he is discussing causal analysis and its mode of employment in the natural sciences, and in the commentary on the *Posterior Analytics,* where these problems are addressed more pointedly as jeopardizing the possibility of demonstrative proof when treating of any natural process.[8] In brief, for Aquinas no special problem is presented when analyses are made in terms of intrinsic (i.e., formal and material) causality, but serious difficulties present themselves when one attempts to demonstrate through extrinsic (i.e., efficient and final) causality, particularly when treating of the sublunary world, for here efficient causes can be impeded from attaining their normal effects. Aquinas' distinctive solution is to propose that demonstrations in the *scientiae naturales* can circumvent the defective operation of efficient causes, whether these arise through material defects or "on the part of time alone," through a technique known as demonstrating *ex suppositione finis.*[9] This technique begins by studying natural processes and noting how they terminate for the

---

[7] For some details, see my "The Cosmological Argument: A Reappraisal," *Proceedings of the American Catholic Philosophical Association* (1972), pp. 43–57.

[8] *In II Physicorum,* lect. 11–15; *In II Posteriorum Analyticorum,* lect. 9–12.

[9] *In I Posteriorum Analyticorum,* lect. 16, n. 6; *In II Posteriorum Analyticorum,* lect. 7, n. 2 and lect. 9, n. 11; *In II Physicorum,* lect. 15, n. 2; see also the references given in note 3 above.

most part. Thus, in biological generation, it is easily noted that men are normally born with two hands, or that olive plants are usually produced from olive seeds provided that these are properly nurtured. From this information, however, one cannot be certain in advance that any particular child will be born with two hands, or that each individual olive seed will produce an olive plant. The reason for this is that the processes whereby perfect organisms are produced are radically contingent, or, stated otherwise, that generating causes do not always attain their effects. But if one starts with an effect that is normally attained, he can use his experience with nature to reason, on the supposition of the effect's attainment, to the various antecedent causes that are required for its production. It is this possibility, and the technique devised to assure it, that permit the *scientiae naturales* to be viewed as sciences in the strict sense. They can investigate the causes behind natural phenomena, they can know with certitude how and why effects have been produced, and they can reason quite apodictically to the requirements for the production of future effects, even despite the fact that nature and its processes sometimes fail in their *de facto* attainment.

To illustrate this technique the favored example of Aquinas, taken over from Aristotle and previous commentators, is the causal analysis of a lunar eclipse. Such eclipses do not always occur, but when they do occur they are caused by the earth's being "diametrically interposed between sun and moon."[10] Thus, if a lunar eclipse is to take place, this will require a certain spatial configuration between sun, moon, and the observer on earth. A similar contingent occurrence is the production of the rainbow in the atmospheric region of the heavens; this is more difficult to explain than the lunar eclipse, since it lacks even the regular movements of the celestial spheres to guarantee its periodic appearance. In fact, rainbows are only rarely formed in the heavens, and sometimes they are only partially formed; when they are formed, moreover, they seem to come about as the result of a contingent process. This notwithstanding, they can still be the subject of investigation

---

[10] *In I Posteriorum Analyticorum,* lect. 16, n. 6.

within a science *propter quid,* if one knows how to go about formulating a demonstration in the proper way. Rainbows do not always occur, but they do occur regularly under certain conditions; they are not always fully formed, but for the most part they form a circular arc across the heavens. An observer noting the regularity of this phenomenon can rightly expect that such a regularity has a cause, and he may proceed to discover what that cause may be. If he moves scientifically, according to Aquinas, he will take as his starting point the more perfect form that nature attains regularly and for the most part, and using this as the end or final cause, will try to discover the antecedent causes that are necessarily entailed in its realization. The necessity of his reasoning is therefore *ex suppositione finis,* namely, based on the supposition that a particular end is to be attained by a natural process. *If* rainbows are to occur, they will be formed by rays of light being reflected and refracted in distinctive ways through spherical raindrops successively occupying predetermined positions in the earth's atmosphere with respect to a particular observer.[11] The reasoning, though phrased hypothetically, is nonetheless certain and apodictic; there is no question of probability in an argument of this type. Such reasoning, of course, does not entail the conclusions that rainbows will always be formed, or that they will necessarily appear as complete arcs across the heavens, or even that a single rainbow need ever again be seen in the future. But if rainbows *are* formed, they will be formed by light rays passing through spherical droplets to the eye of an observer in a predetermined way, and there will be no escaping the necessity of the causal operation by which they are so produced. This process, then, yields scientific or epistemic knowledge of the rainbow, and indeed it is paradigmatic for the way in which the *scientiae naturales* attain truth and certitude concerning the contingent matters that are the proper subject of their investigations.

---

[11] The details of this mechanism were not known to Aquinas but were discovered shortly after his death by another Dominican who had studied at Paris, Dietrich or Theodoric of Freiberg, whose contribution to optical science is discussed in my article in the *Dictionary of Scientific Biography,* Vol. 4 (1971), pp. 92–95. For a full analysis of Theodoric's optical methods, see my *The Scientific Methodology of Theodoric of Freiberg* (Fribourg: The University Press, 1959).

The foregoing may serve to show that Aquinas' discourse, with its concentration on natural processes that take place successively and in time, allows for the possibility of temporal intervals between cause and effect. Unfortunately his examples of the eclipse and the rainbow, concerned as they are with light rays, obscure the point somewhat, since in the Middle Ages light propagation was generally regarded as instantaneous. From other examples, however, one can be assured of Aquinas' awareness of the possibility of a time lag between cause and effect. Thus it comes as no surprise to find him treating this point explicitly in his commentary on the *Posterior Analytics,* and there registering an advance over Aristotle's analysis. The locus is chapter 12 of Book II, where Aristotle treats problems relating to the inference of past and future events, and where he raises the question whether there are, as experience seems to show, causes that are distinct in time from their effects. The answer Aristotle proposes is somewhat ambiguous; consistent with his teaching in the *Physics,* he allows that one may infer the occurrence of an earlier event from that of a later event, but denies that the inference can be made the other way around. Most of his discussion then bears on the latter impossibility, where he argues that, were a later event to be inferred from an earlier, during the interval between them it would not be true to say that the later event either has happened or will happen. Here he likens the two events to the points terminating a line segment and the interval or process between them to the line itself. Two such events cannot be either continuous or contiguous, any more than two points can be, nor can the intervening process be contiguous with either event, any more than a line can be contiguous to a point. Thus there is nothing that can serve to hold events together and so assure that any coming-to-be will actually follow upon a past event. Moreover, there always seems to be the possibility of some third event intervening between the two being considered, which could be the cause of the later event's production and therefore would render the inference invalid.

This line of argument has proved troublesome for many commentators, who question Aristotle's identification of cause and

effect with point-like events and wonder why he never considered
the possibility of cause and effect being more similar to processes,
which then could be considered as successive or continuous.[12] It
is in evaluating this possibility that Aquinas' commentary proves
helpful, for Aquinas does consider the latter case and indeed makes
use of it in coming to a solution. In fact he devotes three *lectiones*
to an exposition of this one chapter in Aristotle, and in the first
two of these even attempts to show how, in accordance with the
Stagirite's principles, a cause that is not simultaneous with its
effect may still serve as a middle term in a demonstration.[13] The
argument Aquinas uses to support his interpretation is relatively
simple: just as in any process prior and subsequent elements can
be identified, so in the causal processes by which natural agents
produce their effects prior and subsequent elements may similarly
be noted. Or, as he puts it,

> since the notions of prior and subsequent are necessarily involved in
> any process, in considering the causes of a process one must accept
> the fact that the cause and the thing caused are likewise related as
> prior and subsequent. For it is obvious that a natural agent cause
> produces its effect through some type of process; and just as the
> thing undergoing change is brought to the terminus of the process
> through the entire process itself, so through the first portion of the
> process it is brought to the second portion, and so on. Hence, just
> as the entire process is the cause of the subsequent state of rest, so
> the first portion of the process is the cause of the subsequent portion,
> and so on.[14]

Aquinas then goes on to note that this line of reasoning is applicable whether one object alone is undergoing change or whether a
series of such objects are acting upon one another successively:

> This analysis is true whether it is confined to one object that is in
> process without interruption from beginning to end, or is applied to
> several objects the first of which initiates change in the second, and
> the second in the third. And although, while the first in the series
> effects change in its object at the same time as the object itself under-

---

[12] See, for example, W. D. Ross, *Aristotle's Prior and Posterior Analytics,* a Revised Text with Introduction and Commentary (Oxford: Clarendon Press, 1949), pp. 80–81 and 648–53; and Hugh Tredennick, *Aristotle's
Posterior Analytics,* The Loeb Classical Library (Cambridge, Mass.: Harvard University Press, 1960), pp. 13–15 and 219–27.
[13] *In II Posteriorum Analyticorum,* lect. 10–12.
[14] *Ibid.,* lect. 10, n. 2.

goes change, nevertheless the object thus changed continues to initiate change in another object even after it ceases to be changed itself. In this way several movable objects undergo change successively, with the one being the cause of the change induced in the other, and so on. . . .[15]

The example Aquinas supplies here is that of the projectile, which, though faulty from the viewpoint of modern science, was readily understood by his contemporaries; the point would be better illustrated in our day with the propagation of water waves by a stone dropped into a mill pond, for the case of the single object, and with the successive falls of a row of dominoes, for the case of the plurality of objects. In such instances, as in the example Aquinas supplies,

> . . . the cause is not simultaneous with that of which it is the cause [i.e., the effect], insofar as the first portion of the process is the cause of the second, or object first undergoing change induces a change in the second.[16]

Having therefore conceded the possibility of antecedent causality, or of a temporal interval between cause and effect, both of which he likens to the parts of a process, Aquinas then takes up the more difficult question as to how antecedent causes can serve as middle terms in scientific demonstrations. To clarify his exposition he introduces an example that is particularly apposite in that it expands the time interval between cause and effect considerably beyond that noted in cases involving the transmission of light rays. The example is that of a person taking medicine and subsequently being cured, either at some specified time, such as "he will be cured on such and such a day," or at some unspecified time, such as simply "he will be cured in the future."[17] In terms of this illustration it is easy for Aquinas to explain why Aristotle has reservations about syllogizing from an earlier to a later event, and why he seems to countenance the possibility of the reverse procedure. Once a person has been cured, it does seem reasonable to attribute the cause of his cure to his prior taking of the medicine. But from the fact that a person takes medicine at a particular time, one may not infer scientifically that he will

---

[15] *Ibid.*
[16] *Ibid.*
[17] *Ibid.*, nn. 8 and 9.

be cured either at some specified later date or indefinitely in the future. The reason for this is that, as Aristotle indicates, after taking the medicine there will always be some intervening time "in which it is true to say that he had drunk the medicine but not yet true to say that he has been cured," [18] or, and this is Aquinas' emendation, that "having posited what is prior, the subsequent does not necessarily follow in cases where the effects of the causes can be impeded." [19]

A difficulty yet remains, however, and this relates to the type of syllogizing to which Aristotle apparently has given approval, namely, that of drawing an inference from a later to an earlier event. Here too, in the intervening time, it would seem always possible to find an intermediate event, different from the taking of the medicine, that could yet serve as the cause of the person's cure. If this possibility exists, then one can never be sure that he was cured by the taking of the medicine, and thus scientific knowledge would seem to be precluded even through this *a posteriori* reasoning process. [20]

The problem, of course, already exists for Aristotle, but the solution he devises is not at all clear, and one suspects that this is why he prefers to insist on the simultaneity of cause and effect whenever necessary demonstrations are required. [21] Here Aquinas' commentary again proves helpful, for the Common Doctor attempts to meet the objection and thus still guarantee the possibility of demonstrating in natural science through antecedent causality. Aquinas admits that if one conceives of events as point-like completions of processes, there will always be an infinite number of such completions or partial completions, and on this basis alone it will be impossible to know where to start or to terminate in any demonstrative process. The practical problem is not insoluble for him, however, for he notes that one can always begin with the point-like event that corresponds to the moment "now," and from this reason back to a cause that is ultimately

---

[18] *Ibid.*, n. 8.
[19] *Ibid.*, n. 9.
[20] *Ibid.*, lect. 11, n. 5.
[21] Cf. *ibid.*, lect. 10, n. 9.

immediate with respect to the process that produces the noted effect. To illustrate this he extends the example of the person taking the medicine to include a further process consecutive on his being cured, namely, "his performing the tasks of a healthy man." [22] Should the sick person now be observed performing such tasks, one can reason back that it was necessary for him to have been cured at some time previously, and if he has been so cured, it is further necessary that he previously have taken the medicine. Thus, if D stands for "performing the tasks of a healthy man," C for "being cured," and A for "taking medicine," C can function as a *causa cognoscendi* that serves to connect D with A as its ultimate cause. On this basis, writes Aquinas,

> we can conclude that if D has come to pass, it is necessary that A have previously come to pass; and we take as cause that which took place in the interim, namely, C. For D having come to be, it is necessary that C have previously come to be; and C having come to be, it is necessary that A have previously come to be; therefore, D having come to be, it is necessary that A have previously come to be. For example, if this person has now performed the tasks of a healthy man, it follows that previously he had been cured; and if he was cured, it is necessary that previously he had taken the medicine. [23]

The foregoing is merely illustrative of the procedure Aquinas would recommend to pass through various mediate events or processes until one finally is able to demonstrate the immediate cause of the effect being investigated. So he continues:

> Therefore, by always taking a middle in this way, for example, something else between C and A, as C was taken as middle between D and A, one will come to rest somewhere at something immediate. [24]

This is as far as Aquinas goes with that particular example, but perhaps its further consideration in the light of present-day knowledge may serve to clarify his point. Let us assume, in Aquinas' example, that the person who takes the medicine is incapacitated by severe stomach acidity, and that the medicine he drinks is some form of alkalizer. If one is to believe television commercials, the essential mechanism of the resulting cure will be provided by some intermediate process or event, which may be

---

[22] *Ibid.*, lect. 11, n. 4.
[23] *Ibid.*
[24] *Ibid.*

designated as *B,* and which will consist in a chemical reaction whereby the alkali ions neutralize the acid ions in the sick person's stomach, and thereupon gradually restore him to health. Thus understood, the entire process of the cure may be seen as made up of four partial processes: *A,* the ingestion of the medicine; *B,* the neutralization of the stomach acidity; *C,* the restoration of normal functioning to the other organs of the body; and *D,* the performance of the tasks of a healthy man. All of these components, it may be noted, are themselves processes, although they begin and terminate with point-like events, up to and including the moment ''now'' from which the reasoning process started. From the viewpoint of modern medicine, what is most important is that the proper or immediate cause of the cure is best seen microscopically as the event-like combination or neutralization of the alkali and acid ions, where for each particular combination the particles come into contact, and where, in this micro-process, partial cause and partial effect are themselves simultaneous. But such individual micro-processes aside, the entire neutralization process is *not* simultaneous, being made up of a series of such micro-processes taking place over a time interval, and the same is true of the taking of the medicine and the final effecting of the cure, both of which depend on the movement of medicine and the redistribution of organic fluids, and thus are time-consuming processes.

On an understanding such as this, based on Aquinas' recommended method, it would seem possible to have scientific knowledge of processes wherein efficient causality is exercised over a period of time, and where the initiating cause is temporally antecedent to the completed effect. The methodology of demonstrating *ex suppositione finis* then can be seen as applying to such cases, just as it does to the cases of the lunar eclipse and the production of the rainbow. Some medicines, it is true, prove to be ineffective, and some people are not cured—a state of affairs completely analogous to that in the example, based purely on nature's operation, that not every human being is born with two hands. But such defects arising either from matter or from the fact that nature acts over an extended period of time, while complicating the methodology whereby demonstrations can be attained, in no way nullify the possibility of scientific or epistemic knowledge of nature and its processes.

126

III

This much said, some differences between the Humean and the Aristotelian views of causality may now be clarified in the light of Aquinas' commentary. Hume, it would appear, was accurate in his intuition that the exercise of efficient causality, as observable at the phenomenal level and so of particular interest to the scientist, would involve sequential series of events wherein the cause would generally be apprehended prior to the effect. Once he had decided on an event-like analysis of cause and effect, moreover, he was correct in maintaining that such an analysis can never yield knowledge of necessary connections in nature. Aristotle's difficulty in analyzing cases where cause and effect are punctiform, with the infinite number of possibilities they provide between the extremes of any natural process no matter how short, already signals the conclusion to which Hume would be forced once he had restricted himself to a consideration of atomic events alone. On the other hand, Hume's limitation lay in being too precipitate when urging that the only meaningful analysis of causation would have to remain at the phenomenal level, and there invoke merely an event ontology. The experience of recent science has shown, for example, the poverty of such dogmatic empiricism for providing knowledge of the entities and mechanisms that underlie observable events and that now serve to reveal their actual connectedness.

Aristotle, as has been observed, is enigmatic with respect to the problem considered in this essay. One could maintain, and indeed some Aristotelian Thomists would be so inclined, that the interpretations here attributed to Aquinas are actually those of Aristotle himself. That this is unlikely may be seen from an examination of the commentaries on the Greek text of the *Posterior Analytics*, and also from a study of the major commentators in the Latin West, including Averroës, Robert Grosseteste, Albert the Great, and extending even to Jacopo Zabarella. Aquinas' interpretations may be seminal in Aristotle, but their distinctive articulation is not to be found elsewhere in the commentatorial tradition. With regard to the *ipsa verba* of Aristotle, it should be noted that he himself suggested event-like analyses as appropriate for dealing with problems of antecedent causality, and thus is partly responsible for the difficulties into which an exclusive concern with such analyses would later lead. The reason for this suggestion is probably associated with his view of substantial generation or change, which takes place at an instant of time and therefore is best described as a point-like event. Since such substantial change is the normal terminus of many of the natural processes studied in the *scientiae naturales,* it is not surprising that punctiform events should have emerged large in Aristotle's thought. In his favor, however, it should be noted that he himself was quick to realize the difficulties inherent in event analysis, and possibly for this reason consistently de-emphasized antecedent causality, preferring rather to discuss cases where cause and effect are simultaneous. Such a preference, as it turns out, was methodologically sound, for the reduction of causal processes to their immediate initiators at the micro-level brings one ultimately to instantiations of simultaneous causality. The search for such deeper levels of explanation also takes one beyond the phenomenal order to regions of ontological depth where otherwise hidden mechanisms can be explored and the ways in which these serve to connect phenomenal events made apparent.

Aquinas, as we have attempted to show, combines both Humean and Aristotelian elements in his treatment of causal processes. The cases of temporal succession that interest Hume and that led to his causation doctrine were clearly of interest to Aquinas also. The ambiguity in Aristotle as to whether some causes actually do precede their effects or merely appear to do so, is resolved by Aquinas in a way that legitimizes the temporal-succession aspect of Hume's analysis. Moreover, in view of Aquinas' interest in process, and then considering the subsequent development of modern science with its pervasive spatio-temporal descriptions of physical events, it is probable that Aquinas would have admitted that antecedent causality *is* more frequently encountered in the investigation of natural processes that interest the scientist. On the other hand, Aquinas's empiricism could not restrict itself to a Humean form of phenomenalism, but would use the succession of observable events as a springboard to search for their deeper underlying connections. In such a search his sympathies would be with Aristotle and the ultimate resolution of antecedent causation to cases of simultaneous causality. Otherwise the advantage of Aquinas' "middle of the road" view is that it provides a framework in which both ways of studying causal processes acquire a certain legitimacy. The phenomenal method, with its stress on the regularity of succession of events in temporal sequences, and thus in its concern with antecedent causation, serves to isolate instances of natural phenomena whose study may lead to scientific or epistemic knowledge, whereas the more noumenal method, with its search for causal efficacy, underlying mechanisms, and micro-processes that lay bare the connections between events, and this in terms of simultaneous causality, itself results in the sought-after knowledge.

Finally, contemporary analytic discussions of causal relations are not without relevance to the problematic under discussion. For the most part analytical philosophers have given up on Hume's insistence that temporal sequence is essential to causation and its recognition, and are now willing to countenance the view that cause and effect, even when seen uniquely as events, can be simultaneous.[25] Recently, however, an attempt has been made to argue "for a qualified endorsement of Hume's intuition," by showing that there must always be a time difference between cause and effect for the cases "in which cause and effect are modifications of the same physical object."[26] The case proposed is rather peculiar and, although discussed with considerable analytical acumen, seems to have been contrived mainly to accommodate a growing body of what the author regards as "non-problematic" statements concerned essentially with event ontology.[27] It would take us too far afield to survey this literature and evaluate the various moves made therein for the description and recognition of events,[28] but the general impression one gets is that it shows little awareness of the actual problems one encounters when employing causal reasoning in scientific explanation. Much more attractive than this Humean exercise are the proposals of other recent writers

---

[25] For example, Arthur Pap, *Elements of Analytic Philosophy* (New York: The Macmillan Company, 1949), pp. 220–24.

[26] Carl G. Hedman, "On When There Must Be a Time-Difference Between Cause and Effect," *Philosophy of Science* (1972), p. 507.

[27] *Ibid.*, pp. 507, 510.

[28] Hedman gives a brief bibliography on p. 511.

who question the adequacy of any event ontology to deal with causal processes, and turn instead to an investigation of generative mechanisms and structures at the micro-level that explain natural phenomena in terms of the factors that can actually account for their production.[29]

It would be too much to say that all of this problematic has been adumbrated by Aquinas and its solution already anticipated by this renowned thirteenth century thinker. Yet, temporally situated as he was between Aristotle and Hume, Aquinas does provide an original intermediate viewpoint. While not completely embracing the opposed positions, perhaps his thought can serve to illumine the strengths and weaknesses of both extremes and so reconcile some of the competing claims that continue to be made on behalf of antecedent and simultaneous causality.

---

[29] For a survey of this literature, see Edward H. Madden, "Scientific Explanations," *The Review of Metaphysics* (1973), pp. 723–43.

DEMONSTRATING IN THE SCIENCE OF NATURE

AT PRESENT it is generally agreed that modern science differs radically from the science of nature developed in the Aristotelian-Thomistic tradition. The "scientific" character of modern science is likewise commonly accepted, but so striking is the difference between it and Aristotle's treatment of the world of nature that many now hesitate to dignify the latter by the name " science." In fact, the remnant of Aristotle's natural doctrine, staunchly defended by faithful adherents as perennial truth, is much more commonly referred to as " philosophy," or by the more specialized terms, " cosmology " and " psychology "; other parts, seemingly of an observational character, have been relegated to the antiquaries as monuments of purely historical interest. Modern science, on the other hand, has pursued an autonomous course from its inception in the seventeenth century, and has developed so extensively as to crowd from the current scene all other knowledge of the world of nature. Thus the word " science " is by and large now taken to mean empiriological knowledge attained by the use of experiment, measurement and postulational procedures, and any other signification, if allowed at all, is regarded as sheer equivocation.

In the peaceful atmosphere created by such common acceptance, any attempt to force a different understanding of the term " science " might easily be regarded as an impertinence. Yet there are compelling reasons for urging a re-examination of the concept of science as it was initially developed by Aristotle and applied to the world of nature. The first of these is the integrative value of the Aristotelian concept in forging a unity among the speculative disciplines functioning at different levels of abstraction. The second is the no less important unifying effect within each level of abstraction, and particularly at the first level where the study of nature properly belongs. The divisive character of modern specialization has resulted in a proliferation of so-called "sciences," all pursuing a common dialectical method, but otherwise without essential connection or immediate relevance one to the other. A third reason is the value of the Aristotelian concept of science in eliminating artificial barriers between "philosophy" and "science," and the consequent endless pre-occupation with the problem of what constitutes a "philosophical" question, as opposed to a "scientific" one. To these reasons may be added a fourth, of great importance to educators, which is the value of the Aristotelian concept in focussing attention on what is true and certain within an area of rational investigation, and therefore on what is teachable and what should be taught.

Granted the efficacy of this motivation, however, almost insuperable difficulties are encountered when an attempt is made to apply the methods and concepts currently taught in cosmology and psychology to productive use in the domain of modern science. This would seem to offer proof positive that the Aristotelian and modern approaches are irreducibly different, that they might possibly be complementary and capable of compatible interpretation, but that they are hardly subsumable under a generalized concept of science, Aristotelian or otherwise.

Yet, to one acquainted with the science of nature originally proposed by Aristotle, as distinguished from its modern counterparts, another alternative suggests itself. The difficulty might be one of comparatively recent origin, arising from a failure of contemporary thinkers to appreciate the way in which Aristotle's approach to the world of nature was truly scientific according to his own definition of science, viz., *certain knowledge through causes and effected by demonstration.* Under this conception, not only would modern science be inappreciative of Aristotelian methodology, but modern cosmology and psychology would likewise have dispensed with his search for causes and demonstrative procedures. And this thesis is capable of elaborate defense, if one only analyze the manuals and textbooks presently available for teaching these subjects in seminaries and colleges. In most instances the order of Aristotle is completely reversed, the properties of changeable things being treated before their principles or causes; [1] and in all cases, the

---

[1] P. Hoenen, S. J., *Cosmologia* (Romae: Apud Aedes Pont. Univ. Gregorianae, 1949) ; F. Saintonge, S. J., *Summa Cosmologiae* (Montreal: Imprimerie du Mes-

notion that strict demonstration is the characteristic of science has been omitted entirely, for nowhere is a single demonstration noted or explained, nor is demonstrative argument regarded as an essential element in the development of this branch of philosophy.[2]

Such being the case, it would appear that the proper place to start in re-evaluating the *scientific* character of cosmology, psychology and modern science is not at the level of their material content, but rather through a reconstruction of the methodological apparatus initially employed by Aristotle in elaborating his science of nature. This in turn entails a fresh understanding of the way in which Aristotle used demonstrations in studying nature, the various types of demonstration he recognized as permitted by its subject matter, and the special procedures he was forced to adopt because of the difficulties inherent in attaining a scientific knowledge of changing, contingent things. Obviously the key to such an undertaking lies in the *Organon,* and particularly in the *Posterior Analytics.* But its implementation further requires a tracing of the demonstrative process through the complete science of nature as it was proposed and at least tentatively worked out in the Aristotelian tradition.

Such an enterprise is essentially the burden of this study. It begins by indicating the various types of demonstration explicitly noted by Aristotle, classifying these in a general way, and furnishing in each instance a prototype to be used for comparative purposes. Then an examination is made of the eight books of the *Physics* to ascertain the principal demonstrations contained therein.[3] This

sager, 1941); J. A. McWilliams, S. J., *Cosmology* (New York: The Macmillan Company, 1933); K. Dougherty, S. A., *Cosmology* (Peekskill: Graymoor Press, 1952).

[2] J. Gredt, O. S. B., *Elementa Philosophiae Aristotelico-Thomisticae* (Freiburg: B. Herder and Co., 1937); F.-X. Maquart, *Elementa Philosophiae* (Paris: Facultatis Theologiae Bibliopola, 1937); E. Hugon, O. P., *Cursus Philosophiae Thomisticae* (Paris: Lethielleux, 1922); T. Zigliara, O. P., *Summa Philosophica* (Paris: Beauchesne, 1912); D. Nys, *Cosmology* (Milwaukee: Bruce Publishing Co., 1942); A. G. Van Melsen, *The Philosophy of Nature* (Pittsburgh: Duquesne University Press, 1953).

[3] It should be noted that Aristotle rarely signalized his use of demonstration in any of the scientific tracts he elaborated, and St. Thomas likewise does not usually point it out explicitly. The explanation of this is undoubtedly to be found in the principle of economy followed by Aristotle, wherein general methodological procedures are logically stated beforehand *in actu signato,* and then applied in each science *in actu exercito.* The *Organon* is thus presupposed to all scientific works, and logical questions are not raised in scientific tracts.

analysis is further extended to the subject matter of the tracts *On the Heavens, On Generation and Corruption, The Meteorology, On the Parts of Animals, On the Soul,* and *On Sense and Sensation.* Because the parvity of early experimental data severely limited the development of demonstrative arguments in these tracts, it was found useful to assimilate considerable material discovered by modern investigators. This matter, however, has been subjected to analysis following Aristotelian methodology, and selected arguments are proposed in the form of demonstrative syllogisms. The result is not intended as a taxative listing of all demonstrations in the science of nature, nor should it be regarded as a definitive study of even the principal demonstrations. But it will serve as a tentative reconstruction of Aristotelian-Thomistic science, and thus will offer the basis for some observations to follow on the *scientific* character of early and modern knowledge about the world of nature.

I. TYPES OF DEMONSTRATION

There are two main types of demonstration in Aristotle's science of nature, the one from effect to cause and known as *a posteriori* demonstration, and the other from cause to effect, and known as *a priori* demonstration.[4] The two are closely connected in the study of nature, in the sense that the latter type is usually the product of the former, in the normal order of knowing.[5] Yet, for purposes of analysis, this connection is overlooked and the two are considered formally as distinct and independent types of demonstration.

A. *A Priori* DEMONSTRATIONS:

A priori demonstrations may be further divided into two kinds, one through a proper cause convertible with the effect and known as *propter quid*, the other through a common or remote cause not convertible with the effect and known as *quia*.[6] *Propter quid* demonstrations, in turn, may be divided into different types depending on the type of causality involved in the demonstration.[7] This is possible insofar as natural science demonstrates through all four causes; it uses either the final, efficient, formal or material cause as a middle term in giving the *propter quid* explanation of a conclusion.[8]

---

[4] *I Post. Anal.*, lect. 4, n. 16.
[5] *Ibid.*, lect. 23, nn. 7-9.
[6] *Ibid.*, n. 3.

[7] *II Post. Anal.*, lect. 9.
[8] *Ibid.*, lect. 11, n. 1.

1. If the material cause is the middle term of a demonstration, the predicate must be a property; it cannot express an essential part of the definition of the subject.[9] If the predicate of the conclusion is a property, however, it is not necessary that the middle term be the material cause; it may be this or one of the other causes. This type of demonstration, where a property is demonstrated through a cause, shall be referred to as *TYPE A*. The following is a sample of the type: [10]

S	M	P
(A) Every natural primary unit	is A thing generated from contraries	is corruptible.
(subject)	(material cause)	(property)

This and subsequent demonstrations are written in an abbreviated form frequently employed by Aristotle.[11] All should be read according to the mode *Barbara* of the first figure, viz.: "(All) M is P, but (all) S is M; therefore (all) S is P." Also, for purposes of more complete notation, a demonstration of property through material cause shall be designated Type A_1; through formal cause, Type A_2; through efficient cause, Type A_3; and through final cause, Type A_4.

a. In this type of *propter quid* demonstration, the predicate of the major premise is predicated in the fourth mode of *per se*.[12] This mode signifies that the predicate is the proper effect of the causal action of the subject, and indicates the causal (consequential) connection between subject and predicate.[13] The predicate of the major premise in this type is thus considered formally as an effect, rather than as a part of the definition.

b. The predicate of the minor premise, on the other hand, is predicated in the first mode of *per se*.[14] This mode signifies that the predicate expresses the definition or part of the definition of the subject.[15]

c. The predicate of the conclusion is predicated in the second mode of *per se*.[16] It signifies that the subject is the material cause or the proper subject of whatever is attributed to it in the predicate.[17] If the predicate is an accident, the proper subject is not only

[9] *Ibid.*, lect. 9, n. 4.
[10] *Ibid.*
[11] *Ibid.*, lect. 7, n. 8.
[12] *I Post. Anal.*, lect. 13, n. 3.
[13] *Ibid.*, lect. 10, n. 7.
[14] *Ibid.*, lect. 13, n. 3.
[15] *Ibid.*, lect. 10, n. 3.
[16] *Ibid.*, lect. 13, n. 3.
[17] *Ibid.*, lect. 10, n. 4.

placed in its definition, but it also exerts a true causality on the predicate, and thus the predication is in the fourth mode of *per se*, as well as in the second.[18]

2. If the middle term of the demonstration is not the material cause, but one of the other causes, it is not necessary that the predicate of the conclusion be an accidental property. The predicate may express a part of the definition, in terms of one or other of the causes. This is possible because the causes have a certain order among themselves, and the *ratio* of one is taken from another. The order is from final cause, to efficient, to formal, to material, the *ratio* in each case being taken from the prior cause.[19]

A sample of this type of demonstration in which the middle term is the final cause, to be referred to as *TYPE B*, is the following: [20]

(B)	Virtue	is	A habit conducive to happiness	is	a stable way of acting according to right reason.
	(subject)		(final cause)		(formal cause)

In order to specify this notation more completely, when the efficient cause is demonstrated through the final cause, the designation shall be Type B_1; when the formal cause is demonstrated through the final cause, Type B_2; and when the material cause is demonstrated through the final cause, Type B_3.

3. The efficient cause may also occupy the place of the middle term. A sample of this type, to be referred to as *TYPE C*, is the following: [21]

(C)	Thunder	is	What is produced by a discharge of lightning from clouds	is	a rumbling sound in the heavens.
	(subject)		(efficient cause)		(formal cause)

Again for purposes of more accurate designation, when the formal cause is demonstrated through the efficient cause, the demonstration shall be referred to as type C_1; and when the material cause is demonstrated, Type C_2.

4. The formal cause can also be used as a middle term. A sample of this type, to be referred to as *TYPE D*, is the following: [22]

---

[18] *Ibid.*, n. 8.
[19] *Ibid.*, lect. 16, n. 5.
[20] *II Post. Anal.*, lect. 7, n. 3.
[21] *Ibid.*, n. 8.
[22] *In III Phys.*, lect. 4, n. 1.

(D)	Motion or change	is	The actuation of a potential thing insofar as it is potential	is	the act of a thing moved insofar as it is moved, not the act of the mover (or, motion is properly in the *moved*).
	(subject)		(formal cause)		(material cause)

Note that in this last type of demonstration, when the subject of the demonstration is in one of the categories of accident, the demonstration is obliquely the same as Type A, the only difference being that in the latter the subject is not the accident itself, but the substance in which it exists.[23]

A special difficulty arises in the consideration of demonstrations of Types B, C, and D. For it appears that in these cases a cause is being demonstrated *a priori*, or that a definition (*per se nota* of itself) is being demonstrated *a priori*, both of which lead to serious inconveniences. Thus it is necessary to make clear that in no case is a cause being demonstrated precisely as cause, but rather under the aspect of itself being an effect of the exercise of a prior causality. The causal action, in other words, is restricted to the particular type of causality expressed in the middle term,[24] and this is sufficient for demonstrative knowledge if the three conditions normally required are present, namely, that we know the cause, that it is the cause, and that what is known cannot be otherwise.[25]

It should also be made clear that there are three types of real definitions that can be given, one of which is the principle of a demonstration, another the conclusion of a demonstration, and the third only differing from a demonstration by the order of its terms.[26] The last named not only indicates the *quod quid est* of the subject, but also includes the *propter quid*; it differs from a demonstration only modally and cannot itself be demonstrated.[27] The first named, i. e., the definition that is a principle of demonstration, expresses the *quid est* of the subject, taken suppositively or *ex suppositione*;[28] it cannot be demonstrated either. It is only the

---

[23] Compare Dem. 70 *infra* with the demonstration usually given in logic textbooks: " Every rational animal is risible; but man is a rational animal; therefore man is risible." But Type A is more *scientific* than Type D; cf. *II Post. Anal.*, lect. 1, n. 9.

[24] *II Post. Anal.*, lect. 7, n. 3.

[25] *I Post. Anal.*, lect. 4, n. 5.

[26] *Ibid.*, lect. 16, n. 4; cf. *II de Anima*, lect. 1, n. 212.

[27] *II Post. Anal.*, lect. 8, n. 9.

[28] *Ibid.*, lect. 7, n. 3.

second named definition that can be the conclusion of a demonstration, and this only insofar as it signifies the *quod quid est,* and this exclusively, without the inclusion of a *propter quid.*[29]

The method of natural science is such that it normally utilizes demonstrations of Types B, C, and D to discover definitions which are the conclusions of demonstrations.[30] A twofold reason for this can be assigned. The first is that in the generation of natural things, the form intended (the end or final cause of the generation) and the agent generating (the efficient cause of the generation), are both specifically the same as the form attained, the formal cause of the thing generated.[31] Thus the *quod quid est* of a natural thing can be considered under aspects that are not merely those of formal causality, but of final and efficient causality as well. The second reason is that the necessity which is proper to natural science is not an absolute necessity, because of the possibility of interference from chance or fortune, but rather is a hypothetical necessity, or one *ex suppositione.*[32] This necessitates the use of a *quod quid est* taken suppositionally, in the order of final cause to be attained, and deriving the other causes on the basis of their necessity, *if* this end is to be attained.[33] Because of this peculiar type of necessity that is proper to natural science (also found to a degree in moral science, however [34]), it is possible to demonstrate conclusions which are sometimes impeded in actual fact, but which are nevertheless verified frequently, or for the most part. These conclusions are necessary with a physical necessity, and truly " cannot be otherwise than they are," [35] if they are understood in the order of a hypothetical necessity taken *ex suppositione* from the end, and abstracting from defects arising either from time or from the failure of one of the causes prior in the actual order of generation.[36]

5. Besides the types of *a priori* demonstration already enumerated, there is the possibility of another type in natural science, in which the middle term pertains to the genus of formal cause, but is in the order of quantity. Quantity is the subject of investigation

[29] *Ibid.,* lect. 8, n. 11.
[30] *Ibid.,* lect. 9, n. 12.
[31] *In II Phys.,* lect. 11, n. 2
[32] *Ibid.,* lect. 15, n. 2.
[33] *Ibid.,* n. 6.
[34] *In II Post. Anal.,* lect. 9, n. 13.
[35] *I Post. Anal.,* lect. 4, n. 5.
[36] *Ibid.,* lect. 6, n. 8.

in two sciences, namely, natural science and mathematics, although it is considered differently in the two.[37] What is true of mathematical quantity is verified also of physical quantity, however, and thus it is possible to give a *propter quid* demonstration for a conclusion verified in natural science by employing a mathematical middle term.[38] These demonstrations are called physico-mathematical demonstrations because of their composite character, and shall be designated as *TYPE E.* The following is a sample: [39]

(E)	A circular wound	is	A wound that presents the smallest healing surface for its area	is	one that heals more slowly than other wounds.
	(subject)		(formal cause, mathematical)		(property)

B. *A Posteriori* DEMONSTRATIONS:

6. Because, in the study of natural things, effects are usually more known to us than their causes, it is possible to demonstrate the existence of certain causes from their effects, or *a posteriori*.[40] Such demonstrations only serve to establish the fact, and thus are *quia*, although they may be converted to *propter quid* if they argue from an effect convertible with the cause.[41] Most frequently, the type of causality made manifest by these demonstrations is efficient causality, and the effect is usually in a subject distinct from the cause whose existence is demonstrated. The middle term in such demonstrations, which is the effect, is usually also the nominal definition of the cause, insofar as we generally name hidden causes from their effects.[42] The type of *a posteriori* demonstration based on efficient causality shall be designated as *TYPE F.* An example is the following: [43]

(F)	Whatever is moved	is	A moving thing that is moved by at best a finite series of moved movers	is	moved by a first Mover completely unmoved (named " God ").
	(subject)		(effect: motion received)		(first efficient cause)

7. It is also possible to demonstrate *a posteriori* through a formal

---

[37] *II Phys.*, lect. 3, n. 5; cf. *I de Caelo*, lect. 1, n. 2.
[38] *I Post. Anal.*, lect. 25, n. 4; cf. *I de Caelo*, lect. 3, n. 6.
[39] *I Post. Anal.*, lect. 25, n. 6.
[40] *II de Anima*, lect. 3, n. 245.
[41] *I Post. Anal.*, lect. 23, n. 7.
[42] *Summa Theol.*, I, q. 2, a. 2, ad 2.
[43] *VII Phys.*, lect. 2, n. 1.

effect, and thus come to the knowledge of the formal cause and its proper matter.[44] A definition can be demonstrated in this fashion for a substantial or an accidental form.[45] This type of demonstration through a formal effect shall be designated as *TYPE G.* The following is an example: [46]

| (G) | The soul | is | That by which a living thing performs vegetative, sensitive, locomotive, or intellective functions | is | the act (form) of its proper matter (a physical organic body potentially living). |
| | (subject) | | (formal effect) | | (formal cause and proper subject) |

8. Finally there remains a type of *a posteriori* demonstration which is the reverse of Type E, using a mathematical middle term, and concluding to a formal cause pertaining to the genus of quantity. This type shall be designated as *TYPE H,* and an example is the following: [47]

| (H) | The earth | is | A body which casts a circular shadow on the moon in all orientations | is | spherical. |
| | (subject) | | (formal effect: mathematical) | | (formal cause: physical quantity) |

It should be noted that an exercise of efficient causality is the physical basis for demonstrations of Type G and Type H, but the effect is considered precisely as a formal effect and thus the predicate of the conclusion is in the order of formal cause.

II. LIST OF DEMONSTRATIONS [48]

A. FUNDAMENTAL SCIENCE OF NATURE (*Cosmology* [49])

The starting point in a strict science of nature is a generalized treatment of all things that are common to the specialized natural sciences; this is done partly because the common features of things

---

[44] *II de Anima,* lect. 1, n. 213; lect. 3, n. 253.
[45] *Ibid.*
[46] *Ibid.,*
[47] *Summa Theol.,* I, q. 1, a. 1, ad 2.
[48] The purpose of this list is to supply a skeletal outline of the science of nature, the bare bones on which a complete organic whole should be developed. Generally, in the interests of brevity, only the main members of the skeleton have been indicated, but in a few places the structure has been given in detail to show how further articulation is possible. Of the 75 demonstrations listed, 57

are more knowable in themselves, and partly because of the economy afforded, insofar as it avoids repetition in each specialized science.[50] Thus the first part of the science of nature considers changeable being *in general,* without particular concern for the type of motion or change that is characteristic of different kinds of natural bodies. It is concerned, in the main, with problems concerning the primary principles or causes of natural things and the general properties which flow from these principles. Therefore it first determines the intrinsic constituents which make natural bodies capable of undergoing change or motion (Dem. 1), and also the principles by which we come to know the world of nature, such as the concept of nature itself (Dem. 2). Then the properties of natural bodies in general are demonstrated, the foremost one being motion, and associated things such as the infinite, place, and time, all of which must be understood in order to comprehend the nature of motion (Dem. 3 through 10). After this the parts of motion are considered (Dem. 11 through 13), and finally the conditions for motion, the most important of which is the existence of the First Unmoved Mover (Dem. 14 through 16).

1. Type G; explicit in Aristotle and St. Thomas: [51]

---

are *a priori* and 18 are *a posteriori*; the balance was kept in favor of the former because it is the more perfect type of reasoning, to which the latter type is already presupposed in natural science. Similarly, 59 demonstrations are taken from the physical sciences, and only 16 from the biological sciences. This is partly because of the author's greater familiarity with the matter of Cosmology, Physics, Astronomy and Chemistry, but no less to give food for thought to those who would admit valid demonstrations in the biological sciences and deny their possibility in the physical sciences. A few of the demonstrations in the list are modelled after similar arguments given by M. A. Glutz, C. P., in *The Manner of Demonstrating in Natural Science* (#8. The Aquinas Library. St. Gabriel Monastery. Des Moines 10, Iowa). The number of physico-mathematical demonstrations was kept deliberately low; any textbook on theoretical physics will furnish countless arguments of this type for those who are interested in further development.

[49] The equivalent modern disciplines are indicated in this manner at their appropriate places in the list.

[50] This order of development is summarized in *I Meteor.,* lect. 1. Cf. *I Phys.,* lect. 1, n. 4.

[51] I *Phys.,* lect. 13, nn. 2-3; cf. lect. 10, n. 1. Note that in this and all subsequent demonstrations, no attempt is made to prove the premises or to indicate the dialectical reasoning that is the normal propaedeutic to their acceptance by the reader. Such proofs have been omitted deliberately in order to keep the article to reasonable length, while yet indicating the vast scope of the science as it is systematically developed. Many of the references cited, however, will be of assistance to those who wish to elaborate arguments to justify the premises.

| Every natural primary unit | is | A thing that is substantially changeable | is | composed of prime matter and substantial form as from first positive principles. |

2. Type G; explicit in Aristotle and St. Thomas: [52]

| What is done by nature | is | What is done always or for the most part, and for what is best and most suitable | is | for a determined goal or for an end (i. e., cannot be merely by chance). |

3. Type D; explicit in Aristotle and St. Thomas: [53]

| Motion or change | is | The actuation of a potential thing insofar as it is potential | is | the act of a thing moved insofar as it is moved, not the act of the mover. |

4. Type D; explicit in Aristotle and St. Thomas: [54]

| The infinite | is | That which is potential in the order of magnitude conceived under the aspect of privation [55] | is | properly in the sensible continuum (i. e., really exists in this subject, although potentially). |

5. Type D; explicit in Aristotle and St. Thomas: [56]

| Place | is | The first immobile surface of the surrounding physical environment | is | proper to each body externally contained by other bodies. |

6. Type D; explicit in Aristotle and St. Thomas: [57]

| Place | is | The first immobile surface of the surrounding physical environment | is | proper to a body that has a natural local motion and rest in the universe. |

7. Type D; explicit in Aristotle and St. Thomas: [58]

| Time | is | The measure of motion according to before and after | is | the *per se* measure of the existence of all things that are generable and corruptible. |

---

[52] *II Phys.*, lect. 13, n. 2; cf. lect. 12, n. 3.
[53] *III Phys.*, lect. 4, n. 1.
[54] *Ibid.*, lect. 12, n. 10.
[55] I. e., the proper physical definition of the infinite: that outside of which there is always something.
[56] *IV Phys.*, lect. 7, n. 2.
[57] *Ibid.*, lect. 8, nn. 6-7.
[58] *Ibid.*, lect. 20, n. 12.

8. Type A₁; explicit in Aristotle and St. Thomas: [59]

Every change or motion [60]	is That which is measurable according to before and after	is in time.

9. Type A₁; explicit in Aristotle and St. Thomas: [61]

Time	is The measure of the locally movable	is everywhere.

10. Type D; explicit in Aristotle and St. Thomas: [62]

Universal time	is The measure of all other times and motions	is found in the first, most regular and continuous motion in the universe.

11. Type D; explicit in Aristotle and St. Thomas: [63]

Every motion or change (i. e., continuous or sensible change)	is A transition from one state to another	is *per se* in a category of being that permits strict contrariety (quantity, quality and location) .

12. Type A₂; explicit in Aristotle and St. Thomas: [64]

Whatever undergoes continuous (local) motion	is A thing that successively passes through the parts of a continuum	is divisible, or a quantified body.

13. Type A₁; explicit in Aristotle and St. Thomas: [65]

The quantity of motion (and time)	is That which is measured by the sensible continuum	is infinite or finite under the same aspects as sensible quantity.

14. Type A₁; explicit in Aristotle and St. Thomas: [66]

Whatever is in motion	is A thing divisible into parts on which depends the motion of the whole	is moved (not *per se primo*, but) by another.

---

[59] *Ibid.,* lect. 22, n. 5.
[60] I. e., continuous, or successive, or sensible motion.
[61] *IV Phys.,* lect. 23, n. 2.
[62] *Ibid.,* n. 11.
[63] *V Phys.,* lect. 4, n. 1.
[64] *VI Phys.,* lect. 5, n. 10; cf. *I Phys.,* lect. 1, n. 4.
[65] *VI Phys.,* lect. 9, n. 10.
[66] *VII Phys.,* lect. 1, n. 3.

15. Type F; explicit in Aristotle and St. Thomas: [67]

| Whatever is moved | is | A moving thing that is moved by at best a finite series of moved movers | is | moved by a first Mover completely unmoved (named "God"). |

16. Type A_1; explicit in Aristotle and St. Thomas: [68]

| The first unmoved Mover | is | An indivisible mover with unlimited power | is | outside the genus of quantified things, i. e., incorporeal. |

B. THE SPECIAL SCIENCES OF NATURE:

The special sciences of nature take up where fundamental science leaves off. The latter part of the science of nature is more or less abstract, and thus does not pay particular attention to the differences in the objects which it studies, nor to the detailed aspects of the types of motion or change that are found in the physical world. But with generalized and abstract considerations certainly established, the problem for the specialized sciences becomes one of concretion. In other words, the special sciences consider particular types of bodies existing in the physical world concretely, and the different kinds of natural motion they undergo in the concrete.

a. THE SPECIAL SCIENCE OF LOCAL MOTION

In all scientific inquiries, it is reasonable to proceed from the more common features of things to specialized variations, to go from what is more common to what is more special. Now of the three types of sensible motion discovered in the general science of nature (Dem. 11), local motion is the most common, being found in even the most simple bodies that do not exhibit alteration or growth, and in every other kind of body also. Thus the science which studies local motion should be studied immediately after the generalized considerations of the fundamental science of nature. This first of the special sciences is therefore concerned with the physical universe and its component parts, both elemental and composed bodies, as they are in local motion.

i. The Elements (*Physics*)

The study of local motion in general is undertaken by analyzing the behavior of macroscopic bodies and ascertaining the natural

[67] *Ibid.*, lect. 2, n. 1; cf. *Summa Theol.*, I, q. 2, a. 3.
[68] *VIII Phys.*, lect. 23, n. 9.

local motion (Dem. 17 and 18). Further investigation reveals the proper subject in which natural motion is found, the elemental bodies or atoms, and leads to the demonstration of certain properties of composed bodies insofar as they are constituted of such elemental bodies (Dem. 19 through 22).

17. Type E; implicit in work of Galileo and Newton (16-17th cent.):

Every known physical body on earth or in the solar system, regardless of size and composition	is	A physical body that obeys uniform laws of motion tending to a center of gravity in a local region	is	composed of ponderous matter in virtue of which it falls, or has gravity.

18. Type B_2; implicit in Aristotle and St. Thomas: [69]

Gravitational motion	is	Regular local motion to rest at the center of gravity of the physical environment	is	a natural motion, or motion from an intrinsic principle.

19. Type D; implicit in Aristotle and St. Thomas: [70]

An element	is	The first material part of a ponderable body that is capable of stable existence	is	the smallest body that can *per se* undergo gravitational motion (or the proper subject of natural local motion).

20. Type A_1 (also E); implicit in work of Newton (17th cent.):

The natural place of a macroscopic body in local motion	is	The natural place of a body made up of elements in a given physical environment	is	distant from the center of gravity in inverse relation to the weight of its composing elements per unit volume.

21. Type H; implicit in work of Dalton and successors (18-19th cent.):

The relative mass of a chemical compound	is	The sum of relative masses combined in integral and fixed proportions by weight	is	caused by simple bodies or elements of unit relative masses (named " atoms ").

22. Type G (also H); based on work of Aston (20th cent.):

The relative mass of an atom	is	The measurement of the gravitational tendency of an elemental body to the center of the physical environment	is	distinctive for each known species of stable isotope.

---

[69] *III de Caelo*, c. 2; this is an application of *II Phys.*, lect. 13, nn. 5-6.
[70] *III de Caelo*, c. 2.

ii. The Cosmic Bodies (*Astronomy*)

The study of local motion also permits a scientific treatment of the heavenly bodies, largely *a posteriori,* through which new facts are discovered about the earth, moon, planets (Dem. 23 through 29) and more remote parts of the universe.

23. Type G; implicit in Aristotle and St. Thomas: [71]

The earth	is	A body to which falling bodies gravitate perpendicularly over its entire surface	is	a spherical physical body.

24. Type H; based on work of Foucault (19th cent.) :

The earth	is	A spherical body on which a freely swinging pendulum deviates clockwise in the northern hemisphere inversely as the sine of the latitude	is	spinning on its axis counterclockwise (looking down on the north pole) once every 24 hours.

25. Type H; based on work of Bessel and others (19th cent.) :

The earth	is	A body from which stars on the pole of the ecliptic appear to have an annual rotation (of 20.5″) as well as a diurnal rotation	is	a spinning body annually traversing a closed orbit (at about 18.5 miles per second).

26. Type A$_3$; adapted from Aristotle and St. Thomas: [72]

A summer day	is	A day that occurs when the pole of the earth is inclined towards the sun	is	longer and warmer than a winter day.

27. Type H; explicit in Aristotle and St. Thomas: [73]

The moon	is	A body that waxes and wanes through crescent phases	is	a spherical physical body illuminated by an external source (i. e., the sun) .

28. Type A$_2$; explicit in Aristotle and St. Thomas: [74]

A planet	is	A heavenly body that is near enough to be seen as a disk	is	a heavenly body that does not twinkle (reflects light steadily) .

---

[71] *II de Caelo,* c. 14; cf. *Summa Theol.,* I, q. 1, a. 1, ad 2.
[72] *II Phys.,* lect. 11, n. 7.
[73] *I Post. Anal.,* lect. 23, n. 8.
[74] *Ibid.,* n. 7.

29. Type H; explicit in work of Lowell (20th cent.) :

The perturbation in Neptune's orbital motion	is	A regularly occurring motion not explanable by gravitational effects from the inner planets	is	caused by a planet more remote from the sun (named " Pluto ").

b. THE SPECIAL SCIENCE OF ALTERATION

After local motion, the next motion that should receive detailed treatment is change in quality, or alteration. That this is more common than augmentation or growth should be clear from the fact that all living organisms undergo alterations, but not everything that changes in quality is alive and undergoing changes in quantity associated with growth.

i. The Qualities (*Physics*)

In order to understand alterations, or changes in quality, it is first necessary to investigate the sensible qualities themselves to ascertain their natures and various properties (Dem. 30 through 37). More intensive research leads to similar knowledge of qualities that are reductively sensible, and thence to the existence of entities associated with these qualities by *a posteriori* demonstration (Dem. 38 through 44).

30. Type D (also G); based on work of Rumford and others (18-19th cent.) :

Heat	is	The quality in things that is properly sensible to the thermal sense of touch	is	properly found in composed bodies whose molecules are in random translational motion.

31. Type C_1; adapted from Aristotle and modern investigators: [75]

Light	is	What is emitted by a (black) body heated to a high temperature (e. g., the sun)	is	that *by which* a colored object is rendered actually visible.

32. Type H; based on work of Roemer (17th cent.) :

Light	is	What is reflected by the regularly eclipsed satellites of Jupiter 16 minutes later when the earth is 50,000 miles farther away	is	propagated at a finite velocity of 186,000 miles per second.

---

[75] *De Sensu et Sensato*, lect. 2, n. 28; compare this syllogism with the more generalized argument in Dem. 43, *infra*.

33. Type A$_1$; explicit in work of Newton (17th cent.):

White light	is	Light composed of various colored rays each with a different index of refractibility.	is	light which produces a band of colors when passed through a prism.

34. Type C$_1$; adapted from Aristotle and modern investigators: [76]

Sound	is	What is produced by a vibrating body and a resonator	is	the quality in things which is properly sensible to the sense of hearing.

35. Type D (also G); based on work of Boyle and others (17-18th cent.):

Sound	is	The quality in things which is properly sensible to the sense of hearing	is	properly found in a medium undergoing regular vibratory motion (between 20 and 20,000 vibrations per second).

36. Type A$_3$; based on work of Laplace (18-19th cent.):

Sound	is	A series of condensations and rarefactions propagated through the local motion of integral parts of the subject	is	propagated faster in a gas when it is compressed than when it is diffuse.

37. Type E; explicit in work of Laplace (18-19th cent.):

Sound	is	A travelling disturbance in a medium which is accurately described by the wave equation	is	propagated in a gas at a velocity whose square is equal to the gas constant multiplied by the pressure and divided by the density.

38. Type C$_1$; adapted from Aristotle and St. Thomas: [77]

Lightning	is	A discharge of static electricity causing a violent disturbance of the air	is	productive of a noise in the atmosphere (called " thunder ").

39. Type H; explicit in the work of Millikan (19th cent.):

The electric charge on a minute oil drop	is	Electric charge that varies in discrete integral steps from a minimum value	is	caused by a unit electric charge (named " electron ").

---

[76] *De Sensu et Sensato*, lect. 16, n. 237; cf. *II de Anima*, lect. 16, n. 448.
[77] *II Phys.*, lect. 15, n. 6.

40. Type C_1 (or C_2); adapted from work of Gilbert (16th cent.) and moderns:

Static electriicty	is	What is produced in a dielectric substance by mechanical friction	is	an accumulation of electrons or ions in a particular region of the substance.

41. Type D; adapted from work of Faraday (19th cent.) and others:

Dynamic electricity (or electric current)	is	The local motion of electric charges	is	a drift of " free " electrons through a solid conductor or flow of ions through a gas or non-metallic liquid.

42. Type E; implicit in work of Ampère (19th cent.):

The magnetic field at the center of a circular turn of wire carrying an electric current	is	A field that obeys the inverse-square law and is radiated from a circular source	is	directly proportional to the strength of the source (i. e., the current) and inversely to the radius of curvature.

43. Type C_1; adapted from the work of Hertz and others (19th cent.):

Electromagnetic radiation	is	What is emitted by a hot black body or by the regular vibratory motion of electrons	is	that by which one body can actualize qualitative changes in a distant body without so actualizing intervening bodies.

44. Type F (or H); based on work of Chadwick (20th cent.):

Under certain bombardment conditions the radiation from a block of paraffin	is	An emission of protons ejected at high speeds	is	produced by a massive neutral particle (named " neutron ").

ii. The Generation of Composed Bodies (*Chemistry*)

Alterations, or qualitative changes, are of great importance in the physical world insofar as they bring about more fundamental changes, changes in the category of substance. Such changes are first noted in the generation and corruption of composed bodies. Thus a special part of the science of nature is concerned with the integral parts of composed bodies and the dispositions through which they undergo fundamental change (Dem. 45 through 52). The classification of such composed bodies and their elemental components, and their properties as known through substantial change, also pertain to this science (Dem. 53 through 59).

149

45. Type A₁; based on work of Dalton and others (18th cent.):

The relative mass of a chemical compound (i. e., its molecular weight)	is	The sum of the parts which make up the composite	is	the sum of the relative masses of the composing atoms.

46. Type H; implicit in work of Rutherford (20th cent.):

Metallic foil composed of atoms	is	A substance that directionally reflects massive positively charged particles	is	composed of integral parts with massive positively charged centers (named "nuclei").

47. Type E; based on work of Rutherford (20th cent.):

An atom	is	A neutrally charged body that has a massive positively charged center	is	a body that has negative charges (electrons) in its peripheral structure.

48. Type H; implicit in work of Moseley (20th cent.):

The series of elements in order of increasing atomic numbers	is	A series in which characteristic radiation is absorbed in discrete integral steps	is	a series in which the charge on the central positive nucleus increases in integral steps.

49. Type G (also H); implicit in work of Bohr and others (20th cent.): [78]

The series of elements in order of increasing atomic numbers	is	An atomic series with periodic (repeating) valences and periodic potentials for ionization by removal of an electron	is	a series with a periodic (repeating) peripheral electronic bonding structure (i. e., 2-8-8-18 etc.).

50. Type B₁; adapted from work of Lewis and Langmuir (20th cent.):

Chemical change	is	A fundamental change by which combining atoms tend to attain the most stable peripheral electronic structure	is	effected by electron transfer (electrovalent bond) and/or by sharing of electrons (covalent bond).

51. Type B₁; adapted from the work of the Curies and others (20th cent.):

Radioactive transformation	is	A fundamental change by which groups of nucleons tend to attain a stable nuclear structure	is	effected by throwing off massive parts as radiant energy (called "radio-activity").

---

[78] This argument is intended merely to show the *a posteriori* basis for our knowledge of atomic structure, by indicating the experimental evidence from which it is inferred. No commitment to any *theory* of atomic structure (e. g., Bohr's, Sommerfeld's, Schroedinger's, Heisenberg's, etc.) is thereby implied.

52. Type A_4; adapted from work of Le Chatelier (19th cent.) :

| The direction taken by two opposing chemical reactions | is | The direction that will bring all reagents in a system most quickly to equilibrium | is | the direction that offsets the normal effect of any strain on the system. |

53. Type A_2; based on work of Mendeleyev (19th cent.) :

| An alkali metal | is | An active metallic element with a positive unit valence | is | an element with a strong affinity for elements of the Halogen group. |

54. Type A_2; based on work of Ramsay and others (19th cent.) :

| An inert gas | is | An element with a neutral valence (most stable peripheral electronic structure) | is | chemically inactive. |

55. Type A_2 (or A_1) ; based on work of Van't Hoff (19-20th cent.) :

| A carbon compound formed from one carbon and four different radicals | is | A compound that has two assymetric forms, one the mirror image of the other | is | optically active. |

56. Type A_2; based on work of modern organic chemists:

| A paraffin | is | An open-chain, saturated hydrocarbon | is | insoluble in water and chemcally inert. |

57. Type C_1; based on work of modern inorganic chemists:

| An ionic compound | is | A compound formed by electron transfer | is | a compound with a crystal lattice made up of alternate positive and negative ions. |

58. Type B_2; adapted from work of Haüy (18-19 cent.) and others:

| A crystal | is | A composite body which preserves itself from chemical combination | is | a body which presents a minimum reacting surface to reagents consistent with its elemental composition and physical environment. |

59. Type A_2; based on work of modern inorganic chemists:

| A covalent substance | is | A substance whose constituent atoms are joined by shared electron pairs | is | a poor conductor of electricity. |

151

The last of the special sciences of nature is concerned with the remaining sensible motion, augmentation, or change in quantity, also known as growth. This motion is characteristic of living things, and thus the latter form the proper subject matter of a special science.

i. The Organism in General (*Biology*)

Scientific study of living organisms begins by ascertaining the nature of organic life and the requisites for its origin and development (Dem. 60 through 62). It is also concerned with the classification and properties of living things (Dem. 63 through 68).

60. Type G; explicit in Aristotle and St. Thomas: [79]

The soul	is	That by which a living thing performs vegetative, sensitive, locomotive or intellective functions	is	the act (form) of its proper matter (a physical organic body potentially living).

61. Type B_1; explicit in Aristotle and St. Thomas: [80]

A vegetative soul	is	What is generative of others similar to it in species	is	endowed with a nutritive potency to conserve its own being, grow, and reproduce, through the assimilation of food.

62. Type B_3; based on work of Malphigi (17th cent.) and recent investigators:

A living body	is	A body that must obtain energy from its surroundings and throw off waste products	is	a body with sufficient organization to sustain an exothermic chemical reaction (e. g., respiration).

63. Type B_3; based on work of modern botanists (e. g., Willstätter):

A green plant	is	An organism that prepares its own food (carbohydrates) by photosynthesis	is	an organism that contains a complex chemical substance (named " chlorophyll ").

---

[79] *II de Anima*, lect. 3, n. 253.
[80] *Ibid.*, lect. 9, n. 347.

64. Type B_2; adapted from Aristotle and St. Thomas: [81]

An animal	is	An organism that (not having a photosynthetic process to make its own food) must seek food from its surroundings	is	an organism endowed with sensation.

65. Type D; adapted from Aristotle and St. Thomas: [82]

An animal	is	An organism endowed with sensation (capable of having the form of another as other through physical stimulus)	is	an organism having at least tactile organs and a nervous system.

66. Type A_1; adapted from Aristotle and St. Thomas: [83]

An animal	is	An organism having at least tactile organs and a nervous system	is	irritable.

67. Type A_1; explicit in work of Harvey (17th cent.): [84]

Blood	is	A fluid of limited quantity that flows continuously in one direction	is	moved circularly.

68. Type B_1; based on the work of modern biologists:

Digestion	is	The breakdown of complex food molecules into smaller ones able to pass through the walls of the intestine into the blood	is	effected by a series of chemical changes, aided by organic catalysts called "enzymes."

ii. The Sentient Organism (*Psychology*)

Since there is also found in the physical world a special type of augmentation which is peculiar to things endowed with sensation, i. e., growth in knowledge, a more specialized development of the last part of natural science is possible. This concerns itself with animals and particularly man to ascertain the faculties by which

[81] *III de Anima*, lect. 17, n. 852.
[82] *Ibid.*, lect. 18.
[83] *Ibid.*
[84] It is noteworthy that William Harvey, practically alone among modern scientists, used strict Aristotelian methodology in his researches on the circulation of the blood.

knowledge is acquired (Dem. 69 through 73), and the appetites and other properties that follow on knowledge (Dem. 74 and 75).

69. Type A$_2$; implicit in Aristotle and St. Thomas: [85]

| Man | is | A rational animal | is | capable of natural science. |

70. Type D; adapted from Aristotle and St. Thomas: [86]

| Risibility | is | The ability to elicit delight over a recognized incongruity | is | the act of a rational being as such. |

71. Type B$_2$; implicit in Aristotle and St. Thomas: [87]

| An animal with intelligence | is | An animal that needs sensory data from which to abstract speculative and practical truth | is | one endowed with complete sensory powers. |

72. Type G; explicit in Aristotle and St. Thomas: [88]

| Man | is | A being who performs immaterial cognitive acts | is | a being with an immaterial cognitive faculty. |

73. Type D; explicit in Aristotle and St. Thomas: [89]

| Man | is | A being with an immaterial cognitive faculty | is | a being with an immaterial substance that is the subject of that faculty (not his body, therefore soul is a spiritual substance). |

74. Type A$_2$; explicit in Aristotle and St. Thomas: [90]

| The soul of man | is | A spiritual substance or an immaterial form | is | incorruptible or immortal. |

75. Type A$_2$; explicit in St. Thomas: [91]

| The human will | is | An appetitive faculty that follows a judgment not determined by nature | is | free. |

* * *

[85] *II Post. Anal.*, lect. 20, n. 15; cf. *II de Anima*, lect. 11; *III de Anima*, lect. 13.
[86] *I Post. Anal.*, lect. 8, n. 8.
[87] *I de Anima*, lect. 14.
[88] *II de Anima*, lect. 12; *III de Anima*, lect. 7.
[89] *III de Anima*, lect. 7; cf. *Summa Theol.*, I, q. 75, a. 2.
[90] *III de Anima*, lect. 10.
[91] *Summa Theol.*, I, q. 59, a. 3 and q. 83, a. 1; *III Ethic.*, lect. 11.

The first observation that should be made about the foregoing list is that it probably will not be generally accepted as a list of strict demonstrations in the science of nature. For one, the impression created by many of the arguments is that their premises are not self-evident, and thus they do not seem to be strictly demonstrative. At the opposite extreme, the impression created by other arguments is that their premises are sufficiently self-evident, but their conclusions are trivial, and therefore they do not seem to demonstrate anything either. And then there is the objection that many of the arguments employ mathematical middle terms, and thus they do not properly belong to the science of nature but to mathematical physics.

As to the first two difficulties, these are more a confirmation of the fact that the list contains true demonstrations than an argument against it. No one can acquire a scientific knowledge of a particular subject matter merely by reading a list of syllogisms—the road to knowledge is not that easy. As was known to Aristotle,[92] there are almost as many *per se nota* propositions in any science as there are demonstrations in that science. Therefore the only persons who can appreciate demonstrations are those who have gone through sufficient investigation to convince themselves of the truth of the premises.[93] And frequently, a person who has this much knowledge of a particular subject has already reasoned to the conclusion logically implied. To him the conclusion may appear trivial, because he is already quite convinced of its truth on the basis of his former knowledge. But the only way he could have attained this was by implicitly seeing the demonstration himself at some earlier period.

Such knowledge is not trivial. For the one who "sees" the demonstration it may not represent anything new, but it is true and certain knowledge that is not possessed by the uneducated. Moreover, it is knowledge not only of the fact, but of the reason why the fact is so and could not be otherwise, and this is most satisfying to the human mind. It may not stimulate further questions for this very reason, but it does summarize and crystallize the truth already possessed by the mind, and focusses attention on the middle term

[92] *I Post. Anal.*, lect. 4, n. 10; *I Topic.*, c. 1.
[93] The main task of the teacher would seem to be one of leading students to this intellectual vantage point by means of a proper dialectic.

that will be most useful in helping others to attain knowledge of the same conclusion in a certain and positive manner.

It is true that some of the demonstrations in the list are strictly physico-mathematical, and do not pertain *formally* to the science of nature insofar as they are seen in the light of a mathematical middle. Such demonstrations are not *propter quid* in natural science; rather they are *propter quid* in mathematical physics and only *quia* in the science of nature.[94] But they do establish true fact in the physical order and can therefore be used for later argument even at the level of *propter quid*. For instance, once the existence of atoms is demonstrated *quia* physico-mathematically,[95] the latter can be used as the proximate material cause for the massive properties of composed bodies *propter quid*.[96] Moreover, the fact that an argument involves quantity does not make it purely mathematical; physical quantity as such is a proper subject of investigation in the science of nature.[97] Thus St. Thomas refers to two proofs that the earth is round, one physical and the other mathematical,[98] but in both instances the predicate of the conclusion is in the quantitative order. Similarly, arguments respecting physical quantity can be either physical or mathematical, depending on the formal light under which they are considered.[99] The reason for this has been pointed out by St. Thomas in the beginning of his commentary on *De Caelo et Mundo*, a tract in which physico-mathematical arguments are obviously of some importance. He there makes the statement:

It would seem that Aristotle's proof here is not proper, because as he points out in the first book of the *Posterior Analytics*, one cannot demonstrate by having recourse to a higher genus. Thus one cannot properly conclude from a proof based on the division of magnitude, which is a mathematician's argument, to anything about motion which is the natural scientist's proper consideration.—But it should be noted that a science which is related to another by addition uses the principles of the latter in its demonstrations, in the same way as geometry uses the principles

---

[94] *I Post. Anal.*, lect. 25.
[95] Cf. Dem. 21, *supra*.
[96] Cf. Dem. 45, *supra*.
[97] Cf. *II Phys.*, lect. 3.
[98] *Summa Theol.*, I, q. 1, a. 1, ad 2; cf. Dem. H and Dem. 23 *supra*. Note that in neither case would the conclusion intend to assert that the earth is a *perfect* sphere in such a way that it would be invalidated by Clairaut's later proof that the earth is actually an oblate spheroid.
[99] Cf. Dem. 36 and 37, *supra*.

of arithmetic; it can do this because extended quantity adds position to number, for which reason a point is said to be a unit with position. In a similar way, a natural body has sensible matter added to its mathematical extension; and therefore it is not improper for the natural scientist to use mathematical principles in his demonstrations, for this is not a case of a completely different genus, but of one that is contained in a certain way within the other.[100]

With this brief refutation of difficulties concerning the demonstrative character of the proposed arguments, a second observation suggests itself. This is the obvious inference obtained from the list that there is a certain continuity between Aristotelian and modern thought, and that *in the things regarded as true and certain by modern science*, the original contributors were possibly more Aristotelian in their thinking than anyone hitherto has suspected.

There are some who might object to this assertion by denying that there is *anything* true or certain in modern science. This is tantamount to saying that speculative progress in uncovering the secrets of nature ended with Aristotle and St. Thomas, a statement which borders on the ridiculous. Those who would maintain such a position quite possibly entertain a distorted notion of physical certitude, and perhaps are too prone to adopt the skeptical attitude of some theoreticians, who, not knowing *everything* about the physical world, are loath to admit they know *anything*. Whether such investigators are seeking metaphysical or mathematical certitude is of little importance; at least they impose more stringent criteria for demonstration in physical science than the simple ones set by Aristotle in the second book of the *Physics*. Insofar as they would therefore be more Aristotelian than Aristotle, their position has little relevance to the present study.[101]

But for those who are convinced that the scientific revolution

[100] *I de Caelo*, lect. 3, n. 6.

[101] A similar instance of being more Aristotelian than Aristotle, frequently encountered in neo-scholastic circles, is the attitude of mind that would jump from *propter quid* knowledge at the level of changeable being in general, to an inquiry about the quiddity of a cat or a snail. This is tantamount to expecting an intuitive knowledge of corporeal essences, and asks for a kind of knowledge about animals that not even expert zoologists pretend to have attained. Most of modern science is far removed from the very abstract consideration of changeable being in general, but for the most part it still has not attained to exhaustive knowledge of various species in the concrete. Such detailed knowledge, of course, is not presupposed to the first demonstrations in any science, although it is gradually approachable through the systematic application of Aristotelian methodology.

of the seventeenth century, apart from its preoccupation with a dialectical method, has produced *some* certain knowledge about the physical world, a further conclusion is inescapable. For it is impossible that certain, mediate knowledge arise *per se* from dialectics; the dialectical process may well be the occasion for discovering such truth, but the certitude itself is attained by seeing the cause or reason why the reality comes to be as it is. The person who grasps a conclusion in this way has *demonstrative* knowledge at least implicitly. And no one should object to a reasonable insistence on rendering such argumentation explicit, particularly when this enhances the rigor of a science and makes the truth of its conclusions more communicable to others.

A third observation on the *scientific* character of modern science automatically arises from what has just been said. If modern science and the classical science of nature both attain to demonstrative knowledge of the physical world, since both are studying essentially the same objects, they are specifically one and the same science in the Aristotelian sense of the term. The accidental difference would seem to be that modern science makes greater use of mathematical modes of reasoning because of its more extensive use of measurement, and then camouflages the demonstrative character of its proofs by presenting them in a dialectical form. Such a procedure permits advances in knowledge to be proposed tentatively, without necessitating an immediate judgment on the certitude of the conclusion. Nevertheless, even though a single conclusion may not be certainly established in the lifetime of one investigator, there is *de facto* a growth in certain knowledge over the centuries. Dalton, Avogadro and Gay-Lussac may well have had some doubts about the existence of atoms, but a competent modern scientist can no longer have an open mind on this subject once he evaluates the data that are presently available.[102]

This means, of course, that considerable residues of dialectical conclusions are a part of the science of nature, vastly exceeding in bulk the conclusions that are known with certitude. But this is not a unique situation; indeed the science of sacred theology is not significantly better off in this respect. It is of central importance, however, that dialectical knowledge be assimilated to the body of knowledge established with certitude; otherwise there is no reference point, no point to which one can return in testing the per-

---

[102] Cf. Dem. 21, *supra*.

manance of a contribution and in adding to the structure of the science.

Neither Aristotle nor St. Thomas, moreover, would be surprised at this state of affairs in the science of nature, for neither had any dream that man could know all the secrets of nature with certitude. As St. Thomas observes in his commentary on the *Meteorology*:

He (Aristotle) says that after we have gotten through what he has already written (the *Physics, On the Heavens, On Generation and Corruption,* and the *Meteorology*), then we shall speculate further according to our ability, following the method outlined in the preceding books. This method is more than a recitation of the opinion of others, but is a real search for causes, the causes of animals and plants, both in general and according to their various species. And then we shall be almost at the end of natural science, which we set out to treat of from the beginning. He says *almost*, however, because not everything about nature can be known by man.[103]

As a fourth and final observation, it should be noted that a re-affirmation of the validity of Aristotelian methodology, and the science of nature implied by it, is of vital importance for education, particularly at the seminary and collegiate levels. If emphasis is once again centered on truth and certitude in reasoning about the world of nature, all so-called opposition between "science" and "philosophy" vanishes.[104] More important, the minds of students need not then be cluttered with theories that will become anti-quated in a few decades, and they can be given a good foundation in what is known with certitude about the world that God has made. Thus they will possess a truly *scientific* knowledge of the universe, which will at once integrate the various branches of natural science and give positive impetus to theological wisdom. Not only will they see the existence of God demonstrated in their science, but they will have a meaningful intellectual basis for further scientific inquiry about his attributes.[105] Such knowledge, developed by metaphysics and perfected by faith in the science of sacred theology, is the synthesis for which the mind of man is ever striving and by which it alone is capable of being satisfied.

---

[103] *I Meteor.*, lect. 1, n. 9.

[104] Philosophy, then, is strictly scientific, but it is a special kind of science, viz., science through the highest or ultimate causes. Thus the term "philosophy" should be reserved for the science properly concerned with ultimate causes, i. e., metaphysics. Yet the term "natural philosophy" can be and is used to designate the science of nature under its aspect of giving the ultimate explanation of natural things.

[105] Cf. St. Paul, *Epistle to the Romans*, c. 1, v. 20.

PART III

REALISM IN SCIENCE

ESSAY VIII:

IS THE PULL OF
GRAVITY REAL?

The great progress of modern science in our generation has brought into household use terms once found only in treatises on celestial mechanics. Rocketry and space technology now offer exciting new instruments for man to probe the depths of space. Already we are pondering the physiological effects of space travel, the effects of such things as "weightlessness" on the functioning of the human body. Where, in times past, a purely speculative interest motivated discussion of topics like gravity, in our day they are discussed for their bearing on the technology of the future.

With this growth of interest in the nature of cosmic forces, there is also increasing awareness of fundamental mysteries that confront man in his attempt to understand the environment in which he lives. Science is puzzled by such questions as the nature of elementary particles, the sources of the radiation impinging upon our atmosphere, the possibility of life in outer space, the intriguing question of the origin and evolution of the entire universe. And there are yet more fundamental questions, about which man has speculated for ages, to which science still does not have adequate answers.

A Fundamental Question

This evening I intend to discuss one such question. I will state it simply. "What is gravity?" All of us have direct experience of a heavy body falling to earth. A college degree in science is not necessary to ponder the question, "Why does it fall?"

I have asked this question of many students, and quite commonly encounter the answer: "Why that's very simple; a body falls because the earth pulls it." This answer is so common that one rarely hears gravity mentioned except as part of the expression, "the *pull* of gravity." And precisely because it is such a commonly entertained notion, I would like to ask a philosophical question about this pull of gravity. I will put it this way: "Is the pull of gravity *real?*"

As soon as I introduce the word "real" into my discourse, you recognize immediately that I speak as a philosopher. For the real, like the true and the certain, is a perennial topic of philosophical discourse. A non-philosopher might not think of raising the question, "What is real?", and possibly such a general question has never occurred to you. But if I am to answer the question "Is the pull of gravity real?", I should preface my remarks with a brief explanation of what I understand by the term "real."

The simplest way to explain the real is to oppose it to something that is not real. A quick definition of the real would therefore be that it includes whatever exists outside my mind, whatever has existence independently of my thought. This definition, unfortunately, can lead one into epistemological difficulties, and thus I do not endorse it in an unqualified manner. But it has the merit of explaining the real by opposing it to the mental, or the rational, or the logical. To avoid difficulties that will be recognized by professional philosophers, I shall refrain from using the term "mental," and explain the real by opposing it to the rational or the logical. The rational or logical is whatever exists in my mind in such a way that it cannot exist outside my mind. The real, on the other hand, although in my mind when I know it, also exists outside my mind.[1]

Thus, when I ask the question, "Is the pull of gravity real?", I mean: "Does the pull of gravity exist outside my mind?" Is it merely something that I fabricate in my mind to help me understand reality, without being real itself, or does it exist outside my mind in the way in which *you* exist? Can I legitimately say: "You are real, and you are sitting in your seats because the earth is really *pulling* you, balancing the centrifugal force of the earth's rotation and preventing you from flying off into outer space?"

Physical versus Mathematical Reality

Before proceeding further, I would like to make another precision in terminology, and speak of two different kinds of reality, one physical, and the other mathematical. If I am to be consistent in my use of the term real, it seems that I must acknowledge that at least some mathematical entities are real. For example, in common usage we say that numbers are real. One such number is the number of people in this auditorium. I do not know how many people are here, but were I to count them, and do so accurately, I would come to know a number, and that number would be in my mind, but it would also exist outside my mind. In this way it satisfies my definition of the real as that which exists in the mind in such a way that it also exists outside the mind. So, at least in some instances, we can maintain that mathematical entities are real.

It is not my intention to discourse here on the nature of the mathematically real.[2] All I wish to indicate is that, when I ask: "Is the pull of gravity real?", I do not mean: "Is the real in the way in which a mathematical entity might be real?" I mean: "Is it *physically* real?" Does it exist in the order of nature in such a way that it affects physical being and is the cause, for example, of your being held in your seats?

Serious answers to questions of this type were not attempted by thinkers until the sixteenth or seventeenth century. Through the preceding centuries, however, there was considerable discussion of the distinction between physical and mathematical reality, particularly as this is relevant to an understanding of the motions of planets and falling bodies. Since this development influenced early discussions of gravity, I shall trace it quickly, and, in so doing, give a brief history of early astronomy.

Early Astronomy

Skipping over the earliest conceptions of the universe, as described in Babylonian myths and the Hebraic account in the Book of Genesis, the earliest "scientific" views of the structure of the universe date from the Greek philosophers, Plato and Aristotle. In Greek astronomy, the picture is one in which the earth is at the center, around which rotate, in series of concentric spheres, the moon, sun, planets and fixed stars. Early in the history of Greek thought the nature of the so-called celestial spheres was subjected to close scrutiny. Plato does not seem to have raised the question whether they were real in a physical, as opposed to a mathematical, sense.[3] But his student, Aristotle, investigated this distinction rather thoroughly, and came to the conclusion that the celestial spheres are not merely mathematical entities, but are physically real. Thus, in attempting to explain the causes of motion on earth, he traces efficient causality through the celestial spheres until he finally comes to the *primum movens immobile,* or first unmoved mover.[4] If physical causality is transmitted through such spheres, then they must be physically real. I have just used this argument when questioning the reality of gravitational pull: if physical causality is actually exerted on you, holding you in your seats by the pull of gravity, then that pull must be physically real.

165

Such theories of the structure of the universe, however, did not stop with Aristotle. Because of interest in the motions of stars and planets, a considerable body of data was soon amassed which showed that Aristotle's conception of heavenly bodies rotating about the earth in uniform motion on concentric spheres could not possibly account for movements actually observed. Astronomers such as Eudoxus, Callipus, and later, Ptolemy, were thus stimulated to elaborate more complicated geometrical schemes that could account for the observed motions. At this stage in the development of astronomy, the notions of eccentric[5] and epicycle[5] were introduced to explain the observational data.

We cannot dwell here on the long history of these concepts from the time of the Greeks to that of Copernicus and Galileo. Suffice it to say that eccentrics and epicycles aroused much speculative discussion, almost all centering on their physical significance. Although many thinkers had been convinced that the celestial spheres were physical entities, following the view of Aristotle, the general feeling seems to have been that eccentrics and epicycles were not physically real. Rather they were regarded as mathematical explanations — today we might say theoretical explanations — that can be used to "explain the appearances," without themselves being physical realities. Thus they played an important role in preserving the Aristotelian distinction between physical and mathematical reality.

Nicholas Copernicus

But, as more and more astronomical data were accumulated through the Middle Ages and more complicated schemes were devised to explain them, astronomers became increasingly dissatisfied with the multiplication of eccentrices and epicycles. In such an intellectual climate Nicholas Copernicus proposed a picture of the universe that provoked a crisis in Christendom. Copernicus urged a return to a very early conception, proposed by Aristarchus of Samos, in which the sun occupies the center of the universe, and the earth, together with the planets and the fixed stars, rotate about the sun. This heliocentric universe was diametrically opposed to the geocentric universe to which men had been committed for close to twenty centuries. Even more important historically, it appeared to be opposed to the picture of the universe sketched in the Book of Genesis.

The theological controversies that this provoked are too involved to discuss, but I should like to mention a philosophical problem that inevitably presented itself. If, according to Copernicus, the sun is at the center of the universe, then the earth is displaced from its privileged position and actually rotates around the sun. But the moon, in all theories, had always been conceived as going around the earth. In the Copernicus system, therefore, the moon rotates about the earth, as the earth in turn rotates about the sun. This means that all bodies in the universe do not rotate about the absolute center of the universe, but at least one, the moon, goes about another center rotating in turn about the first. Now the moon was early recognized as going about the earth in a physical way, and not just as a mathematical epicycle. Thus, in the Copernican system, a physical motion — and not merely a mathematical one — was now displaced from the center of the universe.

This posed a serious philosophical problem, but for the time being it was avoided because of more pressing religious controversies. As the theological implications of the heliocentric theory were worked out, Copernicus' writings came on the verge of condemnation by Catholic and Protestant authorities alike. In order to prevent such condemnation, however, Osiander wrote an introduction to the published version of *On the Revolution of the Celestial Spheres,* in which he states that Copernicus there proposes nothing more than a mathematical theory "to save the appearances." Although this, in all probability, was a falsification of Copernicus' own view, it did succeed in allowing the Copernican theory of the structure of the universe to co-exist with the biblical account.[7] But such peaceful coexistence did not long endure, for trouble soon appeared on the horizon in the fiery figure of Galileo Galilei.

Galileo Galilei

It would be impossible for us here to do justice to Galileo's views on the subject of gravity. Needless to say, they were quite profound, and strongly influential in promoting the development of empirical science along lines it has taken since the seventeenth century. Galileo, in this sense, was a great theoretician, but he also possessed unparalleled skill as an experimentalist and inventor. For our purposes, his most significant contribution was his invention of the refracting telescope, with the aid of which he studied the moon, the planets, and the fixed stars. In 1610, he published the results of his investigations in the *Nuncius Sidereus,* which is variously translated as the *Sidereal Messenger* of the *Message of the Stars.* This made a great impact on the intellectuals of Florence, and through a peculiar sequence of events, did more to lead to his condemnation by the Inquisition than any of his other discoveries. In it, he writes:

> I have discovered four planets, neither known nor observed by any one of the astronomers before my time, which have their orbits around a certain bright star, one of those previously known, like Venus and Mercury around the Sun, and are sometimes in front of it, some-

167

times behind it, though they never depart from it beyond certain limits. All which facts were discovered and observed a few days ago by the help of a telescope devised by me, through God's grace first enlightening my mind.[8]

What was the importance of this discovery? Galileo, by it, has shown not merely that the moon goes around the earth, but that four small planets rotate about the planet Jupiter. Here we have the type of phenomenon traditionally explained by the epicycle. But now, with Galileo's new evidence, the epicycle can no longer be regarded merely as a mathematical explanation. Why? Because Galileo had seen with his own eyes, through his telescope, something really happening in the universe. When one comprehends the nature of Galileo's discovery, it is a simple matter to reconstruct its effect on the intellectual life of Florence, and even on the Aristotelian professors who refused to look through the telescope at the new evidence he had to offer.[9]

Sir Isaac Newton

With this development, the stage is set for the epic-making work of Sir Isaac Newton, which brings us back to the question we have been discussing. Galileo's heliocentric theory of the structure of the universe had already anticipated the major points to be found in the Newtonian view. Newton's debt to Copernicus and Galileo is that from them he became convinced that the planets are physically rotating about the sun, and not about the earth, and that satellites are physically rotating about some of the planets in the solar system. Newton also knew from Kepler, that the paths of these bodies could no longer be regarded as perfect circles, but that they must be ellipses. His attempt to explain why planets followed such elliptical paths led to the discovery for which he is most famous, and brings us forcibly to the question that concerns us.

Having reduced the science of mechanics to its fundamental principles, the celebrated laws of motion, Newton possessed a distinct advantage over his predecessors when attempting to explain why a planet is kept physically in elliptical orbit. His first law of motion, stating that a body in motion will continue in motion in a straight line unless acted upon by some external force, already explained one component of a planet's motion. According to this, however, each planet would tend to fly off into space in straight line motion. Without another physical factor being operative, planets would quickly leave the solar system. Thus something must act physically to keep them in their paths. What is the physical entity that keeps planets in proper orbit? For Newton, the answer is gravity. His great discovery, as I am sure you all know was the universal law of gravitation.

168

Now that brings us to the question we raised earlier. What is gravity? Is this merely a mathematical entity, like an eccentric or an epicycle? No, for Newton it cannot be merely a mathematical entity. It must be real, physically real. So what keeps a planet in orbit? Newton's answer is: two things. A tendency to fly off into space, together with a tendency towards some center of attraction. In the case of the planets, a massive body, the sun, occupies the focus of the elliptical orbit, and is therefore at the center of gravity. And if the planet's motion is real, if the momentum that would carry it off into space is real, then its physical attraction to the center of the solar system must be real also. After the time of Newton, it seems that gravity had to be regarded as something as physically real and existent as motion.

But our question is not: "Is gravity real?" but rather: "Is the *pull* of gravity real?" Many people tend to merge the two questions into one, and answer both in the affirmative. Newton himself did not make this identification. As I have shown, he proposed gravity as a physical explanation for why bodies stay in planetary orbit. For him, gravity is physical and real. But what about the *cause* of gravity? What causes gravity? Newton's answer is given in the General Scholium he appended to the second edition of the *Mathematical Principles of Natural Philosophy,* as follows:

> Hitherto we have explained the phenomena of the heavens and of our sea by the power of gravity, but have not yet assigned the cause of this power. This is certain, that it must proceed from a cause . . . but hitherto I have not been able to discover the cause of those properties of gravity from phenomena, and I frame no hypotheses; for whatever is not deduced from the phenomena is to be called an hypothesis; and hypotheses, whether metaphysical or physical, whether of occult qualities or mechanical, have no place in experimental philosophy.[10]

So Newton does not deny that gravity has a cause. He merely does not pretend to know what that cause might be.

But as to gravitational effects being caused by a physical *pull,* Newton is more explicit. When speaking of the force of gravity, he returns to the Aristotelian distinction between physical and mathematical entities, and says: "I here design only to give a mathematical notion of those forces without considering their physical causes and seats," and a few lines later makes the point that he is "considering those forces not physically, but mathematically."[11] Yet he did enunciate the inverse square law of gravitational attraction, and did speak of all bodies in the universe as "attracting" one another in accordance with this law. Such attraction was commonly interpreted by his readers as meaning some type of physical pull that accounted for gravitational phenomena. Possibly to dissuade readers from such an interpretation, Newton made an explicit declaration in the second edition of the *Principia* concerning the precise meaning of the word "attraction:"

> I here use the word *attraction* in general for any endeavor whatever, made by bodies to approach each other, whether that endeavor arise from the action of the bodies themselves, as tending to each other or agitating each other by spirits emitted, or whether it arises from the action of the ether or of the air or of any medium whatever, whether corporeal or incorporeal, in any manner impelling bodies placed therein towards each other.[12]

Here Newton enumerates a variety of causes that might account for gravity. He prefers to take an agnostic attitude as to which of these might be its true cause, but in one of his letters to Richard Bentley, he reveals himself opposed to the "pull concept" because of the philosophical difficulties posed by the concept of action at a distance. Thus he writes to Bentley:

> That one body may act upon another at a distance through the vacuum, without the mediation of anything else, by and through which their action and force may be conveyed from one to the other, is to me so great an absurdity, that I believe no man, who has in philosophical matters a competent faculty of thinking, can ever fall into it.[13]

From this, I think we are justified in inferring that, though Newton regarded gravity as physical and real, he was not at all convinced that the pull of gravity was physical and real. And yet his reservations on this subject seem to have passed unnoticed by his disciples and later scientists. In spite of some early opposition from Leibniz and others, the notion of attractive force, and its implied action at a distance was gradually accepted as basic to classical mechanics. Laplace in his *Mécanique céleste* and Lagrange in his *Mécanique analytique* both regarded such a concept as fundamental. This mentality has been preserved in our schools down to the present day. Thus I am quite sure that most of you, as you ponder the question: "Is the pull of gravity real?", are not only willing to say that gravity is physically real, but that its pull is physically real also. The cause of gravity, in your minds, presents no problem. You are in your seats because the earth is physically pulling on you and keeping you there.

St. Thomas Aquinas

With this background we can now present the teaching of St. Thomas Aquinas on the pull of gravity. As you well know, he did not possess the

170

experimental findings that provoked the successive astronomical theories of Copernicus, Kepler, Galileo and Newton. But living at the height of the scholastic period, when foundations were being laid for the scientific development of the next few centuries, he was alert to the basic physical problems involved in an explanation of gravitation.

A central factor in St. Thomas' explanation of gravitational motion is his indentification of this as a natural motion. For him, as for Aristotle, nature is defined as a principle of motion and rest that is proper and intrinsic to a body, and not found there merely in incidental fashion. Being a *principle*, nature is always understood by St. Thomas as something relative, understandable only through its relational aspects.[14] He states that we should "deride those who wish to correct Aristotle's definition, and attempt to define it as something absolute, saying that nature is a *vis insita*, or something of this kind."[15]

Since St. Thomas regards nature as a principle of motion, he is careful to point out that this principle may be understood in either of two ways: as active or as passive.[16] Nature is an active principle of motion only in those things capable of initiating their own movements, namely, living things. In non-living things, such as stone and iron, nature is merely a passive principle of motion.[17] But because a heavy object possesses such a principle, it can be moved naturally, provided some extrinsic agent actuates its natural potency. How this is effected, I shall explain in more detail later.

Natural Place

The second concept required to explain St. Thomas' analysis of falling motion in his notion of place. The term "place" can probably best be translated into modern terminology as "physical space." It is defined by St. Thomas as the "innermost surface of the containing body, itself immovable, and primarily so."[18] The immobility of a particular place, or the reason why it is primarily immobile, again implies a relational aspect. Place, or physical space, exists only in the order of nature. If many bodies did not make up the universe, and if these bodies did not have specific natures as principles of their proper activities, place or physical space would not exist.

Aquinas, on this account, makes a clear distinction between physical space and mathematical space. In mathematical space, he points out, there are six (Euclidean) dimensions, all determined in arbitrary fashion, depending on how we situate mathematical entities when considering them. The dimensionality of physical space, on the other hand, cannot be purely arbitrary. As he says, "such dimensions are determined by nature in the universe, and not merely with respect to us.[19] Thus, in the order of nature, up and down

171

is fixed by the motion of heavy and light bodies. Although mathematically we may conceive any part of the universe as up or down, physically we cannot do so, because "up is always the direction in which light things go, and down is the direction in which heavy things go."[20] Moreover, since such directions are not arbitrary, but are determined by nature, it follows that place has some influence on bodies. In his understanding, St. Thomas would admit that the place to which the heavy body tends, say the center of the earth, exerts an attractive influence on it.[21] In such a context he discusses the pull of gravity, but as we shall see, does not conceive this in mere mechanical fashion.

With his two notions of nature and place, we can now sketch how St. Thomas explains why a heavy body falls to earth. He regards the universe as a plenum, made up of the bodies which it contains. Since these bodies are contiguous, the place of each body in the universe is determined by its surrounding bodies. But this place, at any moment, may not be the proper or connatural place of the particular body. When speaking of proper or connatural place, St. Thomas maintains that "the order of situation in the universe is determined by the order of nature."[22] Thus, were all bodies in their proper places, those of a certain nature would occupy positions closest to the center of gravity, while other natures would be situated, in ascending hierarchy, more remotely from the center.[23]

In the usual case, however, most bodies in the universe do not occupy their proper places. The general relationships of nature and physical space which then hold between such bodies, always in direct contact with one another, ultimately explains why they move one another. Thus St. Thomas' explanation of why a heavy body falls is intimately connected with its position in its physical environment. It falls because it is tending towards its proper place; if it were not where it now is, but in a different position, it might be moved otherwise. His concept of gravitation, in this respect, is relational and dynamic. The motion of any one body can never be discussed independently of its position in the entire universe, or independently of other bodies to which it is related. Ultimately it moves because of an interaction between itself and other bodies, all as parts of the universe, all acting upon each other through direct contact.[24]

Medieval Theories of Gravity

These views of St. Thomas, closely related to those of Aristotle, were not completely shared by his contemporaries. It will be worthwhile for us to examine two different currents of thought, for the assistance they give in explaining St. Thomas' concept of gravitational force and its relation to the pull of gravity.[25]

The first current derives from the Arab philosopher, Averroes, who traced the mover in gravitational motion to an active form within the body undergoing motion, thereby giving impetus to nominalist explanations and preparing the way for Galileo and his theories. The second current originated with such authors as St. Bonaventure and Roger Bacon, who attempted to explain gravitation through some type of push or pull, and in this way anticipated the mechanistic theories of the sixteenth and seventeenth centuries. St. Thomas knew of, and rejected, both these explanations.

Averroes, himself an Aristotelian, attempted to work out a more detailed explanation for gravitational motion than was to be found in Aristotle. His writings were widely read through the Middle Ages, and one of his statements, in particular, was generally accepted by most authors. This goes as follows:

> The generator is what gives to the simple body generated its form and all the accidents accompanying the form, of which one is change in place.[26]

In this statement, Averroes focuses on the form of the falling body as a principal factor explaining its gravitation. His emphasis on form comes from his attempt to reconcile the presence of a natural source of movement within a falling body with its being moved by another. In one formulation,, he proposes to meet this difficulty by the distinction between act and potency. Thus he holds that "the stone moves itself insofar as it is actually heavy, while it in turn is moved insofar as it is potentially in a lower place." In another formulation, attempting to give a fuller explanation, he invokes the medium through which the body falls. The falling stone, actually heavy, moves the medium, while the medium in turn moves the stone, and thus its motion is from another. Averroes has in mind the kind of motion executed by a rower in a boat, for in this case the rower moves the boat through the medium, while he in turn is moved with the boat through and by the surrounding medium.[27]

In the above explanations, it should be noted, Averroes means by "form" the substantial form of the body in question. Also, his insistence on the medium in gravitational motion requires him to maintain that the medium plays an essential role in such motion, so that without it there would be no falling motion. St. Thomas explicitly rejects this position, maintaining that the medium is not necessarily required for the motion of a falling stone. He says that Averroes' view is based on a fundamental error regarding the mover in gravitational motion. Thus he states:

> [Averroes] thought that the form of a heavy and light body is the active principle of motion after the fashion of a mover . . . but this

173

is completely false. Because the form of a heavy and light thing is not the principle of the motion as an agent mover, but as that *by which* the mover moves, as color is the principle of vision, by which something is seen.[28]

Here Thomas rejects Averroes' explanation because the latter interprets falling motion as natural in the sense that it comes from an *active* principle within the falling body. Aquinas, on the other hand, maintains that the motion is natural only in the sense that it proceeds from a *passive* principle within the body. This passive principle, moreover, is not the substantial form, but proximately the gravity of the body, an accidental form that comes to the body when it is generated outside of its natural place, and ultimately its matter. Thus he states:

> Some inquire why heavy and light bodies are moved to their proper places. The cause of this is that they have a natural aptitude toward such places. For to be light is to have an aptitude to go up; and this is also the explanation of heaviness, to have an aptitude to go down. Whence to ask why the heavy thing moves downward is to ask nothing more than to ask why it is heavy. And therefore the same thing that makes it be heavy is what makes it be moved downwards.[29]

This explanation, according to St. Thomas, is completely consistent with the teaching of Aristotle. According to this teaching:

> Neither of these, namely heavy and light bodies, move themselves; nevertheless their motion is natural because they have a principle of motion within themselves; not indeed a motor or active principle but a passive principle which is a potency to their proper act.[30]

He then goes on:

> From this it is patently against the intention of the philosopher [Aristotle] to maintain that there is an active principle in matter, which some say is necessary for there to be natural motion. For this a passive principle suffices, which is nothing more than a natural potency to act.[31]

Despite St. Thomas' rejection of Averroes' doctrine, the latter was taken up by a series of writers who exerted considerable influence in the fourteenth and fifteenth centuries. Among the first of these is John of Jandun who regards gravity as proceeding from an "active potency" within the falling body.[32] Likewise Peter Aureoli follows Averroes' explanation almost verbatim.[33] William of Ockham focuses attention on gravity as the immediate *active* principle of falling motion.[34] Other thinkers, such as Walter Burley,[35] Gregory of Rimini,[36] and John Buridan[37] stress the active nature of the substantial

174

form in falling motion. By the time of Albert of Saxony[38] and Nicholas of Oresme,[39] the notion is fairly common that heavy bodies actually move themselves through some intrinsic principle. These thinkers regarded the cause of falling motion as some type of active force within the body itself, thus preparing the way for animist theories of gravitation such as that proposed by William Gilbert at the turn of the seventeenth century.

Attraction and Repulsion

The second current against which St. Thomas reacted, attempted to explain falling motion through repulsion or attraction. Among the first thinkers to propose such an explanation was St. Bonaventure, a contemporary of St. Thomas, who states in his commentary on the *Sentences*:

> It must be said that gravity or a proper quality alone does not suffice for the motion of a heavy object. In fact, beyond the two movers which the philosopher [Aristotle] posits, namely, whatever generates the heavy and whatever removes impediments to motion, there are further required the virtue of the attracting place, and the virtue of the expelling place and the virtue of the fifth body.[40]

St. Bonaventure here regards gravitation as caused at least partly by a two-fold repelling force, one coming from the heavenly spheres, and the other from the place formerly occupied by the body, which the Seraphic Doctor says is endowed with power to expel bodies. He also regards the attracting place as exerting a similar influence on the falling motion.[41]

Such a notion of repulsion and attraction was commonly rejected by medieval thinkers, partly because it invoked action at a distance, partly because it seemed contrary to the facts of ordinary experience. Thus, if a repulsive force from the heavenly spheres actually causes falling motion, then it would seem that the motion should be faster at the beginning of the motion when the body is closer to the repulsive influence. Similarly, if attraction is actually exerted by place, then a body should be heavier the closer it comes to its natural place, which again is not verifiable in ordinary experience.

In the writings of St. Bonaventure, as also in those of Richard of Mediaville, it is not completely clear that the attractive force exerts true efficient causality. But in such authors as Roger Bacon, John Baconthorp, and the Pseudo-Grosseteste, the attraction is conceived as a physical pull. Thus the Pseudo-Grosseteste, refers to "the marvelous power of place, which not only acts as an end" but also "after the fashion of an efficient cause."[42] Baconthorp, clearly impressed by the analogy of the magnet attracting iron, thought that the body "sought its proper place as its end and form," but

175

that this need not exclude that it also "was attracted to it" in a physical sense.[43]

Within this group, the person who most developed the attraction theory was Roger Bacon. His problem was one of explaining the mechanism whereby an attractive force could be transmitted from natural place to the object attracted. He did this by locating the attraction in the surrounding medium itself, as he explains in the following text:

> It should be said that gravity and levity are not only found in the thing, but also in the medium, because the more the body gets to the lower portion of the medium, the more it acquires that form which is diffused from the center to the circumference of the medium containing the thing moved, and this is the immaterial virtue by which each thing is brought to its place.[44]

The Pull of Gravity

There is no reason to assume that St. Thomas was not acquainted with these theories of his contemporaries. In fact, his treatment of the concept of attraction in the commentary on the seventh book of the *Physics* seems aimed at just such theories.[45] Here he explicitly distinguishes the pull of gravity from the pull of the magnet. In an earlier passage, as we have seen, he allows that place does exert some type of attractive influence on a heavy body. Thus he remarks in the commentary on the fourth book of the *Physics*:

> From this it is apparent that place has a certain power of conserving the body in place; and because of this the body tends to its proper place with a desire for self conservation. But this does not show that place has an attractive power *except in the way in which an end is said to attract.*[46]

St. Thomas' analysis of magnetic attraction, although expressed in terms unfamiliar to the modern mind, is nonetheless quite in keeping with recent thought. Even William Gilbert, in his classical treatise *De magnete* written in 1600, remarks:

> Thomas Aquinas in his *Physica*, Book Seven, treating briefly of the lodestone, gets at the nature of it fairly well: with his God-like and perspicacious mind he would have developed many a point had he been acquainted with magnetic experiments.[47]

Gilbert's appreciation of Aquinas' work seems to be confirmed by what we now know about magnetic, as opposed to gravitational, attraction. Thomas actually selects only three points for comment.[48] First, a magnet does not attract iron from any distance whatsoever, whereas gravitational attraction

176

does. Secondly, a magnet may be affected — today we would say shielded — by extrinsic bodies, and thus will not exert its influence, which is not the case for any known gravitational phenomena. Thirdly, the relative position of the iron with respect to the magnet alters the attractive force, whereas orientation does not affect the influence of gravity. All three points show an efficient causality on the part of the magnet that is not to be found in gravitational attraction. Therefore, St. Thomas remains uncommitted to any type of efficient causality in gravitational attraction. He is willing to concede that the center of gravity attracts after the fashion of a final cause, and let the matter rest at that.[49]

Thus it seems quite clear that St. Thomas would reject the notion of "pull of gravity", if the latter be understood as a physical cause exerting true efficient causality. For those of you who are firmly committed to the "pull" concept, I do not suppose that his arguments are convincing. To persuade you further, therefore, I should like now to show that St. Thomas' view is consistent with the most recent interpretations of mechanics and relativity theory given by philosophers of science. I can best do this by resuming my account of the development of the "pull" concept after the time of Newton, and bringing it up to the present day.

Modern Mechanics

Although some scientists, now identified as Newtonians, enthusiastically supported a mechanical philosophy, attempting to reduce all of mechanics to basic forces like those of gravity, other thinkers immediately took a critical view of this procedure. One of the first was the English philosopher and divine, Bishop George Berkeley. Berkeley had earlier objected to Newton's conceptions of absolute space and absolute time, but he was no less critical of Newton's use of the concept of force. In his work *De motu* he makes the observation:

> Force, gravity, attraction and similar terms are convenient for purposes of reasoning and for computations of motion and of moving bodies, but not for the understanding of the nature of motion itself.[50]

He recalls Newton's insistence that he had invoked attraction merely as a mathematical hypothesis, and not as a true physical quality. In view of this, he prefers to accord the notion of force the same status in science as the notion of epicycle in astronomy.[51] So, with Berkeley, we come back to the distinction between physical and mathematical entities. Gravitational pull is relegated to the area of mathematical explanation, having no physical counterpart in the order of nature.

Berkeley did not stop here, however. He went further, and insisted

177

that science can never come to a knowledge of causes. The method of science, in his mind, precludes a critical study of causal phenomena, which must therefore be left to the metaphysical. As is well known, this speculation of Berkeley led David Hume to generalize the analysis and make a more sweeping denial of the concept of causality. Hume, in turn, influenced Maupertuis, who again attacked the concept of force, maintaining that it was only a word used to conceal our ignorance of what is happening in nature. These criticisms gradually led to the formulation of the present-day positivist doctrine, through a succession of thinkers including Kirchhoff, Mach, Hertz, Poincaré, and Russell. Ernst Mach was probably the most outspoken of these critics, adopting the view that the concepts of cause and force represent mere conventions and are devoid of all temporal, causal, and teleological implications. For him, force, including gravitational attraction, is only a means to signify the product of mass and acceleration. Any other name, in his estimation, would have served just as well. [52]

A recent writer, surveying the thought of physicists from the time of Mach to the present, comes to the conclusion that the notion of force has no extra-mental significance for the modern scientist, but is merely a logical or rational entity. Thus he states:

> The concept of force in contemporary physics plays the role of a methodological intermediate comparable to the so-called middle term in the traditional syllogism.[53]

This judgment of recent classical mechanics would therefore seem to support St. Thomas' questioning the "pull of gravity" as having no counterpart in physical reality.

The same judgment can be derived more directly from Einstein's theory of general relativity, which likewise dispenses with attractive force as a mere conceptual entity. Einstein's theory is so heavily mathematical that it does not lend itself to exposition in a lecture of this type. Suffice it to point out that in the theory of general relativity there is no room for a pull of gravity. Why, then do bodies fall? Not because a body pulls them, but because they follow a natural course determined by a space-time geodesic.[54] With Einstein, we thus come back again to the relational aspect of falling motion advocated seven centuries ago by St. Thomas Aquinas.

A Rapprochement?

I am not the only one, by the way, who has noted this reversion to scholastic concepts. In a recent book Max Jammer makes a similar comparison between the Aristotelian theory of natural place and Einstein's theory of relativity. There he says:

It is perhaps not wholly unjustified to suggest a comparison between the notion of physical space in Aristotle's cosmology and the notion of Einstein's 'spherical space' as expounded in early relativistic cosmology. In both theories a question of what is 'outside' finite space is nonsensical. Furthermore, the idea of 'geodesic lines,' determined by the geometry of space, and their importance for the description of the path of material particles or light rays, suggest a certain analogy to the notion of 'natural places' and the paths leading to them.[55]

And, what is perhaps more important, in an introduction to this book, Albert Einstein himself gives the accolade to the "Aristotelian School" for developing a consistent dynamical theory without having resort to the absolute space of Newtonian physics.[56]

With this, I come to the end of my argument. At the outset of this lecture, I asked the simple question: "Is the pull of gravity real?" I think I then made it quite clear that I meant real, as opposed to merely rational or logical, and physically real as opposed to what might be called mathematically real. When science was at the golden age of its classical development, such a question would unhesitatingly have been answered in the affirmative. But for St. Thomas Aquinas, for the expert in modern classical mechanics, and for the relativity physicist, the answer is firmly negative. Which answer is correct I leave you to decide for yourselves.

FOOTNOTES

1. I define the rational, or the logical, as that which exists in my mind in such a way that it cannot possibly exist outside my mind. An example of such a being would be a negation like "non-circle" or "no man." I can conceive "no man" or "non-circle' in my mind, but it is impossible for "no man" to exist outside my mind. In terms of this understanding of the rational or logical, I then define the real as that which exists in my mind in such a way that it also exists outside my mind. Thus, while "no man" is not real, I know that a person to whom I am talking is real. I know that he is real because, first of all, I know him, and therefore he is in my mind. But he is in my mind and also outside my mind. Thus, when I say I know *him,* something different from myself is the object of my knowing act. If the real is not inside my mind, then I cannot know it, and if it is not outside my mind, I do not know *it.* Thus I define the real as what is inside the mind in such a way as also to be outside the mind. The rational or the logical, on the other hand, is inside the mind, but does not exist outside the mind.

2. Having opposed mathematical reality to physical reality, I should like to explain the way in which I understand the difference. Although the mathematical entities of which I have spoken are real, they are abstract in themselves. The number of people in this room is a number, a "pure" number if you like. When that number is known, it is conceived in such a way that it abstracts from the physical entity to which it is applied. Let us suppose the number

is six hundred and twenty-three. In itself, six hundred and twenty-three is abstract and ideal. It does not necessarily involve the notion of people, or of chairs, or anything of that type. Similarly, when I say that the earth is a sphere or an oblate spheroid, the sphere I conceive in my mind is an abstract and idealized sphere. So while such mathematical entities are real, they are abstract and idealized in their very conception. As opposed to this, when I say that something is physically real, I mean that is exists outside my mind, not in an abstract or idealized way, but in a concrete and individualized way. When I know you, I know you as physically real. Although I can include you under a class or grouping, which in a certain way is a fabrication of my mind, I also know each of you as you exist in the order of nature, without idealizing or abstractly conceiving you.

3. Plato's cosmological theories are exposed in the *Timaeus,* which is available in English in *The Dialogues of Plato,* trans. Benjamin Jowett (New York: 1937). See also F. M. Cornford, *Plato's Cosmology* (New York: 1937), and A. E. Taylor, *A Commentary to Plato's Timaeus* (Oxford: 1928), for a critical analysis of Plato's views.

4. This teaching of Aristotle is explained at length in his *Physics,* Books 7 and 8, and his *Metaphysics,* Book Lambda. Mention should be made of the readable translations by Richard Hope, *Aristotle's Physics* (Lincoln: 1961) and *Aristotle — Metaphysics* (New York: 1952).

5. When accurate track is kept of planetary positions, it is found that some planets do not always maintain the same speed, but speed up and slow down in different parts of their orbits. One can account for a motion of this type, while still using uniform circular motions, by merely displacing the center of circular motion on an eccentric axis. The circle thus displaced is referred to as an eccentric. A person remaining at the original center, and viewing the object moving in uniform motion on the eccentric circle, sees it appear to move faster when it is closer to him and slower when it is farther away, even though the planet itself is always moving at uniform speed. For a full explanation of the concept of eccentric, and its related notion, the epicycle, see Thomas S. Kuhn, *The Copernican Revolution* (Cambridge, Mass.: 1957).

6. The epicycle performed a function similar to that of the eccentric and was used to explain a peculiarity in the observed motion of the planet Mars. When this is observed from Earth against the background of the fixed stars, it is found that Mars does not proceed in one direction alone, but occasionally slows down, stops its forward motion, starts to go backward, then in turn slows down, stops, and resumes its forward motion again. It would seem difficult to explain such a peculiar motion in terms of perfect circular rotations, but Greek astronomers succeeded in doing so through the concept of epicycle. The epicycle is a circular motion whose center is carried along on another circle, known as the deferent. As applied to the planet Mars, this theory has the planet rotating about a center which in turn rotates around Earth. In such a case, if one is on Earth, watching the apparent motion of Mars against the background of the fixed stars, the planet will go forward for a while, then will stop, go backward, stop again, and start to go forward again. Like the eccentric, the epicycle gives an ingenious mathematical explanation of the observed motions of planets in terms of perfect circular uniform motions, which the Greeks attributed to the heavenly bodies.

180

7. For more details, see T. S. Kuhn, *op. cit.,* and Pierre Conway, O.P., "Aristotle, Copernicus and Galileo," *The New Scholasticism,* 23 (1949) 38-61, 129-146.
8. *The Sidereal Messenger* of Galileo Galilei, translated by E. S. Carlos (1880), reprinted in part in *Readings in the Literature of Science,* ed. William C. Dampier (New York: 1959), p. 16.
9. This is vividly described by Alexandre Koyre in his essay on Galileo in *From the Closed World to the Infinite Universe,* (Baltimore: 1957), pp. 88-109. For a more controversial account of the historical background surrounding Galileo and his trial, see Georgio de Santillana, *The Crime of Galileo* (Chicago: 1955).
10. *Sir Isaac Newton's 'Mathematical Principles of Natural Philosophy,'* trans. Andrew Motte, revised by Florian Cajori (Berkeley: 1934), p. 546.
11. *Ibid.,* p. 5.
12. *Ibid.,* p. 192.
13. *The Works of Richard Bentley,* ed. Alexander Dyce (London: 1838), Vol. 3, p. 211; also in *Isaac Newton's Papers and letters on Natural Philosophy,* ed. I. B. Cohen (Cambridge, Mass.: 1958), pp. 302-303.
14. St. Thomas expounds his conception of nature in his *Commentary on the Physics of Aristotle,* Book II, Lect. 1, nn. 285-307 (Latin edition of A. M. Pirotta, Naples: 1953). All references below are to this edition, and the translations are my own. For a full account of Aristotle's and Thomas' analysis of nature as this is relevant to gravitational motion, see James A. Weisheipl, O.P., *Nature and Gravitation* (River Forest: 1955), particularly pp. 1-32.
15. *In II Phys.,* lect. 1, n. 296.
16. And therefore it must be said that in natural things there is a principle of motion in the way in which it is proper for them to move. In those things to which it is proper to be movers, there is an active principle of motion; in those things that are more properly moved, there is a passive principle which is matter. This principle, insofar as it has a natural potency to such form and motion, makes the motion be natural . . . . — *In II Phys.,* lect. 1, n. 292.
17. In heavy and light bodies, there is a formal principle of motion; but this formal principle cannot be said to be an active potency from which such motion proceeds, but is included under passive potency. For heaviness in earth is not a principle which makes it be a mover, but more properly something moved; because, as other accidents follow on the substantial form, so also does place, and, as a consequence on this, motion to place. Not in such a manner, however, that the natural form be the mover, because the mover is the generator which gives such a form, on which follows motion of this kind — *Ibid.,* n. 293.
18. *In IV Phys.,* lect. 6, n. 901.
19. *Ibid.,* lect. 1, n. 795.
20. *Ibid.,* n. 797.
21. Since the motion of certain bodies shows place to exit, as has been said, the local motion of natural simple bodies, as fire and earth, and others of the type of heavy and light bodies, not only show that place is something, but also that place has a certain power or virtue. For we see that each of these is taken to its proper place when it is not impeded, the heavy going down and the light up. — *Ibid.,* n. 793.
22. *In IV Phys.,* lect. 8, n. 938.

23. For St. Thomas, when bodies of similar nature are close together, they do not react chemically with one another, but tend to conserve their own natures. When, on the other hand, they come into proximity with bodies of different natures, they are liable to interact and undergo chemical change. In this way he associated variations in the position of bodies in physical space with their capacity for chemical activity, as well as their potentiality for mechanical motion. See *Ibid.*, n. 939.

24. The proximity of nature which holds between the containing body and the contained is the cause why a body is naturally moved to its place: because it is necessary that the grades of natural places correspond to the grades of the natures of things that are in place, as has been said (n. 939). But this reason cannot be assigned if one were to say that space is place: because in the dimensions of separated space no order of nature can be recognized. — *Ibid.*, n. 940.

25. A comprehensive survey of medieval theories of gravitation is given by Anneliese Maier in her essay on "Das Problem der Gravitation," in *An der Grenze von Scholastik und Naturwissenschaft*, 2. Aufl. (Rome: 1952), p. 141-254. This work, hereafter referred to simply as Maier, includes copious citations of Latin texts bearing on the problem of gravitational motion. Some of these are rendered into English by the writer in what follows.

26. *In VIII Phys.*, comm. 32, *Opera* IV (Venice: 1550), Maier p. 152.

27. *In III de Caelo*, comm. 28,*Opera* V: see Maier, pp. 152-154.

28. *In III de Caelo et Mundo*, lect. 7, n. 9 (ed. Spiazzi).

29. *In VIII Phys.*, lect. 8, n. 2173; see also *In II Phys.*, lect. 1, n. 292, cited *supra* in fn. 16.

30. *Ibid.*, n. 2177.

31. *Ibid.*, n. 2178.

32. *In VIII Phys.*, quaest. 11 (Ed. Venice: 1551), Maier, pp. 165-166.

33. *In II Sent.*, dist. 25, q. 1, a. 1; Maier, p. 166.

34. *Quaestiones in Physicam,* Cod. Vat. Lat. 956, fol. 53vb-54ra; Maier, pp. 166-167.

35. *In VIII Phys.*, Ed. Venice: 1482, fol. N3va ff.; Ed. Venice: 1491 fol. AA3va ff.; Maier, p. 167.

36. *In II Sent.*, dist. 6, q. 1, a. 3; Maier, p. 167.

37. *In VIII Phys.*, quaest. 5 (Ed. Paris: 1509); Maier, p. 168.

38. *In VIII Phys.*, quaest. 6 (Ed. Venice: 1504) and *In III de Caelo,* quaest. 7-9 (Ed. Venice: 1492); Maier, p. 169.

39. *Quodlibeta* 22; for reference to the codices, see Maier, p. 171.

40. In this citation, from *In II Sent.*, dist. 14, p. 1, a. 3, q. 2, the 'fifth body' is to be understood as the elementary constituent of the heavenly spheres. See Maier, p. 174.

41. The same type of explanation is adopted by a fellow Franciscan, Richard of Mediaville, who writes: "It seems to me that one should say that, although elements are determined by the generator to their natural motions, nevertheless they carry out the motions to which they have been determined by the generator through their own power and through some participation of the influence which resides in their proper places." — *In II Sent.*, dist. 14, a. 2, q. 4 (Ed. Brescia: 1591); Maier, p. 174.

42. *Summa philosophiae,* cap. 260; Maier, p. 182.

43. *In LL Sent.*, dist. 22, q. 1; Maier, p. 182.

44. *Quaestiones supra VIII Phys.,* ed. Delorme-Steele (1928); Maier, p. 181, pp. 177-182.

45. Since this is so important for an understanding of St. Thomas' position on gravitational attraction, I cite it in its entirety: "A thing is said to pull when it moves another to itself. But to move something to itself in the positional sense can happen in three different ways.

In one way as the end moves, whence the end is also said to pull. . . In this way it can be said that place attracts that which is naturally moved to it.

"In another way something can be said to pull because it moves something to itself by altering it in some way, whence it happens that the thing altered is moved to a new position. In this way the magnet is said to attract iron. For as the generator moves heavy and light things insofar as it gives them a form by which they are moved to place, so the magnet also gives some quality to iron by which it is moved to itself. And that this is so is apparent from three indications.

"The first is that the magnet does not attract iron from any distance whatsoever, but only when close to it. If, however, iron were moved to the magnet only as to an end, as the heavy body is moved to its place, it would tend to it from any distance whatsoever. The second is that if the magnet be affected by other bodies is cannot attract the iron, as if the other things impede its alterative force or even change it in the opposite direction. The third is that in order for the magnet to attract iron, it is necessary that first the iron be lined up with the magnet, particularly if the magnet is small, as if the iron receives some virtue from the magnet which enables it to be drawn to it. Thus the magnet attracts iron not only as an end, but also as a mover and an alterating agent.

"A thing is said to attract in the third way when it moves it to itself by local motion alone. And in this way pulling is here defined as one body moving another body in such a way that the puller moves simultaneously with the thing moved." — *In VII Phys.,* lect. 3, nn. 1810-1814.

46. *In IV Phys.,* lect. 1, n. 794.
47. Book I, chap. 1, trans. P. F. Mottelay (New York: 1893), p. 5.
48. See the text given in full in fn. 45, *supra.*
49. See *In IV Phys.,* lect. 1, n. 794. Before leaving St. Thomas' analysis of the efficiency involved in gravitation, it will be well to raise a question that has probably occurred to the reader, namely: "What, for St. Thomas, is the *ultimate* cause of gravitational motion?" I believe St. Thomas would answer this question in two ways: in one way as a natural philosopher and in another as a metaphysician and theologian. Looking at gravitational motion as a natural philosopher, he would probably say that nature itself is an irreducible notion in the natural order. Thus when we say that gravitational motion comes from nature, we have already given the ultimate explanation available to the natural philosopher. Even in this understanding, however, because gravitational motion proceeds from a passive natural principle, it is still necessary that the heavy body be moved by another. For the natural philosopher, "another" means nothing more than other bodies surrounding the falling body which constitute its place, and through their own motions initiate, assist, or retard its falling motion. At the end of the *Physics,* St. Thomas shows, following Aristotle, that if all motions were of the type that are moved by another, then motion

183

itself would be an impossibility. Thus he argues to the existence of a first unmoved mover which is necessary to maintain motion in the order of nature.

How the first unmoved mover functions in the motion of natural entities is a metaphysical problem for St. Thomas. Thus he does not attempt to resolve it in his commentary on the *Physics,* but rather takes up such questions in his commentary on the *Metaphysics* of Aristotle. Since at the end of the *Physics* he has shown that the first unmoved mover must be incorporeal, there are only two possibilities open to him. Either this incorporeal and spiritual mover is a principle intrinsic to the universe, somewhat like a world soul moving all of its parts to their proper places, as the soul of an animal moves its body, or the first mover is some spiritual substance separated from the universe, moving its parts extrinsically and directing them to their proper places. St. Thomas rejects the first possibility, and looks to the separated substances as movers of all natural motion, themselves moved, however, by the first completely unmoved mover, which he identifies with God.

It is worth noting here that St. Thomas does not conceive of separated substances, or heavenly bodies, as acting on the world of nature in any preternatural or supernatural way, such as we would associate with spiritual activity. Thus, in discussing occult phenomena, he maintains that one cannot say "that such activities result from the power of heavenly bodies, because they act only in a natural way on those inferior things" (*De occultis operibus naturae,* n. 18, trans. J. B. McAllister, Washington: 1939). Thus, their mode of activity is one completely consonant with the operation of nature, and is not detectable through bizarre and occult manifestations.

50. Sec. 17. See *The Works of George Berkeley,* ed. A. C. Fraser (Oxford: 1901), Vol. 1, p. 506.

51. *Siris,* sec. 228, *Ibid.,* Vol. 3, p. 230; also reference in previous note.

52. Cf. Ernst Mach, *Popular Scientific Lectures,* trans. T. J. McCormack (La Salle: 1943), p. 254.

53. Max Jammer, *Concepts of Force* (Cambridge, Mass.: 1957), p. 244.

54. A simplified analysis of this theory is given by Sir Arthur Stanley Eddington in his *Space, Time and Gravitation* (Cambridge: 1920), as follows: "A race of flat-fish once lived in an ocean in which there were only two dimensions. It was noted that in general fishes swam in straight lines, unless there was something obviously interfering with their free courses. This seemed a very natural behavior. But there was a certain region where all the fish seemed to be bewitched; some passed through the region but changed the direction of their swim, others swam round and round indefinitely. One fish invented a theory of vortices, and said that there were whirlpools in that region which carried everything round in curves. By and by a far better theory was proposed; it was said that the fishes were all attracted towards a particularly large fish — a sun-fish — which was lying asleep in the middle of the region; and that is what caused the deviation of their paths.

"The theory might not have sounded particularly plausible at first, but it was confirmed with marvelous exactitude by all kinds of experimental tests. All fish were found to possess this attractive power in proportion to their sizes; the law of attraction was extremely simple, and yet it was found to explain all the motions with an accuracy never approached before in any scientific investigation. Some fish grumbled that they did not see how there could be such an influence at a distance; but it was generally agreed that the influence was communicated through the ocean and might be better understood when more was known about the nature of water. Accordingly, nearly every 'fish who wanted to explain the attraction started by proposing some kind of mechanism for transmitting it through the water.

"But there was one fish who thought of quite another plan. He was impressed by the fact that whether the fish were big or little they always took the same course, although it would naturally take a bigger force to deflect the bigger fish. *He therefore concentrated attention on the courses rather than on the forces.* And then he arrived at a striking explanation of the whole thing. There was a mound in the world round about where the sun-fish lay. Flat fish could not appreciate it directly because they were two-dimensional; but whenever a fish went swimming over the slopes of the mound, although he did his best to swim straight on, he got turned around a bit. . . . This was the secret of the mysterious attraction, or bending of the paths, which was experienced in the region.

"The parable is not perfect, because it refers to a hummock in space alone, whereas we have to deal with hummocks in space-time. But it illustrates how a curvature of the world we live in may give *an illusion of attractive force,* and indeed can only be discovered through some such effect." — pp. 95-96. Emphasis added.

55. *Concepts of Space,* (Cambridge, Mass.: 1954), p. 20.
56. *Ibid.,* Foreword to Revised Edition (New York: 1960), p. xv.

ESSAY IX:

ARE ELEMENTARY
PARTICLES REAL?

That philosophers of science continue to show interest in the ontological status of entities such as the electron, the positron, and the neutrino, is evidenced by the extensive literature that has developed on this subject.[1] Yet most discussions are based on the general suppositions of neo-empiricism, and invoke a theory of knowledge different from that of moderate or

28 (*II Sent.*, 1, 1, 3, c).

29 ". . . quia potentia ad esse non solum accipitur secundum modum potentiae passivae, quae est ex parte materiae, sed etiam secundum modum potentiae activae, quae est ex parte formae" (*De Pot.*, 5, 4, ad 1). "Esse secundum se, non est finitum nec infinitum quia non est quantum, nisi in quantum subjacet motui, vel ut est rei quantae" (In VIII Phys., lect. 21). "Et ideo aliter dicendum quod ex infinitate temporis non ostenditur habere infinitatem nisi illud quod tempore mensuratur vel per se, sicut motus, vel per accidens, sicut esse rerum quae motui subjacent, quae aliqua periodo motus durant, ultra quam durare non possunt" (*De Pot.*, 5, 4, ad 1). "In rebus compositis ex materia et forma, genus sumitur a materia, et differentia a forma, ita tamen quod per materiam non intelligitur materia prima, sed secundum quod per formam recipit quoddam esse imperfectum et materiale respectu esse specifici" (*De Spirit. Creat.*, 1, ad 24). The *esse* of material things seems to fall short of the *esse* of the species.
"Materia, secundum se considerata, secundum modum suae essentiae habet esse in potentiae, et hoc ipsum est ei ex aliqua participatione primi entis" (*De Sub. Sep.*, 6, 45). "Materia secundum suam substantiam est potentia ad esse substantiale" (*In I Phys.*, 15, 131).

[1] A recent study is that of Grover Maxwell, "The Ontological Status of Theoretical Entities," *Minnesota Studies in the Philosophy of Science,* ed. H. Feigl and G. Maxwell, Vol. 3 (Minneapolis: 1962) pp. 3-27. Other studies worthy of mention are those of B. Mayo, "The Existence of Theoretical Entities," *Science News* 32 (1954) pp. 7-18, and "More about Theoretical Entities," *ibid.,* 39 (1956) pp. 42-55; also the critical analysis of Mayo's views by J. J. C. Smart, "The Reality of Theoretical Entities," *Australasian Journal of Philosophy,* 34 (1956) pp. 1-12.

critical realism. This paper proposes to fill a possible lacuna by investigating, against the epistemological background provided by Thomism, the reality of such elementary particles. So as not to limit the discussion to the increasing number of particles of contemporary physics,[2] of which non-scientists have little knowledge, the discussion is broadened to include such entities as nuclei, atoms, and molecules. Although not so elementary, these are as unobservable as the other entities of which scientists speak, and have entered longer into philosophical discussion. To locate the problem in a general context, the precise difficulty is whether these particles have the ontological status of eccentrics and epicycles, of phlogiston, or of the four Empedoclean elements, or whether they exist extramentally in a way similar to that of the objects of ordinary experience.[3]

General Methodology

Theoretical physicists and neo-empiricists are disposed to answer this question differently from experimentalists and realist philosophers. The theoretical formulation of quantum mechanics, for example, consists of postulates that appear to be internally consistent rules for mathematical manipulation, and prescriptions for obtaining predictions about the possible results of some type of experiment or measurement. Within this mathematical model, entities designated as elementary particles are treated as constructs with properties. These constructs, although not themselves directly observable, nonetheless yield predictions that can be put to experimental test. Should such predictions prove correct, the problem of the quantum philosopher is to ascertain whether there is a one-to-one correspondence between the constructs of the model and the elements of physical reality.

[2] Seven years ago, M. Gell-Mann and E. P. Rosenbaum discussed 30 "well-established" particles and antiparticles in an article entitled "Elementary Particles," *Scientific American* (July, 1957). These included 16 baryons and antibaryons, 7 mesons, 6 leptons and antileptons, and the photon. Since that time another 60 or 70 subatomic entities have been discovered; the characteristics of these are discussed, and an attempt made to classify them systematically, in a recent article by G. F. Chew, M. Gell-Mann, and A. H. Rosenfeld, entitled "Strongly Interacting Particles," *Scientific American* (February, 1964).

[3] Of these two alternatives, the first was adopted by Ernst Mach when he stated: "The atomic theory has in physical science a function which is similar to that of certain mathematical auxiliary representations. It is a mathematical model used for the representation of facts." — cited by A. G. Van Melsen, *From Atomos to Atom* (Pittsburgh: 1952) p. 151. Similarly, Hans Reichenbach, in an article entitled "Are There Atoms?" in *The Structure of Scientific Thought*, ed. E. H. Madden (Boston: 1960) pp. 94-105, observes that "Although during the nineteenth century the theory of the atom had reached a stage at which the existence of the atom appeared unquestionable, recent developments have renewed the controversy and have made the existence of the atom more questionable than ever." (p. 94) Opting for the second alternative is Grover Maxwell, who summarizes the paper already cited in the following terms: "The thesis of this paper, bluntly put, is that electrons, photons, and even electromagnetic fields are just as real, and exist in the same full-blooded sense, as chairs, tables, or sense impressions." *Minnesota Studies in the Philosophy of Science*, Vol. 3, p. vii.

Similarly, the neo-empiricist models his philosophy on the postulational method. He, too, regards unobservable entities such as electrons as constructs, and is concerned with methods of verification that can throw light on their ontological status.

The experimentalist, on the other hand, is more disposed to judge whether such entities are real or not on inductive grounds or on the basis of experimental evidences, and not merely on the grounds of their direct observability. In this he has something in common with the philosophical realist. The Thomistic philosopher, for example, expresses no overriding commitment to sensism or empiricism, and is quite used to validating the reality of unobservable entities. His Aristotelian methodology, with its accent on *a posteriori* demonstration, seems peculiarly well adapted to this task. For this reason, if for no other, it will be profitable to apply such methodology in answering the question: "Are elementary particles real?"

For St. Thomas Aquinas, following the lead of Aristotle, basically only four questions can be asked about anything: (1) Is it?; (2) What is it?; (3) Has it any attributes?; and (4) Why has it these attributes?[4] Since these questions relate to all reality, they can obviously be applied to the entities of modern science. For example, regarding the electron, it is meaningful to ask: "Is it?" Has it existence, understanding existence not merely as mental or rational existence, but as existence outside the mind and independently of the mind's consideration. Some scientists are disposed to answer this question "Yes", and for them the remaining questions can be asked. "What is it?" Some answer: A unit electric charge. "Has it any attributes?" The answer is proposed: Yes, it has a magnetic moment. "Why has it this attribute?" The answer becomes more involved: Because it has spin, or some similar explanation.

In what follows, the first two questions are of more concern than the others. Regarding these two, it is important to note that one cannot be answered in complete independence of the other. For example, should one have no idea whatever as to what he is discussing, he cannot take a position on its real existence. Similarly, if there is no suspicion that a thing may exist, it is futile to ask "What is it?" Yet one can inquire about the existence of such entities as a Himalayan snowman, or an elementary particle. In both cases, the meanings of the terms involved give a sufficient answer to the question "What is it?" to permit an initial investigation of the question "Is it?"

Existence of Elementary Particles

Starting with molecules and atoms, one can propose a proof that these entities enjoy extramental existence in some way or other. This conclusion can be deduced from evidence used to support the generalizations known in modern chemistry as the laws of combining weights and combining proportions. Such evidence began to be accumulated with John Dalton.[5]

[4] *In II Anal. Post.*, Lect. 1, n. 2.

[5] For a significant excerpt from Dalton's *A New System of Chemical Philosophy* (1808), see *Readings in the Literature of Science*, ed. W. C. and M. Dampier (New York: Harper Torchbook, 1959) pp. 93-99.

While insufficient to establish the existence of atoms — then proposed merely as an hypothesis — this provoked further experimental work, and led to important discoveries by Gay-Lussac and Avogadro that served to clarify the conceptual distinction between atoms and molecules.[6] The elaboration and synthesis of these results, effected by Stanislao Cannizzaro and others through the 19th and 20th centuries, furnishes an argument for the existence of atoms and molecules of various chemical elements and compounds.[7]

Reduced to its simplest formulation, this argument proposes that since chemicals always combine in integral and definite proportions by weight or mass, something must exist outside of the mind, or independent of mind's consideration, that accounts for such integral and definite proportions. In other words, the constant recurrence of such proportions can only be explained by the existence of some unit weight or mass. Central to the argument is the mathematical principle that the unit is the principle of positive, whole numbers. If such integral numbers appear in nature, some unit must also exist in nature to account for them.

It may be objected that this argument depends upon measurement, and that measurement itself is only approximate; therefore it cannot yield the type of certainty required in a demonstration, and the argument does not prove conclusively. To this one can reply that measurements are approximate, but that they can be known with certainty within the latitude of errors associated with particular measuring procedures. Thus, notwithstanding the almost infinitely variable circumstances that attend most measurements, it is possible for scientists to make true generalizations from them within experimental accuracy.[8] This accuracy has improved remarkably from the time of John Dalton to the present day. Yet even the crudeness of Dalton's measurements did not prevent him from detecting a certain discrete character in his combining weights. In the present day, with much refined measuring procedures, one can be quite certain that such units exist, and have no hesitancy in coupling them with names such as atom, proton, neutron and electron.

The recognition of the existence of a unit mass, again, is not associated uniquely with any particular method of measurement. Arthur Stanley Eddington's simple parable illustrates the danger that is here involved. He

[6] A clear discussion of this development is that of L. K. Nash, "The Atomic-Molecular Theory," in *Harvard Case Histories in Experimental Science*, ed. J. B. Conant (Cambridge, Mass.: 1957) Vol. 1, pp. 215-321.

[7] For a general survey of the scientific discoveries and their interpretation, see L. L. Whyte, *Essay on Atomism, From Democritus to 1960* (Middletown, Conn.: 1961). The strongest statement of this argument from the realist viewpoint that the author has seen is that of P. Soccorsi, S.J., *De Vi Cognitionis Humanae in Scientia Physica* (Romae: 1958). In this volume of over 300 pages, Father Soccorsi argues that the existence of atoms and molecules can be demonstrated apodictically, without having to invoke any unproved postulates or hypotheses, and without becoming involved in circular reasoning in any way.

[8] For a justification of this view regarding scientific measurement, see the author's paper, "The Measurement and Definition of Sensible Qualities," to appear in *The New Scholasticism* 39 (1965).

told of a fisherman who observed that all fish in his lake were over three inches long, apparently not adverting to the fact that his fishing net had a three-inch mesh. This type of circular reasoning is not present in the detection of unit atomic or molecular weights. These can now be measured in many different ways, with different systems of units, with an accuracy that permits their discrete character to be ascertained without doubt.

A related problem is whether or not such units are ultimate, or whether they may not themselves be later shown to admit of fractional values. While this consideration becomes important when one attempts to answer how "elementary" such entities may be, it is not of primary importance when questions of existence are being raised. In other words, this focuses attention on the question "What is it?" rather than on the question "Is it?" Here our concern is with the extramental existence of anything that might qualify as an elementary particle, in any sense of the term elementary. If unit weights continue to appear, this is an indication that entities corresponding to them do exist in some way. Admittedly there is the further question of accounting for the nature of such entities. But this should not impede the prior attempt to answer the existential question. The existence of molecules is in no way nullified by a later proof that atoms exist, just as the existence of atoms is not nullified by a later proof that electrons exist, and so on. Granted that all these existences have been established, the further questions arise as to which entities are truly elementary, and in what sense they can be called such.[9]

As a final point, it may also be observed that theoretical explanations do not enter into or affect the experimental evidence now being discussed. One need not subscribe to a particular theory of the structure of matter in order to interpret such experimental evidence. One certainly need not conceive matter as being composed of little round balls. The only epistemological demand placed on the observer is his acquaintance with, and commitment to, macroscopic measurements, as these are verified in ordinary experience. Whether matter is a wave or a particle, whether it consist of chunks that are tetrahedal, cubic, or spherical in shape, are questions that are completely extrinsic to the reasoning process here involved.[10]

[9] The terms "elements" and "elementary" are themselves relative, and depend upon the context in which they are used. For example, syllables may be referred to as the elements out of which words are constructed, even though syllables themselves are composed of letters as further elements. Similarly, what is regarded as an element by chemists need not necessarily be taken as elementary by physicists. Although many wish to employ these terms in an absolute sense, it appears that their primary imposition is relative, and that their usage in scientific contexts continues to preserve this relational character.

[10] Much the same comment may be made about theoretical concepts, such as that of mass, when the latter is understood as part of a theoretical system of mechanics that is not itself capable of direct experimental confirmation. Whatever may be the ontological status of mass when conceived in this fashion, since it is always employed in a univocal sense as a unit of measurement, and since this unit cancels out when measurements are placed in ratio to obtain relative weights, the theoretical interpretation one places on the unit is itself irrelevant to the argumentation or reasoning process. Here

Such reasoning therefore leads to the conclusion that a unit mass detected in the laboratory has some counterpart in the order of nature. The experimenter does not bring it into existence; it exists outside the mind. Therefore the entity that possesses the unit mass, or to which the unit mass is ascribed, also exists outside the mind.

Thus far discussion has been restricted to experimental evidence regarding weight or mass. One can make a similar analysis of the procedure employed by Millikan in the oil-drop experiment.[11] The same type of argument is there involved. One measures the electric charge on a very small oil drop, and discovers in the process that this charge is always some integral multiple of a very small unit. The same basic principle is employed: The unit is the principle of discrete, positive integers. The conclusion then follows that a unit electric charge exists, and therefore that an entity corresponding to this charge, named the electron, also exists.

Using such a methodology, it becomes possible to learn something about entities that are hidden from direct observation. The experimentalist learns about these from their influence, or in other words, from their causality — whether this be efficient, formal, or material. He learns of their existence from a peculiar effect that can be attributed to them, and this leads him to speak of something existing outside the mind and possessing the attributes that explain the effect.[12]

This provides the general Thomistic framework for a solution regarding the existence of elementary particles. If history gives a correct indication, molecules are more readily detectable than neutrinos. In modern particle physics, similarly, the extramental existence of lambda, sigma, and xi particles may not be knowable with the same degree of certainty as that of electrons, protons, and neutrons. But to say on this account that all of these are merely constructs, or purely theoretical entities, is to cut oneself off from the reality with which the experimentalist is daily in contact.[13]

The history of science does show, however, that mistakes have been made in the past. One is always faced with the danger of overpopulating the

the constructional aspect is much the same as the logical construction involved in formulating the traditional demonstrative syllogism. Although the syllogism itself is a construct, and even though the middle term may be merely an *ens rationis,* the conclusion has a real or extramental significance that is independent of the logical construction involved.

[11] For a full discussion of the oil-drop experiment and the conclusive character of the proof it implies, see J. D. Stranathan, *The "Particles" of Modern Physics* (Philadelphia: 1942) pp. 46-64.

[12] See P. Soccorsi, S.J., *De Physica Quantica* (Romae: 1956), particularly pp. 253-276.

[13] Mario Bunge censures such an attitude as "the inconsistency of maintaining subjective idealism in connection with the atomic realm and materialism with regard to the macroscopic level." He goes on: "Atoms do not exist apart from instruments, maintain idealists. Now, instruments have avowedly an atomic structure. . . . So that, if one asserts that 'only instruments exist,' then one is implicitly stating that 'atoms exist objectively as well' — which is contradictory to the former sentence." — *Metascientific Queries* (Springfield, Ill.: 1959) pp. 183-184.

universe with modern counterparts of eccentrics and epicycles, or of phlogiston. How can this be avoided? There is no simple answer to this question. Yet if scientists keep experimenting, measuring, and checking, ultimately they seem to get rid of superfluous entities. They may have thought that these were something, and later find out that something was actually involved, but something quite different from what had first been thought. But here again one passes from the existential question to the question regarding the nature of the existent: from "Is it?" to "What is it?" A change in the way one answers the subsequent question, "What is it?", need not nullify the reasoning process that led to its investigation in the first place.

Nature of Elementary Particles

This raises the second, and considerably more difficult, question: What is an elementary particle? Physicists and chemists possibly seek different answers to a question of this type. A chemist, interested as he is in the structure of matter, thinks of elementary particles as these are components of macroscopic bodies. The physicist, on the other hand, is more concerned with the interpretation of experiments in which these particles are conceived as subsistent entities. This difference of viewpoint suggests a twofold consideration of the nature of elementary particles: first, as these are parts of a composed body; and secondly, as they are entities that subsist in one way or other.[14]

Virtual Parts. Speaking in general on the first point, one can say that an elementary particle is a part of a physical body. This answer, based on ordinary experience, employs no technical terms from modern science. Part is taken to be correlative with whole, and a physical body is understood simply as juxtaposed to a mathematical body. The latter is made up of parts, all homogenous, endowed only with extension as their unique property. The number of such parts in a mathematical body is indefinite, or potentially infinite. A mathematical body can be divided without limit, since its parts have only extension, and extension is always divisible.[15]

---

[14] Although this distinction has been proposed in the context of modern physics and chemistry, it is significant that medieval thinkers made a similar distinction when discussing *minima naturalia.* Thus they spoke of *minima inexistentia,* meaning *minima* as these might exist within a body, and *minima per se existentia,* which are *minima* as these exist when separated from a body. In the 14th century, thinkers such as John of Jandun commonly taught that separated *minima* could exist, but that *minima inexistentia* were not present within a body. Because of this infelicitous view, the 14th century did not continue the work on minimal parts inaugurated in the 13th by Albert the Great, Thomas Aquinas, and Giles of Rome, and was consequently sterile in the development of atomic theory. For details, see Anneliese Maier, *Die Vorläufer Galileis im 14. Jahrhundert* (Roma: 1949), pp. 185-190.

[15] In discussing the difference between a body considered mathematically and a body considered physically, St. Thomas Aquinas remarks: "Although a body, understood mathematically, is infinitely divisible, a natural body is not divisible to infinity. For in a mathematical body all that is considered is quantity, and in this there is nothing that is repugnant to division, whereas in a natural body there is a natural form that requires a determinate quan-

When one says that a molecule or atom or electron is a part of a physical body, the implication is that this part is a different type of entity from the part of a mathematical body. Like the mathematical body, the physical body is divisible, but it is not infinitely divisible; after a finite number of divisions, one comes to a part that is not further divisible. To be more concrete, one can consider a physical body such as lead or water. Are all the parts of lead, lead? Can one divide a piece of lead, and carry on this process indefinitely, and always get lead as a result of the process of division? An answer consistent with modern science, it seems, would be that one can divide lead very many times; yet experiment shows that there are parts beyond which one cannot go and still retain lead. Physical bodies seem therefore to be made up of minimal parts, beyond which division cannot be effected and still retain parts that are homogeneous in nature with the whole.[16]

The same analysis can be applied to water — perhaps a more provocative example, because many feel that they can identify the parts of water. Assuming that water is divided, one comes ultimately to its minimal part; to this the name "molecule" is commonly applied, and association made with the unit molecular weight mentioned above. Although this molecule of water is then found to be further divisible, the important point is that when it is further divided it ceases to be water, but becomes something else, say, hydrogen and oxygen. This, it would seem, does not permit one to say that hydrogen and oxygen are actually *in* water; the only legitimate inference is that water, when divided, breaks down *into* hydrogen and oxygen, or that water is made *out of* hydrogen and oxygen. Assuming that one calls the minimal part of hydrogen, or oxygen, or lead, the "atom," one can then say that molecules are made out of atoms, or break down into atoms.[17] Using

tity, just as it requires other accidents. Wherefore quantity cannot be found under the species of flesh unless within certain determined limits." — *In I Phys.*, Lect. 9, n. 9.

16 The doctrine of minimal parts, deriving from Aristotle (*Physics,* Book I, Chap. 4) was developed by the Arab philosopher, Averroës, and perfected by 13th-century scholastic thinkers such as Roger Bacon, St. Albert the Great, St. Thomas Aquinas, Giles of Rome, Siger of Brabant, Richard of Middleton, and Duns Scotus. For a treatment of the scholastic development, see Maier, *op. cit.,* pp. 179-196; for a statement of the influence of this doctrine on later atomic theories, see Van Melsen, *op. cit.,* pp. 58-91.

17 The earliest thinker, to the author's knowledge, who identified minimal parts with atoms was St. Albert the Great. Thus Albert states: "Although there is no minimum part of a body precisely as it is a body . . . nevertheless in a physical body one can have flesh so small that if it become any smaller it cannot carry out the activity of flesh: and this is minimal not precisely in the sense of being a body, but in the sense of being physical. This is what Democritus called the atom. And because this is material to the entire body, and the whole is composed of material parts, so he said that physical bodies are composed of such. In this he would not have been wrong if he had understood it in the sense of a quantitative and physical composition: but he did err in not discerning the primary essential composition that results from matter and form, for the minimal flesh is composed of matter and form." — *In I de Gen.*, Tract. 1, cap. 12 (ed. Borgnet, Vol. 4, p. 354b).

this manner of speaking, however, one passes from considering how elementary particles are parts of composed bodies to considering how they may be separated from bodies and begin to exist as subsistent entities.

Yet it is sometimes said that atoms are present in molecules, or that water is composed of hydrogen and oxygen in the sense that both are present in water and are fully real as its parts. Can such a statement be validly made? This problem, basically the question of the manner of existence of elements in compounds, is as old as Aristotle, and has been treated at length by scholastic philosophers. Aristotle himself maintained that elements were present in compounds by their *dunamis*, a Greek word that is equivalent to the English expression "powers of action." [18] This term has been variously understood and translated by different commentators. Avicenna understood it to mean that elements are actually present in compounds, while Averroës asserted that elements were present only potentially. St. Thomas Aquinas took a middle position, maintaining that elements were present in compounds neither actually nor potentially, but virtually, in the sense that their forces or powers (*virtutes*) are conserved in the compound.[19] The latter interpretation represents the common position of scholastic philosophers, and will be assumed to be essentially correct in what follows.[20]

The concept of virtual presence suggests a general answer to the question, "What is an elementary particle?", considering such a particle as part of a composed body. It is a real part of such a body, as an integral component. Although real, however, it is not fully actual, nor is it merely potential; rather it has a virtual existence. In the case of a molecule composed of different atoms, the molecule is of a different nature from its components when these exist separately; yet, when incorporated into the nature of the molecule as integral parts, the components become virtual parts of that nature. Since they are not fully actual, one can maintain that they are not fully real. At the same time, because they have some type of existence outside the mind, they are not merely rational or logical entities. To say that they are real but virtual thus characterizes their special mode of existence, and gives a general idea of their nature.

Primary Matter. Such a reply to the question "What is it?" is based on the type of concern exhibited by the chemist. When one passes to the speculations of modern physics, however, the answer becomes considerably more difficult. The reason for this lies in the fact that the physicist is concerned with these entities as they exist (or subsist) in a transient state as quasi-independent particles. The complexity of the phenomena he studies in high energy experiments enables him to identify between thirty and ninety particles and anti-particles that may be grouped in various ways.[21]

18 *De Generatione et Corruptione*, Book I, Chap. 10, 327b 31.

19 *In I de Gen.*, Lect. 24, n. 6.

20 For the details of the various teachings of high scholastic thinkers, see Anneliese Maier, *An der Grenze von Scholastik und Naturwissenschaft*, 2. Aufl. (Roma: 1952), pp. 1-140.

21 See the articles cited in fn. 2, *supra*. For an elementary explanation of the reasoning that led to the identification of the 30 particles and anti-

What are these particles? Are they truly fundamental and elementary? If so, what is meant by the expression "elementary particle"?

In a context such as this, Werner Heisenberg has recently proposed an answer that is intelligible to the Thomistic philosopher. As a theoretical physicist, he associates such particles with a mathematical function known as the psi-function and interpreted as a probability wave. Explaining the nature of this wave, Heisenberg says:

> This concept of the probability wave was something entirely new in theoretical physics since Newton. Probability in mathematics or in statistical mechanics means a statement about our degree of knowledge of the actual situation. . . . The probability wave of Bohr, Kramers, and Slater, however, meant more than that; it meant a tendency for something. It was a quantitative version of the old concept of *potentia* in Aristotelian philosophy. It introduced something standing in the middle between the idea of the event and the actual event, a strange kind of physical reality just in the middle between possibility and reality.[22]

Here and in other places Heisenberg points to something with a merely potential character, such as primary matter, as the physical analogue of the psi-function. This enables him to investigate the nature of elementary particles at a deeper ontological level than those who propose explanations in terms of a Democritean notion of atom. Heisenberg notes that Democritus had deprived his atom of the normal properties of color, odor, and taste, because Democritus believed that atoms could explain these properties by their motions and arrangements. But while depriving the atom of such qualities, notes Heisenberg, Democritus did not deprive it of being, or of extension in space, or of shape or motion. The reason for this, in Heisenberg's estimation, is that in Democritus's day it would have been difficult to discuss the atom if such attributes were taken away from it. In the present day, however, the situation has changed, and one can give a more profound explanation of the ultimate entities of which physics speaks. In Heisenberg's words:

> Let us discuss the question: What is an elementary particle? We say, for instance, simply "a neutron" but we can give no well-defined picture of what we mean by the word. We can use several pictures and describe it once as a particle, once as a wave or as a wave packet. But we know that none of these descriptions is accurate. Certainly the neutron has no color, no smell, no taste. In this respect it resembles the atom of Greek philosophy. But even the other qualities are taken from the elementary particle, at least to some extent; the concepts of geometry and kinematics, like shape or motion in space, cannot be applied to it consistently. If one wants to give an accurate description of the elementary particle — and here the emphasis is on the word accurate — the only thing which can be written down as description is a probability function. But then one sees that not even the quality of

---

particles that were believed to be elementary a few years ago, see Chen Ning Yang, *Elementary Particles:* A Short History of Some Discoveries in Atomic Physics (Princeton: 1962).

[22] *Physics and Philosophy* (New York: 1958; Torchbook edition 1962), pp. 40-41.

being, if it [being] may be called a quality, belongs to what is described. It is a possibility for being or a tendency for being.[23]

Here again, Heisenberg's answer regarding the nature of elementary particles identifies these as elementary or transitional states that are assumed by some basic potency such as primary matter.

The sense in which these are elementary or primary states of matter can be further clarified by inquiring whether all the so-called elementary particles are truly elementary or whether some are more fundamental than others. Heisenberg uses the term elementary to designate the primary manifestations of a basic potency represented by the psi-function. Thus he does not deny that elementary particles can be divided. They can be divided, and still remain elementary, if the fragments into which they divide have characteristics similar to their own, enabling these in turn to be called elementary particles. On this broad interpretation, it is possible to refer to all the particles of which physicists speak as truly elementary.

Yet physicists are now searching for hierarchies among the various particles they identify as elementary, and it seems likely that the next few decades will witness further clarification and simplification. A recent proposal by Victor Weisskopf, of MIT, reveals the lines along which a resolution may be made.[24] Weisskopf would simplify the number of elementary particles by first eliminating all anti-particles, then all particles that can be shown to be excited states of others. Thus he regards the sigma particle, the lambda particle, and the xi particle as different excited states of the proton. He further suggests that there are only two elementary particles, the baryon and the lepton, both with a variety of states or configurations. For him, the proton and the neutron are variant states of the baryon similar to the spin-up and spin-down of the electron in the ground state of hydrogen. The lambda particle, the xi particle, and the sigma particle in turn represent excited states of the baryon. Similarly, leptons occur in different forms: as electrons, as neutrinos, and as heavy electrons (sometimes referred to as mu-mesons).

Weisskopf also distinguishes between particles that represent fundamental states of matter and those that are named particles but are in reality field quanta. The most familiar field quantum is the photon. Just as this is the light quantum of the electromagnetic field, so Weisskopf identifies the pi-meson and the k-meson as quanta of the nuclear field. He also suspects, somewhat along the lines suggested by Heisenberg, that underlying both is something different from the particle and from the field. This he describes as "some new thing, which is as far from the field as the field is from the particle, consequently something new, but that embraces the whole." [25]

23 Ibid., p. 70.

24 "The Quantum Ladder," *International Science and Technology* (No. 18, June 1963) pp. 62-70.

25 Ibid., p. 70.

To summarize, at the present state of science, one can define an elementary particle as a real but virtual component of a physical body; as such it is not merely a mental construct, but exists extramentally in the whole of which it is a part.[26] Alternatively, when considering such particles as subsistent entities in a transient state, one can define them as elemental manifestations of some substratum, or as the basic forms that come to primary matter, when the latter is undergoing substantial mutation of the most elementary kind. Here too, they are not to be regarded as fully real entities that have the actual existence of objects of ordinary experience. At the same time, since they do represent transient states, and furnish some knowledge of the potentialities of the substratum, they cannot be relegated to the domain of mental construct; they do enjoy some type of extramental existence.[27]

Two final questions may be asked about the solutions here offered concerning the reality of elementary particles. The first concerns the certainty that should be attached to such solutions, and the second inquiries about their relation to other contemporary views concerning elementary particles.

Regarding the first, if one maintains that the existence of such particles can be demonstrated, then it would seem that *something* can be known, in general, about their nature. An exact knowledge — say, of the number of elementary forms that can come to primary matter — on the other hand, does not seem attainable at the present state of scientific research. It may well be that baryons and leptons are now the most plausible candidates for the title of most fundamental particle. Yet a later stage of research could well yield simplifications that account for observed phenomena in more elegant fashion. While a general answer can thus be attempted concerning the nature of elementary particles, specific details still remain in the realm of probability.

Regarding the second question, it appears that any discourse about virtual parts and primary matter will be largely unintelligible to the modern scientist. Again, even when these notions are understood, they are not easily reconcilable with the intuitive picture formed by the scientist when thinking of the entities on which he does research. If these difficulties present themselves to the experimentalist, they become even more pronounced for the theoretical physicist because of his preoccupation with mathematical models. For example, T. D. Newton and E. P. Wigner, discussing the meaning of elementary particle as this occurs in mathematical theory, maintain that a physical system is to be called elementary if all its free physical states can be obtained by kinematic transformations (belonging to the inhomogeneous

[26] This position has been defended by Edward MacKinnon, S.J., in his articles, "Atomic Physics and Reality," and "Thomism and Atomism," *The Modern Schoolmen* 38 (1960-61), pp. 37-59, 121-141.

[27] Thus the solution arrived at in this article differs both from the critical empiricism of Mach and Reichenbach and from the extreme realism of Grover Maxwell; it is actually intermediate between the two, being based on the critical or moderate realism that typifies Thomistic epistemology.

Lorentz group) of one basic state; similarly a physical system is to be called a particle if it can be treated as structureless.[28] These notions, it need hardly be pointed out, bear little relation to the concepts of primary matter and virtual part.

Whatever the formalism used by the theoretical physicist, however, this still requires physical interpretation if it is to furnish information about the real world. A postulational system, no matter how sophisticated its postulates, always leaves questions unresolved as to what is objectively real and what is merely a matter of construct. Philosophers in the neo-empiricist tradition, concerned almost exclusively with the postulational approach, have found themselves incapable of giving satisfying answers concerning the reality of elementary particles. The position adopted in this paper is that an analysis of the data of modern science in terms of scholastic concepts that furnish an ontological description of the structure of matter is one means of supplying satisfying answers to this problem. Whether such a fusion of the "new" with the "old" can be made, and to what benefit, is left open to discussion.

CAUSALITY, ANALOGY, AND
SCIENTIFIC GROWTH

The problem of what may be referred to as « the cumulative growth of scientific knowledge »[1] has come into sharp focus in the United States and England within the past decade, following the publication of Thomas S. Kuhn's *The Structure of Scientific Revolutions*[2] and the controversies it has generated. Previous to Kuhn's work, most historians of science were agreed that science is an objective and rational enterprise, employing a methodology that systematically eliminates hazy and idiosyncratic judgments and that ultimately contributes to a cumulative growth of knowledge. Likewise Anglo-American philosophers of science, the majority of whom are logical positivists by inclination or training, have consistently regarded science as a type of critical inquiry that is productive of a publicly verifiable type of knowledge, growing more or less continuously, and thus essentially evolutionary in its mode of development.

By concentrating attention on the revolutionary, as opposed to the evolutionary, character of modern science, Kuhn has effectively launched a frontal attack on this « cumulative growth of knowledge » thesis. The burden of his analysis is to show that the larger part of scientific activity, which he calls « normal science », is essentially puzzle-solving within the context of paradigms or sets of rules that are accepted within a scientific

---

[1] For a fuller treatment of the historical and conceptual background for the thesis developed in this paper, see the author's two-volume study, *Causality and Scientific Explanation*, Vol. I. *Medieval and Early Classical Science*. Vol. II. *Classical and Contemporary Science*. Ann Arbor: The University of Michigan Press, 1972-1974. The author wishes to thank The University of Michigan Press for permission to use portions of Chapter 4, Vol. II, in preparing this paper.

[2] Chicago: University of Chicago Press, 1962; 2d enlarged edition, 1970, which will be cited in what follows.

community. At rare intervals, in his view, scientists break out of this normal pattern and institute a revolution, which is equivalent to re-tooling within the scientific community and adopting a new paradigm that solves yet further puzzles. Through a series of such revolutions, however — and this is the important issue for purposes of this paper — there is not necessarily linear progress or cumulative growth. Scientific revolutions really amount to different ways of looking at things, like Gestalt switches, and one should be wary of regarding them as productive of new truths, or even of seeing them as tending asymptotically to objective truth as the limit of a knowledge-acquisition process. Thus science, for Kuhn, is not evolutionary at all; it is basically revolutionary, ever changing, and not a stable body of knowledge to which additions are being made continuously by an evolutionary process [3].

Kuhn's attack on the concept of truth has provoked a reaction from Karl Popper and some of his disciples in England, most notably Imre Lakatos, who, while sympathetic to certain aspects of Kuhn's thesis, feels that Kuhn fails to take account of the results of rational inquiry in furthering human knowledge [4]. Popper himself focuses on the method of falsification and sees this as a way of approaching truth, at least as an ideal [5]. He, however, disagrees with the main line of logical positivist thought in the United States, and another of his disciples, Paul K. Feyerabend, has attacked the positivist view of scientific theories and the observational-theoretical dichotomy as inadequate accounts of actual scientific practice [6]. Particularly in urging philosophers of science to abandon the coherence condition for successive theories and the notion of meaning invariance even for observational terms, Feyerabend seems to have joined forces with Kuhn, since both effectively question the « cumulative growth of knowledge » view of the scientific enterprise.

The point of this paper will be to argue against both the logical positivist philosophy of science and its recent « revolutionary » critics, while

---

[3] *Ibid.*, pp. 168-173.

[4] See *Criticism and the Growth of Knowledge*, ed. Imre Lakatos and Alan Musgrave, Cambridge: at the University Press, 1970.

[5] Note POPPER'S brief essay in *Criticism and the Growth of Knowledge*, pp. 51-58; for a more extended exposition of his views, see his *Logic of Scientific Discovery*, New York: Basic Books, 1959, and his *Conjectures and Refutations: The Growth of Scientific Knowledge*, New York: Basic Books, 1962.

[6] See FEYERABEND'S « *How to be a Good Empiricist - A Plea for Tolerance in Matters Epistemological* », in B. A. Brody, ed., *Readings in the Philosophy of Science*, Englewood Cliffs: Prentice-Hall, 1970, pp. 329-342.

[7] This has been argued by the author in his « *St. Thomas Aquinas, Galileo, and Einstein* », in *The Thomist*, 24 (1961), pp. 1-22, revised and enlarged as *Einstein, Galileo and Aquinas. Three Views of Scientific Method*. Washington: The Thomist Press, 1963.

[8] ERNEST NAGEL, *The Structure of Science. Problems in the Logic of Scientific Explanation*, New York: Harcourt, Brace and World, 1961, pp. 15, 26-28; note also the essays in Brody, *Readings in the Philosophy of Science*, pp. 8-27, 66-87, 88-104.

defending at the same time the « cumulative growth of knowledge » thesis, and this from a perspective provided by the philosophy of St. Thomas Aquinas. Admittedly it is dangerous to resort to a thirteenth-century thinker for the solution of a' problem in twentieth-century science, and yet the problem itself yields to ready solution when two distinctive teaching of Aquinas, namely, those on causality and analogy, are applied to it. In fact, one may maintain that the scientific methodology outlined in Aquinas's commentary on the *Posterior Analytics* of Aristotle, while unknown to most scientists, is still implicitly used in scientific practice [7]. For although, according to some recent philosophical analyses, the scientist seems to be asking only « that-questions » (*quia*) and « why-questions » (*propter quid*) [8], in answering these he implicitly expresses his own commitment on questions of existence (*an sit*) and definition (*quid sit*). Thus his inquiry continues to center around the four scientific questions that were first pointed out by Aristotle and then employed and elucidated with remarkable clarity by Aquinas [9]. Since this is so, and since these questions can be answered. satisfactorily only in causal terms, one may further argue that a reinstatement of causal analysis is essential to any endeavor that would account for cumulative growth in scientific knowledge. What Kuhn and others have indeed succeeded in showing is that the approach to problems in the philosophy of science through formal logic alone, conceiving scientific explanation on the model of formal deducibility without reference to causality or analogy or the conceptual apparatus of material logic, is quite inadequate to the task of justifying *any* scientific progress. As opposed to this positivist approach and the Humean empiricism that inevitably accompanies it, the moderate realism of Aquinas, with its stress on analogical reasoning and causal analysis, may perhaps be offered as an antidote to Kuhn's revolutionary relativism and as a remarkably durable, though admittedly pre-modern, support for the critical and objective character of contemporary science.

1. *Analogy, Modeling, and the Growth of Knowledge.*

The growth of human knowledge, as it takes place in the individual, is somewhat mysterious but nonetheless an undeniable fact. Knowledge grows in individuals because they perceive, and observe, and learn from the things around them. And generally one perceives, and observes, and learns by noting the similarities and differences among things [10]. When a person encounters something he does not know, he attempts to understand this by conceiving it after the fashion of something he does know. Thus he uses the things he knows to advance into the realm of the unknown.

---

[9] ARISTOTLE, *Posterior Analytics*, Bk. II, ch. 1, 89b 21-25; AQUINAS, *In II Posteriorum Analyticorum*, lect. 1.

[10] Cf. AQUINAS, *In I Metaphysicorum*, lect. 1.

[11] See AQUINAS, *Summa Theologiae*, I, q. 13, a. 5, and parallel places.

When he encounters very special difficulty, and cannot understand something in terms of anything already known, he resorts to analogy. The classical case of this is man's discourse about God[11]. It is not only in theology that man uses analogy, however, for he does this also in the process of scientific discovery. It is true, of course, that the finished language of science avoids analogy and aims for precise formal predication in an unequivocal or univocal way. But in the process of discovery, before this precise language gets formulated, the scientist can be said to employ a type of analogy in his thought processes. He does not use this term explicitly, but he will frequently speak of a model, particularly in connection with a new theory he is proposing, and it is this device, the model, that can shed light on the growth of knowledge in science[12].

The term « modeling » as applied to scientific discovery has two referents, one of which is something known, from which the model is taken, and the other something unknown, at least initially, to which the model is applied. The known factor may be referred to as the source or origin of the model, and the unknown factor may be called its application. Thus a model is taken from one thing, its origin, and used to understand another, its application.

There are many types of model employed in scientific reasoning, and some of these may be indicated in terms of simple relationships that can hold between the origin and the application. If the origin and application, for example, are similar in form, one may refer to this as uniform modeling. The simplest instance of uniform or one-form modeling is that frequently used in applied physics, where an exact replica is constructed, on a smaller or larger scale, in order to study a particular phenomenon. Since an actual replica is involved, both origin and application are similar in form, and only a size or dimensional change serves to distinguish the two. In what may be called difform modeling, on the other hand, the origin and application are different in form. The difference may arise from the fact that the origin pertains to the subject matter of one discipline whereas the application pertains to the subject matter of another. A simple example, also from applied physics, is the use of electrical circuit analysis to study problems of mechanical vibration. The modeling is difform because the origin, an electrical circuit, is different in form from the application, mechanical vibratory motion.

Difform modeling is much more complex than uniform modeling, and has more interesting applications in scientific discovery. Yet uniform modeling has been productive of some discoveries, and these should be given

---

12 The exposition that follows is influenced by MARY B. HESSE, *Models and Analogies in Science*, Notre Dame: University of Notre Dame Press, 1966, but in the main it follows the treatment in ROM HARRÉ, *The Principles of Scientific Thinking*, Chicago: University of Chicago Press, 1970, pp. 33-62, with considerable abbreviation and simplification of terminology.

brief mention. An interesting example of this form of modeling is the discovery of the first correct explanation of the rainbow by Theodoric of Freiberg in the first decade of the fourteenth century[13]. Whereas most of his predecessors regarded the rain cloud as an effective agent in the production of the rainbow, and even saw some similarity between the colors of the bow and the spectrum resulting from the sun's rays as they pass through a spherical flask of water, they all tended to model the flask as a cloud or as a collection of raindrops. Theodoric, on the other hand, was the first to see that a globe of water could be used to model, not a small spherical cloud, but a magnified raindrop. His experiments with rays of sunlight passing through the water-filled globe enabled him to duplicate, in a laboratory situation, and thence to explain, the essential properties of the primary and secondary rainbow. His modeling here was uniform, since the spherical flask of water is similar in form to the raindrop. Another example of such modeling would be the explanation of a planetary perturbation in the solar system by means of a putative planet, or hypothetical planet, not yet known to exist. Here the unknown entity is modeled after a known entity, and upon discovery, say in the case of Neptune, is found to be similar in form to the planet whose motion it was perturbing, namely, Uranus. Sometimes there is an appreciable size difference between the known entity and the unknown, for example, the flask of water and the raindrop, and sometimes there is not, as in the case of Neptune and Uranus. Again, there are times when there will appear to be great differences in size between the model and the thing modeled, which themselves are rectified when the effects of distance on observation are taken into account. Stars, for instance, appear so small that they were first modeled as points of light; with the advance of scientific knowledge, however, they have been more accurately modeled as suns. Now the sun is surely the largest object in any reasonable proximity to us, and compared to this a point of light is as small as one could imagine. Yet, the progress of science has revealed that these points of light are bodies of the same order of magnitude as our sun, so the end result is modeling in the same size range. In fact, we now say that our sun is a star of a certain type, which shows how we tend to model one entity on another, and how the study of one phenomenon leads us to an understanding of others.

In difform modeling, as already noted, there is a change of form between the model and the thing modeled, and this usually because the model is taken from one discipline in an attempt to understand a phenomenon occurring in another. Studying mechanical vibration problems through electrical circuit analogues is, in this sense, difform modeling. A better example, and one associated with a famous scientific discovery, is William

---

[13] For details, see the author's « Dietrich von Freiberg », *Dictionary of Scientific Biography*, Vol. IV, New York: Charles Scribner's Sons, 1971, pp. 92-95.

Harvey's classical work on the circulation of the blood. Here, rather than analyze the flow of blood in mammals as Galen had done on the model of total absorption from a linear flow process, Harvey correctly understood this on the model of a circulatory flow maintained by a mechanical pump. His modeling was difform in the sense that pumps pertain to mechanics whereas the flow of blood pertains to biology or physiology.

More complex types of difform modeling construct models that are based on two or more different disciplines in an attempt to understand a baffling or complex phenomenon. A classical example is the attempt to understand phenomena associated with the elementary constituents of matter on the model of a wave-particle. Here the application is in the area of atomic or nuclear physics, whereas the origin is from a twofold source: particles are usually studied in kinematics or dynamics, whereas waves pertain more to hydrodynamics or electromagnetic theory. Another example would be the Bohr atom when this is used as a model to explain the absorption and emission spectra of various gases. In this case the application is broadly in the area of chemistry, whereas the model itself is based on two disciplines, mechanics for the planetary features of the atom and radiation theory for the way in which it emits and absorbs energy. These types of difform modeling are powerful tools for scientific investigation, but they also pose most interesting questions relating to existential statements and law-like generalizations, which will be taken up in subsequent sections of this paper.

It should be remarked here that every time one employs a novel modeling technique to gain understanding of a phenomenon, he is involved in a new way of looking at things, and even a type of Gestalt switch may be said to take place. It is in this sense that Kuhn is quite correct in seeing scientific revolutions as involving such switches and changed viewpoints. In fact, his paradigm-shifts can very frequently be regarded as modeling-shifts. Feyerabend is also correct in maintaining that there is no strict meaning invariance throughout the history of science, for under a new modeling technique the entities to which one refers do take on new meaning and significance. For example, to say that "A star is a minute hole in the canopy of the heavens" or " A star is a pin-point of light ", is quite different from saying that "A star is a sun". The same should be said for the differences between the following pairs of statements: "A rainbow is light dispersed by a cloud" and "A rainbow is light differentially reflected and refracted by spherical raindrops"; "The flow of blood is a linear absorption process" and "The flow of blood is a circulation resulting from the pumping action of the heart"; and "The Milky Way is a nebula or cloud of star-dust" and "The Milky Way is our galaxy seen on its side". In all these changed viewpoints, however, and the list includes some classical discoveries made by the founding fathers of astronomy, optics, and biology, more is involved than merely subjective change in the

206

viewer. In each pair the second statement represents an advance of objective content as well, it represents a growth of knowledge, and if this growth is not cumulative in the Baconian sense of progress by uniform accretion, it is cumulative in the sense that the first statement can be readily understood in terms of the second, and the second actually offers a better explanation of the whole range of phenomena the first was initially thought to account for.

2. Theories, Existential Statements, and Causal Reasoning.

With these notions as a background, some of the difficulties associated with the use of uniform and difform modeling may now be elaborated in the contexts provided by scientific theories and scientific laws or lawlike generalizations. It will be convenient first to consider theories, and a fruitful way of doing this is to speak of the paths by which new existential statements make their way into the language of science. Since theories involve reference to hypothetical or theoretical entities, attempts to verify the extramental existence of such entities lead to problematic existential statements with which scientists—and not philosophers of science alone—frequently find themselves concerned. The verification of such statements, in turn, quite commonly involves reasoning from effect to cause and thus, by implication at least, the use by scientists of causal argumentation.

The invention of the telescope and the microscope were not essential to the Scientific Revolution, but they did much to accelerate its progress, and they led immediately to the incorporation of a host of new existential statements into the literature of science. One need only mention here the variety of new objects found by Galileo in the heavens with his telescope, described so enticingly in his *Sidereus nuncius,* including myriads of stars, planets of strange shapes, and those mysterious "four Medicean stars" that produced such consternation in Renaissance Florence. The same could be said of Antony van Leeuwenhoek's work with the microscope and the revelation of scores of new microbes, micro-organisms of unheard of types, that gave so much stimulus to the sciences of biology and medicine. Such instruments contributed immeasurably to the growth of scientific knowledge, and this growth was for the most part made cumulative by means of uniform modeling. Because both instruments essentially magnify, they put human observer in contact with objects whose size appears unlike those of ordinary experience, but whose form, on closer observation, is found to be not notably different. Microbes are organisms, but very much smaller than the organisms we ordinarily see. The Medicean star are moons, but imperceptible to the naked eye, and so not seen as the spherical body that illumines nights on earth. Thus the universe is populated with new entities, but they are basically similar to entities already known, and so the modeling is uniform and leads to new existential statements. Such statements, however, frequently have a problematic or hypothetical status, and then it becomes necessary for the scientist to verify or falsify them. For example, in the study of the solar system a planet departs from its projected orbit calculated on the basis of the influences known to be affecting its motion. It is suspected that there might be another planet in the solar system that is actually perturbing its orbit. Such a planet then becomes a hypothetical entity and criteria are established for verifying or falsifying the statement that accords it existence. In general these criteria are of two types, indicative criteria and recognitive criteria [14]. The simplest example of an indicative criterion is pointing, or indicating the spatio-temporal region in which the postulated object is to be found. Along with this goes a recognitive criterion, whereby the object is identified as belonging to the expected type [15]. Such criteria work for verifying existential statements, but they also can serve to falsify them. Assume, for example, that an astronomer's calculations indicate a spatio-temporal region that is to be searched for the hypothetical planet, on the condition that, if there is such an entity, this is where it will be found. The existential statement is falsified if the region is searched and found either to be empty or occupied by something that does not meet the appropriate recognitive criteria. Through the use of such verification and falsification techniques the planets Uranus, Neptune, and Pluto were discovered and are now regarded as parts of the solar system, whereas the putative planet Vulcan, originally postulated to account for other planetary variations, is no longer ascribed a real existence.

The cases discussed so far involve only optical magnification and thus are well suited to illustrate uniform modeling. More sophisticated instruments, such as the spectroscope, also permit uniform modeling, whereby, for example, through the comparison of spectra the sun is identified as a star of a certain type. As more complex instrumentation is utilized, however, and particularly the experimental configurations designed to study the structure of matter, existential statements are encountered that are more difficult to verify or falsify. Consider the statement, based on the interpretation of experiments with diffraction patterns, that "there is a lattice structure in crystals". Or the statements, based on the observation of scintillations and tracks in cloud chambers, to the effect that "this is an alpha particle" or "That is a positron". The verification of such statements involves indicative criteria, but these are not simply pointing to the entity described.

---

[14] Following, but adapting the discussion in HARRÉ, *Principles of Scientific Thinking,* pp. 63-91; a related exposition is that of RICHARD J. BLACKWELL, *Discovery in the Physical Sciences,* Notre Dame: University of Notre Dame Press, 1969.

[15] Using Aristotelian terminology, one could say that indicative criteria of this type establish the *an sit,* whereas the recognitive criteria establish the *an sit talis* or even the *quid sit.*

Rather they are indirect criteria whereby one reasons from effect to cause. Similarly the recognitive criteria are not as simple as in direct pointing, for here the very entity spoken of is quite probably different from anything encountered in ordinary experience. One may speak of a postulated planet as a theoretical entity, but lattice structures, alpha particles, and positrons are seemingly theoretical entities of a different sort. Yet a distinction may be made on the basis of the type of modeling involved, for the putative planet, as already explained, is based on uniform modeling, whereas these other postulated entities are based on difform modeling. And when difform modeling is involved, it is quite possible that different indicative and recognitive criteria will be required to verify and falsify existential statements. Such existential statements, it may be remarked, are implicit answers to the frequently-asked questions concerning the ontological status of theoretical entites.

Indicative and recognitive criteria for theoretical entities, then, should be patterned on criteria used to verify or falsify the existence of ordinary things that fall at least indirectly under sense observation. With indicative criteria there is no special problem, since the indication can only be direct or indirect. With regard to the indirect, moreover, one need have no scruples about employing cause and effect relationships, since these are used to indicate even ordinary types of things. So litmus paper would be inserted into a liquid to verify the presence of an acid or a base, depending on the particular effect of the substance on the paper to supply the indication. It would seem, however, that some type of spatio-temporal localization is necessary for even this indirect pointing, and thus any entity that does not fit into a space-time matrix in one way or another will fail to satisfy indicative criteria. When investigating the types of theoretical entities that enter into the structure of matter, however, such as elementary particles and genes, so long as these are viewed as parts of a whole that is of determinate dimensions and exists over a knowable time span, there would seem to be no insuperable problems with spatio-temporal localization.

Recognitive criteria present a more complex problem, for the range of possibilities becomes great as soon as one speaks of entities different from those already known. It is here that some type of ontology is essential, and for purposes of discussion, following Aristotle and Aquinas, we may propose that any postulated entities should fall generally within one of three categories, namely, those of: (1) substance or thing, which manifests some permanence and independence in being; (2) property or attribute, which shows dependence in being but with a characteristic way of initiating or affecting activity; and (3) motion or change, which gives indication of being a process or event of some type, either transient or on-going. How these categories may be utilized will become apparent from a brief consideration of the various types of difform modeling. Suffice it to state, for the moment, that the most interesting cases are those concerned with classifying entities that enter into the structure of ordinary bodies, or with classifying entities that themselves constitute new subsistent types, even though they be extremely transitory and thus exhibit minimal spatio-temporal localization.

Entities based on difform modeling therefore present the general problem of how to incorporate novel kinds into an ontology, understanding these as species or subspecies within the categories already enumerated. Obviously some types of difformity raise problems of greater complexity than others, particularly when the multiple origin suggests contradictory characteristics. This, of course, is the main source of all the literature on the philosophy of quantum theory. Here it may only be suggested that the need to employ difform modeling in the first place may already be an indication that the novel kind pertains to a different general category than the models that serve as its source. For example, to think of a photon, as an instance of "wave-particle", as a thing or substance because this is the way one thinks of water waves or particles of matter, may be wrong-headed; perhaps photons are better thought of in the categories of attribute or quality, or even in the category of process or event. And when such difformly modeled entities are thought of as components of other things, then perhaps they should not be thought of as subsistent entities at all, but rather as modal transforms that result from looking at the same entity in two or more different ways. As examples of such modal transforms one might cite viewing crystals as lattice structures and colors as wavelengths of light [16].

Even from this brief consideration, however, it should be obvious that difform modeling provides a powerful instrument for delving into the structure of matter and of the universe, and, by offering the opportunity to verify existential statements such as those arising in high-energy physics and in radio astronomy, offers great possibilities for the cumulative growth of scientific knowledge.

3. Laws, Generalizations, and Causal Analysis.

At this point a more difficult topic may be approached, namely, that of generalizations and law-like statements. Scientific knowledge is generally thought to progress along two main paths, one the acceptance of new existential statements and the other the recognition of the validity of new generalizations. Existential statements have already been discussed; here it may suffice to examine only a single question, and that a rather troublesome one, associated with scientific laws, namely, how *any* generalization is possible for one who would maintain that there can be a cumulative growth of scientific knowledge. Generalizations are seemingly based on confirming in-

---

[16] For a discussion of modal transforms and how they differ from causal transforms, see HARRÉ, *op. cit.*, pp. 53-56.

stances, but a person never knows what the future may bring, and the next instance he examines may nullify any generalization already made. One may say, "All sulphur is yellow", but apparently he can never be sure that the next sulphur he examines will not be purple, and thus he cannot make even this descriptive generalization with certitude. This will be recognized as the source of numerous paradoxes relating to confirmation theory and the problem of induction, which have given rise to such an extensive literature in the philosophy of science within the past few decades[17].

In answer to these puzzles, a defensible position is that valid generalizations are possible in science, and these have the character of laws of nature, but they are never easy to arrive at and they involve an on-going process of recategorization and refinement of understanding that is part and parcel of knowledge growth. It is impossible, moreover, to explain these changes in term of formal logic alone, whereas they become quite intelligible to anyone who employs taxonomic principles and causal reasoning in the tradition of Aquinas and his commentary on the *Posterior Analytics*.

These points may be made though the consideration of a few examples. Recent authors commonly distinguish between accidental generalizations and law-like generalizations on the basis that the first cannot sustain counterfactual inference whereas the latter can[18]. An accidental generalization would be "All the screws in Smith's car are rusty", and this is understood to be a mere contingency, such that it would not permit one to state of any screw, "If this were a screw in Smith's car, it would have to be rusty". On the other hand, the law-like statement, "All copper expands when heated", permits one to state of this copper "If it were heated, it would expand". On face value the second case assumes that one possesses some knowledge of the nature of copper, or what causes it to expand when heated, and thus he knows what would happen even if the event did not take place. Empiricists, however, because of their distrust of natures and causes, will not accept this explanation[19]. And, is it not true that there is a finite possibility that the next piece of copper one heats will not expand? If so, how can a law be sustained in the face of disconfirming evidence?

To answer this one may inquire what to do with a generalization such as "All birds are feathered" in similar circumstances[20]. This may be referred to as a taxonomic generalization, and so it is open to the possibility of a disconfirming instance. Suppose that a small bird-like creature is presented to us, and it is not feathered. What are the moves that are then open to us? To save the taxonomic generalization we can say simply, "This is not a bird". Such a move is equivalent to maintaining, "All *true* birds are

[17] See Part III of BRODY, *op. cit.*, pp. 375-538.
[18] RODERICK M. CHISHOLM, « *Law Statements and Counterfactual Inference* », Analysis, 15 (1955), pp. 97-105.
[19] E. g., NAGEL, *op. cit.*, pp. 47-78.
[20] Cf. HARRÉ, *op. cit.*, pp. 139-141.

feathered", but that this is not a true bird even though it looks like a bird.
And then, we may understand "not a true bird" in a variety of ways. If
this is a single instance, or one of extremely rare occurrence, we may say,
"This creature belongs in the category of birds, all right, but actually it is
a freak", on the basis that accidents sometimes happen in natural generation.
Or, alternatively, if we run into such creatures in great numbers and find
that they are of regular occurrence, we divide bird-like creatures into two
classes, those that are feathered and those that are not. It we follow usual
scientific practice, we will retain the name "bird" or "true bird" for the
feathered class and we will invent a new name for the non-feathered; Harré
suggests that we do this by spelling bird backwards and calling the new class
"dribs". So we end up by preserving the generalization "All birds are
feathered" at only the slight expense of adding another generalization, "All
dribs are non-feathered". The well-understood case of heavy water vs. ordinary water seems to parallel precisely this procedure [21].

A similar instance, but closer to the concerns with modeling and scientific
discovery that have been dealt with earlier, is the descriptive generalization,
"All sulphur is yellow" [22]. Now what does such a generalization normally
mean? Nothing more than that this is the hue or color that sulphur manifests to us, where the "this" is what we commonly see and agree to call
"yellow", assuming that none of us is blind or afflicted with an organic
defect known as color-blindness. Assume now the case where sulphur is
presented to someone under a red light, and he sees it not as yellow but
as red. Assume also that this is a sophisticated person who knows that the
specimen is sulphur and that sulphur under white light normally appears
yellow. He may observe the red sulphur and state, "It may look red, but it
is *really* yellow". What could the word "really" means in a context such
as this? The case is somewhat analogous to that of the "true bird", for
what is meant by "really" is "under normal conditions", or "in daylight",
or, if the person happens to be a scientist, "This substance's surface structure
is such that it selectively reflects light of 5745 Angstrom units in wavelength". All three statements are equivalent, upon consideration, to the
affirmation that sulphur by its very nature manifests itself as yellow under
appropriate conditions. Or, enough is known about the nature of sulphur
to assert with confidence how it will appear under various conditions of
illumination.

Following this line of thought, one may go further and maintain that
it is somewhat simplistic to characterize a law of nature as a formal statement of the type "All A is B", or "For all x, if x is *phi* then x is *psi*", or

---

[21] And, as in the case of heavy water, where the explanation of the differences
between it and ordinary water is found in the molecular constitution of the two, so the
explanation of the differences between birds and dribs would be sought in the genetic
factors or materials that led to their speciation.

[22] Cf. HARRÉ, *op. cit.*, pp. 185-188.

"Class *alpha* is included within class *beta*", or "The class of *alpha*'s and non-*beta*'s is an empty set". Rather, the correct way is that of attributing an underlying nature to a subject in the much more suppositional mode expressed in Harré's alternative formulation, "Under conditions *C, A* will manifest sensible quality or characteristic *B* in virtue of its being of nature N" [23]. This statement is based on more than formal analysis, and it attempts to take into account some of the factors behind our thinking when we state generalizations such as "All sulphur is yellow". There are reasons other than mere instance confirmation that encourage us to make such generalizations, and usually these are convictions that the distinctive nature is an intrinsic cause that manifests itself in the internal constitution of the subject, or that something such as sulphur has a particular type of structure or generative mechanism that will dispose it to display, under appropriate conditions, the property or attribute ascribed to it. The term "nature" is apt for referring to such an internal determiner, particularly when taken in the sense of Aristotle's *phusis* or Aquinas's *natura,* which is an internal principle of activity or stability that is characteristic of the type [24]. At the outset of scientific investigation it is not necessary that this principle be comprehended completely, so long as it is seen as a determining internal source of characteristic activity or reactivity. Thus it is that, when we accord a statement law-like status, we treat it as ascribing a property or attribute or process to a subject which we believe has a determinate nature, or generative mechanism, or structure, without feeling bound to state in detail what that mechanism or structure has to be. It is true also that with the growth of scientific knowledge we continually revise our estimates regarding that underlying structure or determiner of whatever type, and that this becomes the basis for successive qualifications in our law-like statements, or recategorizations of the entities they are used to describe. Again, both Kuhn and Feyerabend have hit upon an element of the truth in the sense that these revised views of internal structures, etc., do constitute new ways of looking at things and do result in variations of meaning, even for the objects of ordinary experience. But such changed viewpoints and variations in meaning do not nullify scientific progress; in fact, they are the very means that insure the cumulative growth of knowledge and its enduring character.

With regard to law-like generalizations, therefore, it may be concluded that these are initially based on descriptions that are regularly verified, and thus they are empirically established by instance confirmation, and that it is in this way descriptive knowledge of the natures of things is attained. As science progresses, however, exceptions are found to occur and deeper explanations sought for the new characteristics exhibited. It is in this way

---

[23] *Ibid.,* p. 187.
[24] ARISTOTLE, *Physics*, Bk. II, ch. 1, 192b 20-23; AQUINAS, *In II Physicorum,* lect. 1.

that descriptive definitions give way to real definitions, which attempt to describe, to the extent possible, the nature or real essence that rise to these characteristics. Ultimately the taxa that we use to classify things are established on the basis of internal determiners such as structures and generative mechanisms, the modern-day equivalents of intrinsic (formal and material) causes [25]. So it is that scientists have learned to classify the elements, and all of their manifest properties, in terms of a real essence or nature that they feel is modeled quite accurately by the Bohr atom. Again, they are now beginning to have deeper knowledge of all living species in terms of generative mechanisms that they are reasonably confident are modeled by such structures as the DNA molecule, gene-pools, and so forth. From this may be seen the importance of analogical reasoning based on modeling, since it can give some insight into the natures of the material substances studied, can provide the basis for revising taxa from time to time, and so assure the possibility of valid, law-like generalizations.

The foregoing has been concerned mainly with taxonomic generalizations, but a final word may be added now about generalizations of other types. The most significant among these are law-like statements of concomitant variation, such as Boyle's law, $PV = k,$ which describes the behavior of a gas under various conditions of pressure and volume [26]. Many scientific laws are of this type, and once such a generalization has been discovered, scientists make efforts to qualify it, as necessary, to guard it against falsification. The devices they use are somewhat different, however, from those employed in preserving taxonomic generalizations. Three may be mentioned here, namely, limitation, modification, and idealization [27]. Working experimentally within the framework of Boyle's law, a scientist may discover disconfirming instances in certain areas where the law was first thought to hold. In this case the law is retained, but the range of its application is set by limiting the values that may henceforth be substituted for its variables. This is an instance of law preservation by limitation. Alternatively, the law may be modified so as to be able to subsume the disconfirming instances as special cases. In this way, for example, Boyle's law was modified to yield Van der Waal's equation, which successfully takes care of instances

---

[25] For a discussion of taxa and classes, see HARRÉ, *op. cit.*, pp. 196-200; on the modern equivalents of formal and material causality as well as of the other Aristotelian types, and this in the context of scientific explanation, see N. R. HANSON, *Observation and Explanation, A Guide to Philosophy of Science*, London: George Allen & Unwin, 1972, pp. 28-45.

[26] The earlier example, « All copper expands when heated », is a nontaxanomic generalization of this type, and in the face of an apparent disconfirming instance would be modified in ways similar to those discussed here as applicable to Boyle's law. Another procedure for dealing with the aberrant case, of course, would be to revert to taxonomy and distinguish between « true copper » or « ordinary copper » and other « nonexpanding » types.

[27] Cf. HARRÉ, *op. cit.*, pp. 142-145.

that would seem to disconfirm the initial law. This is the technique of modification. A third move is to retain the law but to claim that it is not directly applicable to substances of ordinary experience, but rather describes the action of an "ideal gas", which serves to model the behavior of ordinary gases and furnishes some insight into their structure on this account. This final technique is that of idealization. It is by devices such as these that most law-like statements in the physical sciences are continually revised and understood, while still retaining their character as true generalizations.

On this note we must bring our paper to a close. Perhaps the foregoing may serve to illustrate how the epistemological realism of Aquinas, brought up-to-date by modernized versions of analogical reasoning and causal analysis, can contribute to the solution of a vexing problem in the philosophy of science, namely, that of the cumulative growth of scientific knowledge. The thesis that underlies Thomistic methodology, of course, is that science is concerned with a study of the real, not with the logical as such, and that real entities can be the subject of true existential predication, that they have natures that can be understood, and that there can be progress in this understanding. Much of this progress comes about through the continued application of modeling techniques, which make new existential claims possible and enable scientists to preserve their generalizations, while modifying them and interpreting them in terms of an ever-deeping understanding. And all of this is done in virtue of man's ability to understand effects in terms of their causes, and so to explain phenomena in terms of the very determiners that make them be what they are. The resulting accretion of law-like generalizations, plus the on-going accumulation of new existential statements, is what makes science essentially evolutionary. This is not to deny that revolutions occur in science. They do, but not in such ways as to destroy, or negate, the long-term growth of science itself. So, in the final analysis, the scientific enterprise is more evolutionary than revolutionary. Its revolutionary aspect need not obscure its evolutionary aspect, when the relationship between the two is understood in the light of principles furnished seven centuries ago by Thomas Aquinas.

215

PART IV

SCIENCE AND MAN

ESSAY XI:

CYBERNETICS AND THE
MODELING OF MAN

The area of technology that has contributed most
to the "second industrial revolution," making of the
twentieth century an age of automation, may be broadly
characterized as that of cybernetics. Concerned as it
is with the study of control and communication in the
animal and the machine, cybernetics is opening up
challenging avenues of systems research into the study
of organisms, nerve impulses, sensation, memory, and
even mind. These developments, not unlike Galileo's
breakthrough in the study of falling bodies, may be expected to advance science and technology at an unprecedented rate during the next few decades.

Such advances in systems engineering would not,
on the surface, appear to have direct relevance to
philosophy. Yet they are not without some bearing on
perennial philosophical topics such as life, knowledge,
mind, and even soul. In a critical review of John von
Neumann's *The Computer and the Brain,* for example,
Ernan McMullin underscores the difficulties that this
book raises for a scholastic philosopher attempting to
prove the immortality of the soul.[1] Similar problems
present themselves in the investigation of other topics
in philosophical psychology.

The purpose of this essay is not to magnify such
difficulties and indirectly promote warfare between
science and philosophy. Rather it proposes to stress
some positive aspects of the problem, and to attempt to
show what cybernetics can do not only to promote the
study of the philosophy of man, but also to provide a
model in terms of which man can be understood, with
proper regard to his rights and dignity, within our
developing technological civilization.

Contributions of Cybernetics

To do this it may prove helpful to show how advances in systems research and automatic control can give powerful stimulus to the study of life processes and of human knowledge. As a preliminary we shall explain a few concepts associated with this new science that may promote a better understanding of animal and human psychology.

Fundamental Notions. The word cybernetics, deriving from the Greek term *kubernētēs* (which means steersman), was coined by Professor Norbert Wiener of M.I.T. for the title of his book, *Cybernetics, or Control and Communication in the Animal and the Machine,* which appeared in 1948. Since a steersman regulates a ship, cybernetic devices are taken to include all regulating mechanisms that effect some measure of automatic control.

The devices most commonly employed in recent research were developed by electrical engineers studying message transmission. In communication systems the simplest way to transmit information is through the use of a signal, itself nothing more than a pulse, which is referred to as a "bit." This term, a contraction for "binary digit," is now taken as the standard unit of information. When a simple signal of the pulse type can be recognized through all types of distortion, noise, and electronic background, then a unit of information is said to be successfully communicated.

The cybernetician couples the notion of information with that of automatic regulation, a concept used by mechanical engineers for decades. The ball governor on a steam engine is an automatic regulator that controls the speed of the engine. Similarly, the thermostat that regulates a home heating unit is a self-regulating device. In cybernetics the essential modification made on such control devices is that the regulator is not used to transfer energy, as it would be employed by the mechanical engineer, but rather to tranfer information. This introduces a new element into the control process which offers exciting possibilities for the study of life and mental processes. The novelty is directly traceable to a type of indeterminism that results from the feed-back of information. Thus mechanisms can be designed that effectively adapt to indeterminate situations in ways that are not themselves dependent on the situation, and therefore are not com-

pletely foreseeable. The resulting indeterminism is
similar to that which characterizes many living and
psychical phenomena.[2]

Simulation of Life Processes. How such simulation is effected is not easily discussed in abstract
terms, and can best be explained through a few examples.
The simplest device is one developed by W. R. Ashby to
study rudimentary life processes.[3] This is called the
"homeostat," because it attemps to achieve a state of
homeostasis found in living organisms. Such organisms
detect slight changes of temperature and chemical state
within themselves, and compensate for these by producing equal and opposite changes. The homeostat attempts
to achieve the same result through mechanisms that preserve the internal stability of a system in spite of
external changes to which it might be subjected. This
operation is described as follows:

> In Ashby's homeostat there are a number of elec-
> tronic circuits similar to the reflex arcs in
> the spinal cord of an animal. These are so com-
> bined with a number of radio tubes and relays
> that out of many thousands of possible connec-
> tions the machine will automatically find one
> that leads to a condition of dynamic internal
> stability. That is, after several trials and
> errors the instrument establishes connections
> which tend to neutralize any change that the
> experimenter tries to impose from outside. It
> is a curious fact that although the machine is
> man-made, the experimenter finds it impossible
> to tell at any moment exactly what the machine's
> circuit is without 'killing' it and dissecting
> out the 'nervous system'; that is, switching
> off the current and tracing out the wires to
> the relays. Nevertheless the homeostat does
> not behave very like an active animal -- it is
> more like a sleeping creature which when dis-
> turbed stirs and finds a comfortable position.[4]

Simulation of Animal Activity. Another device
developed by W. Grey Walter, of the Burden Neurological
Institute in London, attempts to simulate activity in
the waking state.[5] It is referred to as *machina speculatrix* because it duplicates the exploratory, "speculating," behavior that is found in animal activity. It
consists of two receptor elements, one a photocell sensitive to light, the other a relay actuated by touch,
and two effectors or motor devices, one for crawling,

the other for steering. The inventor describes the behavior of this device, which he names "Elmer," as follows:

> [This] is in fact remarkably unpredictable.
> The photocell, or 'eye,' is linked with the
> steering mechanism. In the absence of an
> adequate light-stimulus Elmer explores con-
> tinuously, and at the same time the motor
> drives it forward in a crawling motion. The
> two motions combined give the creature a
> cycloidal gait, while the photocell 'looks'
> in every direction in turn. This process of
> scanning and its synchronization with the
> steering device may be analogous to the mech-
> anism whereby the electrical pulse of the
> brain known as the alpha rhythm sweeps over
> the visual brain areas. . .[6]

Walter goes on to explain how this device can feel its
way in the dark, steer around obstacles, approach a
light source through the type of reflex behavior known
to biologists as "positive trophism," solve the dilemma
presented by two equal but separated light sources, and
so forth. He then concludes:

> These machines are perhaps the simplest that
> can be said to resemble animals. Crude though
> they are, they give an eerie impression of pur-
> posefulness, independence and spontaneity.
> More complex models that we are now construct-
> ing have memory circuits in which associations
> are stored as electric oscillations, so the
> creatures can learn simple tricks, forget them
> slowly and relearn more quickly. This compact,
> plastic and easily accessible form of short-
> term memory may be very similar to the way in
> which the brain establishes the simpler and
> more evanescent conditioned reflexes.[7]

The Mechanical Hand. Yet another device, developed by Claude Shannon and Heinrich Ernst at M.I.T.,
attempts to simulate the operation of the human hand.
The hand itself has been recognized for centuries as
the most flexible appendage in the animal kingdom, one
peculiarly adapted by nature to serve intelligence in
a rational animal. The human hand has so many degrees
of freedom that it is almost impossible to duplicate
its activity mechanically. Yet the mechanical hand developed at M.I.T., part of a one-armed robot with a

"brain" that consists of an electronic computer, is
able to duplicate some motions performed by a human
child. For example, it can feel along a table, recognize a wooden building block, pick it up and place it
on top of another block, and thus form a simple structure. It can also recognize a cardboard box, pick up
all the wooden blocks on the table, and put them into
the cardboard box. If something on the table gets in
the hand's way, it will also move around the obstacle.

To perform such tasks, of course, the robot's
brain must be suitable programmed. The hand then refers to the program in deciding how to treat a block or
box or obstacle. Information on which the brain reacts
is picked up by thirty sensors built into the hand itself. Some of the sensors are kinesthetic, and feed
information to the brain on the position of the hand
and its fingers; others record pressure, and are somewhat similar to the human hand's sense of touch.

Possible Confusions

These few examples will serve to illustrate how
cybernetics supplies novel instruments for investigating life and mental processes. In the long run these
will have beneficial results for promoting knowledge of
man and his rational nature, but in the short run they
cause confusion and apprehension in this area. What
are some sources of difficulty, and how can they be resolved so as to derive maximum benefit from cybernetic
and systems research?

Usually such confusions can be traced to one of
three sources. The first is an uncritical acceptance
of the assumptions that underlie cybernetics and make
it feasible, the second derives from the analogous terminology that this type of research requires, and the
third is associated with erroneous notions in philosophy. I should like to comment on each of these in turn.

Assumptions and Simplifications. The cybernetician
is committed to a program of research in which animal
and human means of communication and acquisition of information are studied through electronic and mechanical
devices. Even superficial observation, however, reveals vast differences between organisms and machines
of the most complicated types. In order to bridge the
gap, the researcher in this area must down-grade living
phenomena until they approach the level of the non-

living, and up-grade mechanical and electrical phenomena to give these the appearance of vital activity.[8]

Thus the assumptions on which the cybernetician
works automatically commit him to a monist view of
reality. He may be aware of profound differences between living and non-living things in his ordinary experience, but when carrying out his research he must
abstract from these differences. Like Galileo, he
first simplifies the phenomena he is studying to arrive
at an idealized generalization, such as the law for
bodies falling in a perfect vacuum, before he can re-
introduce the complexity found in nature to get a more
accurate characterization of a law for bodies falling
in air or water. Such simplification is an integral
part of scientific method. It need be no cause for
concern to either scientist or philosopher if the researcher is aware that he *is* so simplifying.

The Problem of Terminology. The second source of
confusion in this area is closely associated with the
first. It concerns the use of terms hitherto reserved
exclusively for animal or human activity which are now
applied indiscriminately to machines. In the descriptions already given I have spoken of cybernetic devices
being "killed," having a "nervous system," "speculating," "remembering," and possessing a "brain." The
fact that such use, or abuse, of terminology awakens a
reaction from many people is evidenced by the recurrence of articles on "thinking machines" in Sunday sup-
plements and similar mass media.

Although this usage does provoke lively discussion, it should not be cause for alarm on the part of
the philosopher. In the early stages of any scientific
development, the researcher is forced to employ terms
that are generally used in quite different contexts.
For instance, early theories of momentum had to employ
the medieval notions of impetus and violence, which
were inextricably associated with questions about the
efficient cause of inertial motion. Again, when Newton
first arrived at the notion of mass, he had to designate it by the medieval expression *quantitas materiae,*
or quantity of matter, because no other term was available. Similarly, in the beginning of cybernetic research, it seems inevitable that considerable analogy
and even equivocation will be employed before a proper
scientific terminology can be developed. Yet the temper of the scientific mind is not to rest content with
equivocation of any kind. A science reaches perfection

224

when it attaches univocal meanings to the terms it properly employs.

Perhaps this can be illustrated by means of an example.[9] The scientist is typically concerned with statements that can be publicly verified. Let us take the statement: "Chalk dissolves in vinegar." Is this statement true? If we experiment with various types of chalk, we find that it is true of pure precipitated chalk, that it is sometimes true of chalk as it occurs in its natural state, say, in the cliffs of Dover, but that it is not at all true of classroom chalk. As science progresses, instead of using ambiguous terms like chalk the chemist speaks of pure calcium carbonate, and instead of saying that this dissolves in vinegar, he says that it is soluble in acetic acid. For other experiments it becomes necessary for him to be even more precise and to render his meaning of calcium carbonate still more univocal. Thus, in nuclear chemistry, he must indicate the isotope of calcium that occurs in calcium carbonate, spelling out, for example, whether this be calcium-40 or calcium-42.

What has been true in the growth of the science of chemistry will also be found true as cybernetics moves from its infancy to the stage of advanced science. It will develop its own proper terminology -- already the term "programming" illustrates such development. And as this process continues, many of the early confusions will disappear. It is my further contention that precisely this development will be most helpful for clarifying traditional philosophical and psychological notions of man. It will be necessary to return to this when detailing the contributions that philosophy has to offer cybernetics and when developing a model for man based on systems research.

Philosophical Difficulties. The third source of confusion attending the early development of cybernetics does not stem from science or scientists, but rather from the hazy philosophical notions entertained by many who are interested in safeguarding human nature and the dignity of man. Ever since the development of modern philosophy, and this would date from the time of Descartes, an extreme dualism has come into vogue which accentuates the dichotomy between matter and spirit. So extreme is this dualism that those imbued with the spirit of modern philosophy emphasize either the one or the other. Scientists and cyberneticians usually tend toward the polarity of matter, and on this account are identified as materialists. Those with an anti-scientific mentality, on the other hand, generally favor the polarity of spirit. Not uncommonly they believe in the spirit world as something more real than the material universe.

To over-emphasize either matter or spirit, from the viewpoint of a philosophy of man such as Thomism, is to emphasize the matter-spirit duality to an extreme. For the Thomist, man is a substantial unity resulting from a union between matter and spirit that is the most intimate possible. Man has a soul, which is spiritual, but this is not present in his body like "a ghost in a haunted house." Rather it intrinsically informs the body, vitalizes it, renders it capable of performing all of its psychic and psycho-somatic functions. Most scientists, in my experience, reject soul merely because they are not much interested in ghosts or other occult phenomena; and here I am inclined to agree with them. Once they relinquish such erroneous notions of soul, on the other hand, they become more disposed to appreciate valid philosophical insights that bridge the gap between matter and spirit, and can thus be directly relevant to their science.

Contributions of Philosophy

None of the sources of confusion just mentioned need present insurmountable difficulties, and one can be optimistic over the prospects of a rapprochement between cybernetics and philosophical thought. Although presently a challenge, cybernetics can promote a clearer understanding of the nature of thought and living phenomena, and thereby make a positive contribution to philosophy. This introduces a related point which concerns the possible contributions that a philosophy of man can make to cybernetic research. Advances can be made in this area, but they do require a cooperative effort on the part of both philosopher and engineer. The philosopher can learn from techniques developed in modern electronics, but equally significant is the fact that the engineer can learn from the philosopher. This point might be developed by citing a few examples. Those most suited to the present topic concern the concepts of perception, memory, communication, translation, purposiveness, and learning, as these are applied to man and machine.

Machine Perception. An extensive study of machine perception has been carried out by Selfridge and Neis-

ser at the Lincoln Laboratories associated with M.I.T.[10]
The perceptive phenomena there chosen for study was
that of pattern recognition. I will not describe the
computers used in this work, but merely report that
they were designed to recognize simple patterns such as
hand-printed letters. Results showed that, although
present computers cannot segment continuous written
material, they can "learn" to discriminate between various letter patterns, even when these are submitted to
them in random orientation. Their ability to do this,
it goes without saying, is built into them by their
designers. It should also be understood that no claim
is here being made for machine thought or intelligence.[11]
Rather what is at question is whether or not a machine
perceives, the way a man perceives, when it is used for
pattern recognition.

When a machine recognizes a pattern, it compares
a pattern presented to its kinescope with certain test
features which serve to identify this pattern as one of
several possibilities. The comparison is more subtle
than one of mere juxtaposition, such as is done, for
example, when two patterns are placed one on top of the
other and viewed toward a light source. Rather, there
is an indeterminacy in the standard pattern which is
resolved on a probabilistic basis and subsequently cor-
rected whenever the result is found wrong. By trial
and error, the machine advances toward more and more
perfect identification of the pattern.

A study of this process from the viewpoint of
psychology and philosophy reveals that this is not the
mechanism whereby man perceives an object or a pattern.
Human perception involves more than a comparison with
a standard pattern. It does presuppose identification
of the pattern, but above and beyond this it involves
an element of signification or intentionality not to
be found in machine perception.

For example, when the eye sees a coin at a distance, the pattern presented to the eye is in general
oval, or elliptical, because the coin is usually seen
from an angle. But the coin when perceived is not *perceived* as elliptical or oval, but as a circular disc.
Similarly, a square may be presented to the eye as a
rhombus, but it is perceived by the eye as a square.
Thus spatial perception is self-corrective for the effects of perspective, for the angle of vision, for dis-
tortions introduced by the medium (heat waves, mists),
etc. The same can be said for the perception of colors.

A white surface, seen in semi-darkness, reflects less light to the eye than a gray surface seen in daylight. Yet it is perceived by the eye to be lighter than the gray surface.

Human perception thus involves more than pattern recognition. The additional factor is what enables man to recognize the identity of an object perceived whenever it is sensed under different conditions of orientation and lighting. And the philosopher can give an explanation for this. Man can perceive because he is capable of grasping the signification or meaning of a particular representation, of knowing it in an intentional way. Signification or intentionality is the synthesizing factor which unifies many possible representations and enables the perceiver to identify a particular content through any one of them. Machine perception reaches the first stage of comparing representations, but the machine is not capable of grasping the signification or meaning associated with individual representations as can the human being.

Machine Memory. The study of machine memory is another area in which philosophy and psychology can contribute to cybernetics. Computers are said to have a memory when they store information and make it available for future use. They do this by mechanically or electronically locating bits of information that are present and recorded in the machine. Machine memory, on this description, is limited to recording the past as present, that is, it re-presents information in the present. Its operation is much like locating an object that is mechanically present in a filing system.

Philosophical analysis reveals that human memory involves more than this. It does not consist in recalling a representation received in the past as it is now present, but rather perceiving the past as past, that is, as temporally situated in a by-gone present. The person who remembers filing an object does something different from another who merely locates the same object present in the file. The remembering does not concentrate on the present action, that is, locating the material, but rather on identifying a past action, that is, placing the matter in the file, precisely as a past action, that is, as done several days, weeks, or months ago.

A similar illustration can be drawn from the photograph. A photograph is not itself a memory of the

past, even though it is a present repre.'entation of
something past. A person can look at a photo of himself and say: "I do not remember that." A computer
does nothing like this. Rather it records and files
mechanically, and then simply relocates what it has
stored away. But this is basically quite different
from what is involved in remembering.

Even more striking differences are seen when one
examines the opposite of remembering, that is, forget-
ting. Machines "forget" with absolutely no difficulty
whatever. They can erase information contained in
their magnetic drums and never retain a trace of all
they once "knew." Commenting on this fact, Neisser
states:

> Human memory seems much less flexible. A man
> rarely has single-minded control over what he
> wil learn and forget; often he has no control
> at all. Thus he lives willy-nilly in an ac-
> cumulating context of experience which he can-
> not limit even if he would. The result is
> both stupidity and serendipity; if he is inef-
> ficient, he also can become wise in unexpected
> ways. Youth is not doomed to ignorance even
> thought it would like to be, and no one can
> entirely avoid growing up. [12]

Here a computer expert reveals that he is under no illusion as to whether or not machine memory duplicates
the remarkable complexity of human memory.

Transmission of Information. Another area offering possibilities for fruitful interchange between the
philosopher and the engineer centers around the communication of information. Engineers studying message
transmission quickly become involved in semantics, a
discipline with pronounced philosophical overtones.
One way in which the semantic problem presents itself
to them is in developing techniques for interpreting a
message as it is received, i.e., as opposed to the message originally intended by the sender. The two messages are not necessarily the same because distortion,
introduced by noise in the communication network, effectively injects random elements into the message
transmitted. In spite of distortion, however, information content, or intended meaning, can usually be determined by the engineer. He does this either from an
analysis of possible intended meanings, such as those
listed, for instance, in a series of Western Union con-

gratulatory telegrams, or from an analysis of probable word sequences in context, based on the structure of the language and the frequency of occurrence of various letters, words, or expressions. In developing a theory to account for this success, the concept found most useful for reconstructing meaning is that of entropy, a concept borrowed from thermodynamics, which measures the decrease of organization in a message. Noise and random influences disrupt the organization, thereby increase the unavailable information in the message, and hence increase the entropy.[13]

This usage suggests the question: Whence comes the organization whose loss is measured by entropy? Such organization, whose measure could be referred to as negentropy, is already presupposed to any computer analysis and therefore its source is not critically examined by the engineer. But the philosopher can suggest a source of organization that distinguishes human thought from devices used for its transmission, namely, the human intellect. Man's mind effects the organization in a message when it produces the idea or concepts behind the message. Thus mind, in this analysis, is the organizing factor accounting for the low entropy or high negentropy in the initially transmitted message. More proximately it is the human concept that effects this organization, that produces the content or meaning that is independent of its particular expression. Just as different expressions stand in relation to the meaning they contain, so particular messages are related to the information they contain. A philosophical correlation between information and meaning therefore furnishes some insight into the nature of message organization and the possibility of its reconstruction after distortion in transmission.

Machine Translation. Some of the more extravagant claims for machine thought come from those working in the field of machine translation -- another area where the philosopher can assist the cybernetician. Present engineering approaches to translation seem to treat this as basically a problem in decipherment. Despite the considerable progress made with mechanical deciphering devices, however, the cybernetician still encounters serious obstacles whenever he attempts to get a readable translation from a machine. Expressions like "hydraulic ram" continue to turn up as "water goat" in contexts that leave them completely unintelligible to the reader.

The engineer may be perplexed by the magnitude of the task facing him, but the philosopher can give some explanation for his difficulty. Decipherment, although sometimes preliminary to translation, is not to be identified with translation. The former is essentially concerned with the manipulation of symbols, whereas the latter deals with the meaning behind the symbols. Being concerned with meaning, translation requires intellect or intelligence and cannot be performed at a merely mechanical level. This difference is well brought out by a report on a translation project studied at Georgetown University, whose author concludes:

> The process being developed in this research is misnamed translation: it is in fact a deciphering or decoding operation. The machine is not translating speech or language, but is deciphering its unfamiliar symbols and setting up a matching set of familiar symbols. If it is perfected, it will be as valuable as an interpreter who does not understand a word of what he is saying in either language. This is not valueless, but it is not translation or interpretation. The sponsors of this machine are falling into the same error as did the inventors of an earlier age, who first gave the name 'talking machine' to what we now call a phonograph. It is now recognized that the talking machine could not talk, and that no phonograph will ever be able to talk. The Georgetown translation machine does not translate and no translation machine will be able to translate. It is at present a highly ingenious, though still erratic, decipherment machine.[14]

Purposiveness in the Machine. But the relationships between concept and entropy, between translation and decipherment, are not the only means of distinguishing intellectual activity in man from related processes in the machine. Another interesting difference is discerned when one compares purposiveness in human and machine activity. Early experimenters with cybernetic devices were enthusiastic because they apparently had designed purposiveness into a machine. That they were able to do so should not have surprised them because machine behavior is far more purposive than any other activity. No matter how sophisticated the model, the machine does precisely what it was designed to do, and it follows out this purpose relentlessly. Commenting on this difference, Neisser remarks:

> When a program is purposive, it is too purpos-
> ive. People get bored; they drop one task
> and pick up another, or they may just quit
> work for a while. Not so the computer pro-
> gram; it continues indomitably. In some cir-
> cumstances the program may be more effective
> than a man, but is not acting as a man would.
> Nor is such single-mindedness always an ad-
> vantage; the computer is very likely to waste
> time on trivialities and to solve problems
> which are of no importance.[15]

The obvious conclusion to be drawn from this: Although
machines imitate some purposive aspects of human behavior, they can hardly be said to imitate these in a human way.

Machine Learning. A final comment should be made
about machine learning, since this is another area
where the philosopher-psychologist can assist the engineer.[16] Although machines can be designed to show a
development of skill or ability through trial and error, their so-called "learning" does not bear close
comparison with human learning. To see this, all one
need do is observe a child learning to play checkers.
If the child is very young, he cannot be taught to play
such a game because he will not comply with the rules.
Once he finds out that he should try to capture pieces,
he will do so with any move that immediately occurs to
him. Again, he will avoid the loss of a piece by every
possible maneuver, including putting it in his mouth.
If the piece be taken from him, such action notwithstanding, he might go into a tantrum and stop playing.
So far as I know, there is no analogous behavior to be
observed in a computer as it follows out its program
and relentlessly proceeds to score a victory over its
human opponent. Computers may some day be programmed
to play chess as well as a man or better, but the
"thought" processes of the two will remain fundamental-
ly different.[17]

The Modeling of Man

This brings us to our final point, namely, how
cybernetics and the related development of systems research can provide models in terms of which we may gain
a better understanding of man himself, in such a way as

232

to preserve his rights and dignity within our advancing technological society. From what has been said
thus far, it should be clear that men are very different from machines, and yet the differences are not so
great as to preclude the use of computing systems for
gaining an understanding of men and their activities.
The ideas concerning modeling that were developed in
the preceding essay of this volume prove useful here.
If cybernetic devices do not completely mirror man's
nature, they nonetheless can provide analogies that
are helpful for understanding that nature, and indeed
for providing some insight into philosophical concepts
that have been used for centuries to explain human behavior.

   Stimulus-Response Mechanisms. One of the simplest ways of modeling an animal organism is to concep-
tualize it in terms of the stimulus-response mechanism
represented in Fig. 1. Such a model was popular among

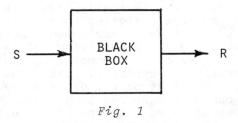

Fig. 1

the early behaviorists, who were wary of occult entities and wished to restrict their research to observable behavior or responses generated by controllable
stimuli. Apart from the stimulus (S) and response (R)
they professed agnosticism with regard to what might
be going on internally within the organism, and so
thought of it simply as a 'black box.' Their research
programs produced some good results, particularly when
studying reflex behavior, but turned out to have limited value when applied to activities that are more indeterminate in their genesis, and so resemble more
closely those that are distinctively animal in character.

   A slightly more sophisticated model can easily
be developed that replaces the 'black box' of Fig. 1
with the two boxes shown on the next page in Fig. 2,
labelled 'receptor' and 'activator' respectively.
Like the 'black box' this is a stimulus-response model,
but it differentiates the basic capabilities of the

233

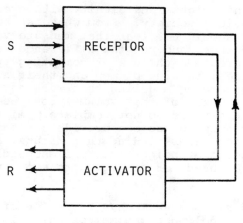

Fig. 2

organism and permits the study of a wider range of interactions between them. Actually Fig. 2 is a schematic diagram of the model referred to earlier in this
essay as the *machina speculatrix* named Elmer: the receptor is the photocell and the relay activated by
touch, and the activator is the motor mechanism that
gives the automaton its cycloidal gait. The connecting circuits to the right of the diagram represent a
computer that can be programmed to generate a variety
of responses depending on the type of stimuli the automaton encounters, and it is this that serves to create the impressions of "purposefulness, independence,
and spontaneity" noted by Walter in his description of
Elmer's activities.

     The next step in the modeling process consists
in developing memory circuits such as those alluded to
by Walter that further complicate the automaton's reactions and enable it to generate activities even more
similar to those of animal organisms. Another deside-
ratum would be the addition of elements that in some
way duplicate emotional reactions, such as those of
the child learning to play checkers described earlier
in this essay. Both of these objectives can be attained by adding 'boxes' to the receptor and activator of
Fig. 2, and so generating the receptor line (A) and
the activator line (B) shown in Fig. 3 on the following page. Here we have broken down the 'receptor' box
of Fig. 2 into a 'sensor' and a 'memory' box, and so
introduced a double capability into the receptor line;
similarly we have broken down the 'activator' box into

234

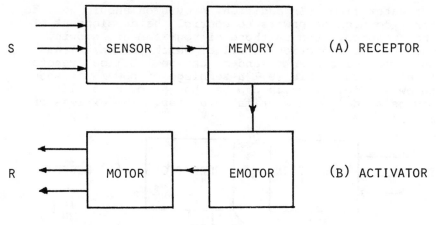

Fig. 3

a 'motor' and an 'emotor' capability to further develop the activator line. Both capabilities, when energized by the required circuitry, can be referred to as
'powers.' Such powers are activated under appropriate
stimuli, and they then become the source of the distinctive response that is elicited from the mechanism,
not only along deterministic lines but also allowing
for varying degrees of spontaneity and indeterminism
as generated by the computing devices that control the
reactions.

Life Powers Models. With the introduction of the
concept of powers we can now begin to speak of cybernetic analogues for animal organisms that model, in the
schematic way of a block diagram, the complex functions
of a living thing. Instead of the mechanical and electrical sensors of Fig. 3 the animal organism is endowed with various powers of sensation associated with its
external senses, such as those of sight, hearing, taste,
touch, and smell. Likewise, instead of the computer
memory circuitry, the animal has a whole range of internal senses, such as those described in Essay 3,
namely, memory, imagination, and the central and estimative senses that are necessary for it to form its
own percepts. These powers have been diagrammed on
p. 43 above, in the context of explaining how knowledge
is acquired by a sensing organism through various processes of sensation and perception. Since all of these
powers pertain to what we have referred to as the receptor line, however, it now becomes necessary to add
corresponding motor and emotor powers to constitute an

235

activator line. In addition, provision should be made
for a complex of powers to control the development of
the organism, such as those of nourishment, growth,
and even reproduction -- all of which the animal has
in common with plants, and so can be labelled 'vegetative' powers. This full assemblage of powers is shown
below in Fig. 4, which can be thought of as a 'life-
powers' model of the animal organism. The expression

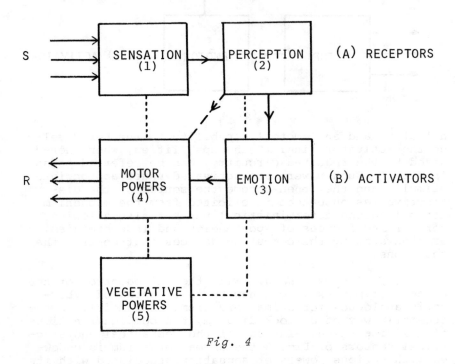

Fig. 4

'life-powers' refers to all of the powers or capabilities of the organism that are necessary for it to perform its life functions. These powers are also the
means whereby it responds to stimuli from the outside
world, and so initiates its distinctive behavior
through emotional reactions and various motor activities.

     To be more specific, the 'outside world' acts on
the animal organism through stimuli (S) that are translated into the various sensations received in the external senses (box 1). These are then processed
through the internal senses to form and retain the percept (box 2) as described in Essay 3 above. The per-

236

cept so apprehended may immediately provide the basis for an autonomous reaction, or reflex activity, that triggers the motor powers (box 4) to act in such a way as to safeguard the good of the whole; this type of response (R) is indicated by the dashed line connecting boxes 2 and 4. Alternatively, the percept may elicit an emotional reaction, according to one or more of the emotions symbolized in box 3, which in turn will influence the motor powers to react in a way appropriate to the stimulus received.[18] This line of action is indicated by the solid lines, with arrows, connecting boxes 1 through 4. Finally, since all of the powers represented by these boxes themselves undergo growth and development, and such development is controlled by yet another capability of the organism, all of the boxes are shown connected by dotted lines to box 5, which represents its vegetative powers, namely, those of nourishment, growth, and reproduction.[19]

The modeling of man's distinctive activities requires a still more complicated block diagram than that for the brute animal. A clue for the development of such a diagram has already been provided in Essay 3, with its discussion of intellectual knowledge and how this differs from sense knowledge. There it was explained that man differs from lower animals in his ability to grasp meanings or ideas or intelligible contents that become the basis for his language, literature, culture, science, and other distinctively human activities. Associated with this power or capability is another power that follows upon it, namely, that of personal decision or of voluntary activity, commonly called 'will power,' whereby man initiates activities that are properly his own and for which he assumes, or is imputed, responsibility. The complex of powers that serve to explain human activity, incorporating these additions, is shown in Fig. 5. This is obviously similar to Fig. 4 except for the addition of boxes 6 and 7. Box 6 is the 'intellect' box, already explained in Essay 3 (pp. 42-45), wherein all of man's conceptualizing and intellectual activity explained in that essay are contained. Box 7, finally, is that of man's will, the source of his voluntary activity.[20] The solid lines, with arrows, connecting boxes 6 and 7 with the others in the receptor and activator lines are similar to those connecting the first four boxes; the broken line joining boxes 6 and 2, however, represents the abstractive process diagrammed on p. 43 above and explained on p. 45 and following. A fully human act would thus involve the activation of all the

237

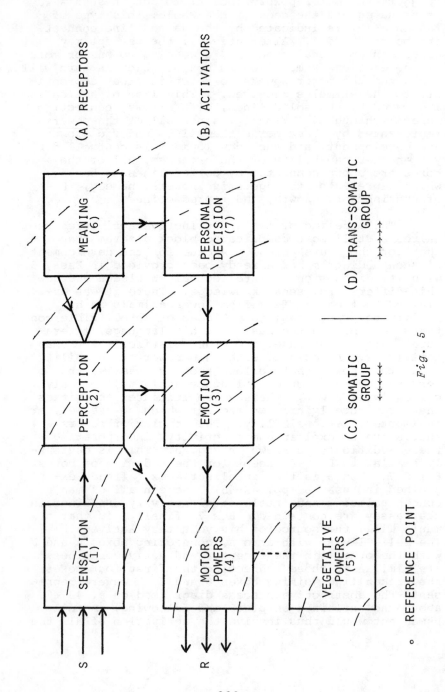

(A) RECEPTORS

(B) ACTIVATORS

MEANING
(6)

PERSONAL
DECISION
(7)

PERCEPTION
(2)

EMOTION
(3)

SENSATION
(1)

MOTOR
POWERS
(4)

VEGETATIVE
POWERS
(5)

S

R

(C) SOMATIC
GROUP
←←←←←

(D) TRANS-SOMATIC
GROUP
→→→→→

o REFERENCE POINT

Fig. 5

238

powers represented by the seven boxes in the block
diagram, although a man might also act in animal fashion, utilizing only boxes 1-2-4 or 1-2-3-4, rather
than those representing his fully human capabilities.

Man's Perfectibility. To gain a deeper insight
into the reality modeled by block-diagram in Fig. 5
one should note that none of man's powers can function
unless the grid shown in that diagram is properly energized. To use the electrical analogy, a computer or
other cybernetic device will not work unless it is
plugged in, unless there is an energy source from which
its circuits are energized. The receptor box of Fig. 2
will not function if the photocell is dead or if there
is no battery to activate the tactile relay, nor will
the activator box move Elmer if it lacks a power supply. To convey this need for some energizing factor,
a reference point (8) has been indicated at the lower
left-hand corner of Fig. 5, and a series of concentric
dashed lines have been shown radiating from it. This
energizing 'radiation,' if you will, represents a theoretical entity of the metaphysical type (see pp. 62-63
above). It models whatever it is that serves to energize the entire network -- the entity that converts
all of the boxes into life powers, functioning powers,
animated powers. The reality of this theoretical entity is such that it makes the human organism alive and
fully human. The traditional name for this entity is
the human soul -- the animating factor that enlivens
man's body and renders it capable of exercising all of
its human activities.

For our purposes it is not necessary to enter
into a full explanation and justification of the soul's
existence and nature; such material can be found in
textbooks on philosophical psychology. Suffice it to
mention that a dead person has all of the organs that
should enable him or her to perform the life functions
represented by boxes 1 through 5 of Fig. 5, and yet the
body is completely inert and performs none of them.
The eye of a cadaver may have a retinal image, but it
sees nothing. Sound waves may cause its ear drum to
vibrate, but it hears nothing. The factor that differentiates the live person from the dead person is the
soul: every capability represented by an organ of the
body has a corresponding capability in a power-part of
the soul. Hence the boxes that have been diagrammed in
Figs. 4 and 5 represent nothing more than the powers of
the soul. Those who are interested in a description of
such powers, and an explanation of how the soul can be
said to have power-parts, may consult *The Elements of*

Philosophy for fuller details. Table I below keys all of the material diagrammed on Fig. 5 to appropriate section numbers of the *Elements*.

TABLE I

THE LIFE-POWERS MODEL OF MAN KEYED TO *THE ELEMENTS OF PHILOSOPHY* (The symbol § refers to section numbers of *The Elements*)

(A) Receptor or Cognitive Group. Function: cognition §23. Product: knowledge §38.
   (1) Sensation. Powers: external senses, §24.3-4. Product: sense knowledge §24.1-5.
   (2) Perception. Powers: internal senses, §24.6-10. Product: unified perception §24.11-12.
   (6) Meaning. Power: mind or intellect §25.1, called reason §2.1. Product: intellection §25, embraces all of logic §2-14, language §57, and culture §71.1-3.

(B) Activator or Appetitive Group. Function: appetition §26. Product: human activity §50-56.
   (3) Emotion. Powers: sensitive appetites §27. Products: acts of emotion §27.3.
   (4) Motor Powers: sources of activites associated with animal life §22.1, §22.6.
   (5) Vegetative Powers: sources of activities associated with plant life §22.1, §22.6.
   (7) Personal Decision. Power: will §28.1. Product: volition §28, including free decision §28.2 and the human act §50.

(C) Somatic Group. Powers that require bodily organs for their operation: (1) to (5) inclusive.

(D) Trans-somatic Group. Powers that do not always require bodily organs for their operation, viz, (6) and (7) -- see §25.5-6, §29.3-7.
   (8) Reference Point. Integration of life powers. Function: life §22.1. Basic animating or energizing source: soul §22. Product: the animated composite, man §29.

Some idea of the explanatory force of a concept such as the soul may be gained from the following considerations. The human body grows and develops following a biological pattern that is well understood: the zygote develops into an embryo, and this becomes a

240

fetus, then an infant, a child, an adolescent, etc.
Such growth and development is initiated and controlled by the life principle or soul, whose powers unfold
and develop with the growth of the body. It would appear that the powers that are closer to the reference
point on Fig. 5 are the ones that develop first, whereas those of intellect and will come to their perfection last. Likewise, at the end of life, when the human organism is no longer able to support its activities, the powers would appear to cease functioning in
the inverse order: first those that represent the
higher faculties, then those of sense and emotional
response, and finally the most rudimentary powers of
movement and nourishment. When the soul departs the
body, traditionally thought to be the moment of death,
it has no organs to energize, and thus no activities,
unless some of the powers it has developed are able to
exercise their functions without bodily organs. (In
Table I it may be noted that two powers of the soul
are listed as 'trans-somatic' powers, namely, intellect and will. In Christian thought these are regarded as the source of the distinctive activities of the
'separated soul,' i.e., of the soul when separated
from the body, which are those of knowing and willing,
and which form the basis for the generally accepted
teaching on the soul's immortality.)

Since the human soul is intimately associated
with the notion of 'person,' what has just been said
assumes great importance when one discusses the moral
issues raised by abortion and euthanasia. If man were
simply a 'black box,' then one could do anything he
wished to it without worrying about questions of rights
and obligations. If, on the other hand, the body is
animated by a human soul, such animation confers on the
organism the special dignity of a human person. For
this reason, if for no other, the position one takes
on the moment when the human soul enters and leaves
the person's body is of great ontological importance
for deciding problems relating to the morality of medical procedures used at the beginning and ending of
human life.[21]

As a final point, it may be mentioned that the
diagram of Fig. 5 can provide the basis for discussing
the full perfection of man, which comes about not only
when his body reaches its terminal development but also
when his powers of soul have been perfected to their
fullest capacity. Many of man's powers, and particularly his higher faculties, are perfectible by habits.

These are either conducive to good and proper actions, and then they are called virtues, or they are conducive to evil and improper actions, in which case they are called vices. The study of virtues and vices pertains to the part of philosophy known as ethics or moral philosophy. Fuller particulars are again contained in *The Elements of Philosophy*, to which the reader is referred for details. So as to relate the block diagram of man's life-powers to the theme that man's actions are perfectible by habits that complement these powers, Fig. 5 has been redrawn as Fig. 6, which indicates, in each of the appropriate boxes, the habits that serve for the full development and perfection of the corresponding powers.

This, then, completes our survey of the ways in which science and philosophy can cooperate, particularly through studies in cybernetics, to a fuller understanding of man and his capabilities. It should now be obvious that attempts to model man through the use of computer devices and systems theories can be of inestimable value for understanding the basic realities that underlie human life. It should also be clear that philosophy has something to contribute to cybernetic research, and that when questions arise that involve human rights and obligations, philosophical reflection becomes indispensable for the development of man's full potentialities in the technological age in which we live.

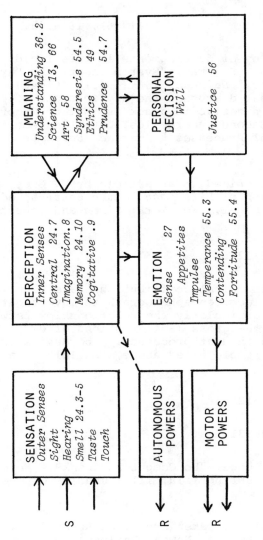

Fig. 6

Numerals in italics refer to section numbers of THE ELEMENTS OF PHILOSOPHY

NOTES

[1] *Philosophical Studies*, 8 (1958), 182-185.

[2] For a survey of developments in this field, see R. W. Jones and J. S. Gray, "System Theory and Physiological Processes," *Science*, 140 (1963), 461-464. Another study that discusses the applications of positive as well as negative feedback is that of Magorah Maruyama, "The Second Cybernetics: Deviation-Amplifying Mutual Causal Processes," *American Scientist*, 51 (1963), 164-179.

[3] This is described in an article by W. Grey Walter, "An Imitation of Life," *Automatic Control*, ed. Dennis Flanagan et al., New York: Simon and Schuster, 1955, 123-131.

[4] *Ibid.*, 125-126.

[5] Walter's principal contributions have been in the use of the electroencephalograph to investigate the brain, and particularly the relationships between brain waves and the gross manifestations of emotion, personality, and thought processes. The device is explained in the article cited above, "An Imitation of Life," 126-127.

[6] *Ibid.*, 127-128.

[7] *Ibid.*, 130-131.

[8] See Mario Bunge, "Do Computers Think?." *Metascientific Queries*, Springfield, Ill.: Charles C. Thomas, 1959, 124-152.

[9] This example is taken from John Russell, S.J., *Science and Metaphysics*, Newman Philosophy of Science Series, No. 1, London: Sheed and Ward, 1958.

[10] This is reported in an article by O. G. Selfridge and Ulric Neisser entitled "Pattern Recognition,"

Scientific American, 203 (1960), 60-68.

[11]Thus the authors themselves conclude: "The effectiveness of all of them [i.e., the computers involved] is forever restricted by the ingenuity or arbitrariness of their programmers. We can barely guess how this restriction might be overcome. Until it is, 'artificial ingelligence' will remain tainted with artifice." -- *loc. cit.,* 68.

[12]U. Neisser, "The Imitation of Man by Machine," *Science,* 140 (1963), 194.

[13]For a technical exposition, see A. I. Khinchin, *Mathematical Foundations of Information Theory,* New York: Dover Publications, 1957.

[14]This excellent but untitled report, which to my knowledge remains unpublished, was prepared by Charles Hamilton of 1432 Newton Street, N.E., Washington, D.C., in February 1959.

[15]"The Imitation of Man by Machine," 194.

[16]For my views on machine teaching, see "A Thomist Looks at Teaching Machines," *Dominican Educational Bulletin* (1963), 13-23.

[17]"The Imitation of Man by Machine," 195.

[18]For an account of the emotions as human powers, see my *The Elements of Philosophy,* New York: Alba House, 1977, §27.

[19]These are the powers characteristic of plant life, described in *Elements,* §§22.1 & 22.6.

[20]For a discussion of will as the appetitive power associated with man's intellect, see *Elements,* §28.

[21]See Gabriel Pastrana, O.P., "Personhood and the Beginning of Life," *The Thomist,* 41 (1977), 247-294.

ESSAY XII:

A MORAL DILEMMA:

THE ATOM BOMB

Eighteen years ago, in the early morning of August 6th, 1945, I was alone in the operations command post of the 313th Heavy Bombardment Wing on the island of Tinian, in the midst of the Pacific ocean. At the time I was a line officer in the U. S. Navy, a naval liaison officer, attached to this B-29 Wing to supervise the aerial minelaying of Japanese home waters with magnetic and acoustic mines. Colonel Wilson, who was in charge of operations, had stepped out for a minute, leaving me momentarily in charge of the post. A field telephone rang, and I picked it up. A some-what muffled voice announced: "This is Washington calling by trans-Pacific cable. Have they dropped it yet?" I did not know: looking up at the operations board I saw that three planes of the 509th Group were over Japan on a so-called 'weather' mission. I got General Davies immediately. The answer, for the moment, was "no," but within the hour, an affirmative response was on the way. The atomic age had begun; the first atom bomb had just been dropped on Hiroshima. It unleashed an unprecedented amount of explosive energy over a military objective. It also unleashed an unprecedented amount of discussion about modern warfare that left men's minds in turmoil long after the 'all quiet' descended in its gruesome way over the Japanese island of Honshu.

The morality of nuclear warfare is certainly one of the most pressing problems of our time, to which no clear-cut solution appears in sight at the moment. The reason for this, in my mind, is intimately connected with the nature of ethics, or moral science, as it relates to problems of human action. I should like therefore to discuss ethics, to explain what kind of science it proposes to be, and what its limitations are. In this way greater light may be shed on the character of our modern morality dilemma, and the steps that must be taken if we are to acquit ourselves, before our own eyes as well as those of the world, in our atomic responsibilities for the future.

Ethics—A Practical Science

If it be permissible to use the term 'science' in a sense broad enough to include philosophy, following the usage, say, of Aristotle or St. Thomas Aquinas, we could say that ethics is a science. As soon as we were to say this, however, we would have to qualify our statement immediately and add: it is not a science like astronomy or biology, which aim at giving us *speculative* knowledge of the universe, but rather it is a *practical* science that tells us how we should act. Ethics, or moral science, is the science of human action, whose entire purpose is to direct man's action so that he attain his proper perfection as a man, i.e., by reasonable, virtuous living in a social context. The difference between a speculative and practical science is considerable: each has its peculiar mode of analysis, each considers basically different types of truth and certitude. Let me try to explain this by means of an analogy. I mean to contrast physics with engineering, then extend the contrast to biology and medicine, and finally show how philosophy is related to ethics, because I think this is of key importance in understanding the moral problem that lies before us.

Physics might be described as an attempt to understand "what is the case" in the physical world. It seeks general and universal knowledge that is public and verifiable always and everywhere for the realm of experience for which it is proposed. Engineering science is different from physics, although in a certain sense it presupposes the knowledge of physics. The engineer must know "what is the case" in order to be an engineer, but his engineering does not stop at knowing this; it must pass into the order of "doing" or "making" if it is to be engineering in the strict sense. An engineer is a practical man. He makes things, and the things that he makes are not general and universal things, but very singular and concrete realities like a bridge or a rocket or a cyclotron. He must possess universal knowledge in order to do this, but his engineering is not concerned primarily with universals. Rather it is concerned with singulars, for these are the only things that man can really make.

The preoccupation of the engineer with doing or making introduces an element of uncertainty into his science that is not found in the pure sciences. The astronautical engineer who would put a man in orbit has a much more complex problem than the pure astronomer who would compute a planetary orbit in order to verify the predictions of general relativity. For one thing, the calculations of the engineer are not enough to put the man in orbit: the project is dependent on the work of technicians who must realize the engineer's ideas in a given practical situation with the money and materials available. The materials used are a source of uncertainty, as are the technicians who manipulate them and even the atmospheric conditions and elements encountered. One need not have great knowledge of the activities at Cape Canaveral to realize that engineering projects have associated with them a different kind of "truth" and "certitude" than do the theoretical researches of the pure physicist.

The same thing might be said of the medical doctor when compared with the biologist, say, or the vertebrate zoologist. The doctor must be a biologist in order to be a doctor, but biological research is not the same thing as "doctoring." The biologist is concerned with knowing how the animal organism normally works, while the doctor is concerned mainly with sickness and health. His is the practical task of restoring the sick or abnormal organism to normality. To do this he must understand the normal functioning of organisms of some general type, but his practical work is concerned, not with the general type, but with one particular malfunctioning organism, and his task is to restore this singular thing to proper operation. To do so, he employs theoretical knowledge, but he is also forced to use singular contingent things, like medicines and instruments and the ministrations of medical technicians. His measure of truth is therefore different from the biologist's. It can be referred to as "practical truth" and it has associated with it a "practical certitude." The good doctor attains practical truth when he knows what should be done, and he has practical certitude when he is certain of his procedure, but his knowledge and certitude are never so good that he infallibly restores every patient to health. The uncertainty inherent in doctoring is well known and is treated sympathetically by the general public—much more so than the uncertainty involved in engineering—whence the engineer's adage: "Only engineers go to jail: doctors bury their mistakes."

I mention these things because they are very relevant to any scientific treatment of man's action and the rules that should govern such action. Just as there can be a theoretical study of the physical universe (call it physics or astronomy or what you will) which has allied with it the practical science of engineering, and just as there can be a theoretical study of the functionings of man's body which has allied with it the practical science of medicine, so there can be a theoretical study of man in his entirety, not merely as he is an animal organism, but as he is a rational animal, endowed with intellectual knowledge and free deliberation, which may be referred to as psychology or philosophical anthropology. This discipline has allied with it a practical science which governs man's actions precisely as they are those of a responsible human being. Such practical science goes under the name of ethics or moral science. It is one of the most difficult types of scientific investigation that can be undertaken by man. Its difficulty is matched only by its importance, for it extends to all of humanity, and perforce is

249

concerned with everything that man does as he attempts to realize his vast capabilities as human.

Ethics and Prudence

Ethical science, like engineering and medicine, does not aim at speculative truth: it is not concerned with "what is the case," but rather, as has been said, with "what should be done." And since human actions are always placed in the concrete, are always singular, and surrounded by a host of mitigating circumstances, the truth and certitude sought in ethics is practical truth and practical certitude. Yet ethics attains such truth and certitude in a distinctive way, and I should like to explain this now in terms of what I have already said about the truth and certitude associated with engineering or medical science.

Engineering science does not itself construct the singular object, say the rocket, about which it reasons: this is constructed through the manual arts of the technicians who build the rocket, granting that such technicians are guided by the knowledge of the engineer. Similarly, the medical doctor does not himself "cure" the sick person: the cure is effected through the art of pharmacy, or through the work of nature using the medicines or incisions of the doctor, thereby assisting the organism to restore itself to normal functioning. Practical sciences such as engineering and medicine must therefore be complemented by some kind of practical art, which attains the singular effect that is sought by the doctor or the engineer. The same thing may be said for ethics or morals. Ethics does not tell anyone what he or she should do in this immediate situation. Like the practical sciences of engineering and medicine, it can guide human action, but it does not touch such action immediately. It too must be complemented by some kind of practical art that attains the singular action directly, and the practical art thus associated with ethics is known by the name of prudence.

Prudence is to ethics as the practical "know-how" of the technician is to engineering science. It is a habit of mind that tells a person how he or she should act reasonably in a given situation in order to attain his proper perfection as human. It operates under the general principle: "good is to be done and evil avoided," effectively equating the "good" with the "reasonable." It presupposes that the person who would act prudently has control of his emotions and his desires, having moderated these in a reasonable way to attain a normal and balanced character or personality. According to many philosophers, the dictates of what we commonly refer to as "conscience" are usually subjective judgments, proceeding from prudence, that point the way to intelligent action by the individual in any given human situation.

Precisely because it is a very personal thing, prudence is difficult to analyze, but without it there can be no science of morals; as I shall attempt now to illustrate by means of an example that is somewhat remote from the problem of nuclear warfare. A moralist seeking to establish a reasonable norm as to how people should act in society might propose the general principle of justice: "give to everyone what belongs to him." This would seem to be an infallible rule for human conduct, and yet there are some situations where it will not work. I pass over the complex problem of what constitutes private property and the subtleties involved in the analysis of the notion of theft to cite a simple case proposed by St. Thomas Aquinas seven hundred years ago. A man deposits a weapon with a friend: he rightfully owns it, is merely loaning it to his friend for safe-keeping, and the understanding is that he may have it back any time he asks for it. Some time later he does come back, under these circumstances: he has just been in a fight with another man, he is enraged, he comes in great passion, demands his weapon back, obviously intent on killing his enemy. Under these circumstances, is it just or reasonable to give to this person what truly belongs to him? Prudence says "no," even though the general principle proposed by abstract ethical argument permits a conclusion to the contrary.

Most people have little to do with the custody of lethal weapons, but become more involved in the next example I shall propose. This respects the moral problems of courtship, or more particularly, the actions of young people while "keeping company." The moralist, from his knowledge of human nature, knowing what has been done in the past, what can very easily happen when young people get together, might propose as a safe principle for reasonable action that "a young man and a young woman should *never* be completely alone." In this way, he neatly sidesteps the messy moral problems of "necking" and "petting" and "kissing," to say nothing of what to do with unwed mothers and other social and psychological problems arising in the sexual order. His principle is a safe principle: the big question is—does it attain practical truth? Courtship is ordered to marriage, and in this day and age, is it reasonable for a person to marry someone who is completely frigid and unaffectionate (relative to him, that is), or whom he does not really know in a personal way, but has only seen in a crowd? Ethical science, as a matter of fact, does not propose such a principle for human conduct. Room is left for personal prudential judgments. Young people who are prudent and virtuous can, in some cir-

251

cumstances, be trusted alone, and it might even be argued that this is necessary for a reasonable courtship. I say, "in some circumstances," and am careful not to specify too carefully just what these circumstances are, because this is a very personal problem. What John might very prudently do with Helen, he might quite imprudently do with Jane, or vice versa. But, if he is reasonable, in any given set of circumstances, he can arrive at "practical truth" as to what he should do, or "how far he can go," and he will have some degree of moral certitude about the rectitude of his decision.

What I have said about courtship can easily be applied to the question of drinking. A teetotalist principle might work for many people, but it cannot be imposed on all as a conclusion of moral science. There are differences among people as well as among the situations they are liable to encounter. Some can prudently drink and be better persons for it, others are very imprudent if they even take, as they say, "a sniff of the stuff."

Ethics, then, is a practical science, but it has to be wary of the principles it proposes for human action. If they are too general, they are practically of no use, and if they are too specific, they probably do not represent practical truth for the individual case. Ultimately it proposes principles that are apt for application to specific action by some human being in a given situation. These principles reinforce the prudent judgment of the individual, but it is the prudent judgment that makes the final decision as to what is actually to be done. The practical truth of morals is the truth of a generalized rule for action that is applicable in most cases: the actual application is made by the prudence of the individual. And both morals and prudence are necessary, in difficult situations, to produce a good human act. An intelligent man, who is slightly sick, can frequently cure himself with a pill; or, if he be mechanically inclined, he can build a gadget for himself. But if he has appendicitis, his normal knowledge is not enough—he has to reinforce it with medical science, as found in the doctor, in order to get well; and if he wants to build and launch an earth satellite, his tinkering ability is not enough either—he must reinforce it considerably with astronautical engineering and other technical skills in order to reach his objective. So it is with difficult problems of human living. Prudence is enough for daily, ordinary affairs. Ethics or moral science must be invoked when difficult problems are involved that cannot be solved by native intelligence and common sense. Together, the two work together to meet the complex demands made on man in modern society.

Even when ethics and prudence are both employed, however, it is important to realize that there can be no *absolute* truth or mathematical certitude about a future action that is to be placed. Moral science, like engineering and doctoring, has a "hit-or-miss" aspect to it. Not every satellite gets into orbit, nor is every patient cured, nor is every action that is ethically and prudently planned found, in the sequel, to produce the best or most reasonable eventuality for all concerned. Many a "Saturday-afternoon-quarterback" has made a prudential decision that lost a football game, on which account he is much maligned by the "Monday-morning-quarterback." Ethical decisions are frequently like that. All that ethics and prudence, like engineering and medicine, can assure is that an action be planned reasonably and well, taking account of all the factors that can be known at the time that the action is to be placed. Sometimes new knowledge or a later development will show that the particular action would have better been placed otherwise, or not at all, but this eventuality does not render the action either imprudent or unethical. Even if it does not turn out well, it can still be *planned* well, and this is the essential ingredient of practical truth— a point which has great bearing on the morality of nuclear warfare.*

Politics and Military Prudence

What I have said so far is very general and applicable to any human situation. As we move into the realm of public affairs, the notions thus far discussed continue to exert their influence on practical decisions to be made. A political or military leader must use ethics and prudence in his own personal life if he would attain his proper stature as a man. Beyond that, however, he must further develop his reasoning about social matters and acquire a special type of prudence, if he is to act reasonably in public affairs and in the interests of the common good. The practical science that he evolves in the course of such speculation is a part of the science of ethics, although classical Greek usage dignifies it by the special name of politics. Since the latter term has fallen into such bad repute in its non-scientific usage, we shall include it under the broad term of "moral science," or, if you will, designate it as "political science," although this has other connotations in modern usage. As a science, however, it remains practical, has for its goal the attainment of practical truth, and must be complemented by a practical art in the one who ultimately makes the decision as to what is to be done. For the broad conduct of affairs of state, this practical art is

---

* For a more technical discussion of the nature of ethics as a practical science, see my *The Role of Demonstration in Moral Theology*. Washington: The Thomist Press, 1962.

known as "political prudence," while for specific questions of military affairs, it is called "military prudence."

Obviously military prudence and the scientific reasoning that reinforces it must always be located in the broader context of moral science. As taught, however, in our service academies, command schools and war colleges, under the name of "military science" (or "naval science" or "air science"), it is concerned with very practical decisions about the deployment of forces and weapons' usage, and traditionally shies away from discussion of broad moral principles and a moral philosophy that should govern the action of the military. I suspect that our concern for "democracy" explains partly our reluctance to commit ourselves, as a nation, to a specific moral philosophy with all the moral principles that this automatically entails. As a matter of fact, however, no nation can function without *some* committment to moral science, and in my opinion, we have, as a nation, at least implicitly subscribed to a moral system that is acceptable to a large percentage of our enlightened citizenry. This goes by the name of "pragmatism," and equivalently defines as "good" whatever "works." If obliteration bombing "works," it is "good" bombing. Our military men, as a rule, have not been given to abstract thought on such questions as the morality of bombing, and have been content, in many situations, to follow the pragmatic rule as the unique criterion for judging their actions. But criticism on the part of other nations of the world, particularly those that have suffered from pragmatic thinking on the part of a former enemy, and criticism from Americans who do not subscribe to pragmatism in their own personal lives, and are indignant that our nation should be stigmatized by its thought, have led to an "examination of conscience" at the national level. The study of moral principles as applied to modern warfare has thus become topical, and any philosopher who has something constructive to offer is given a hearing, so that we as a nation may formulate more precisely the moral principles on which we work.

Warfare and Morality

As soon as we begin to discuss modern warfare in the broader context of moral science, we are back once again at the quasi-dilemma encountered when ethics formulates principles for human action. If such principles are "safe" principles, or are too general, or are too specific, they probably do not represent practical truth for the individual case. The moralist who insists that one should give to everyone whatever belongs to him, under *all* circumstances, or that it is wrong *ever* to drink alcoholic beverages, has

254

not arrived at practical truth, even though he may allege excellent reasons in justification of his principles. Somewhat in this vein, there are moralists who have studied the effects of nuclear weapons, or the present world situation with regard to communism and its opposing ideologies, who propose principles of this type. One school would say that modern technology has developed weapons of such destructive force that there can *never* be moral justification for their use in any circumstances—and this forms a basis for the so-called "pacificist" position on modern warfare. Another school would say that communism is such a menace to the moral welfare of the world that it *must* be wiped out at all costs, that nowadays a "pre-emptive" war against communism is equivalent to a "holy war"—a basis for the so-called "militarist" position on nuclear weapons. The arguments offered in support of such positions can be extremely logical. They are as difficult to refute as the general principle that "everyone must be given what belongs to him." In the abstract they may well be irrefutable. The precise problem is this: do they permit the individual (be he private person, statesman, or military leader) to arrive at practical truth in the concrete situation facing mankind in the twentieth century?

Most American moralists take the position that either of these principles is too extreme, and therefore attempt to reason to other principles that are not so general, thereby allowing for the exercise of a prudential judgment within the limits that they specify. Two such principles are the following: (1) because of the destructive force of nuclear weapons, all wars of "aggression," whether they be just or unjust, are no longer morally justifiable in the present day; (2) yet, since there can be no peace in the world without justice, law and order, a "defensive" war to repress injustice is morally admissible both in principle and in fact. These principles obviously define a middle ground between pacificism and militarism, and allow for the application of the so-called "traditional moral doctrine" on war to the contemporary situation.

Such a doctrine has been sketched rather fully in a book edited by William J. Nagle, entitled *Morality and Modern Warfare* (Helicon: 1960), in which the proponents of the doctrine are, among others, Father John Courtney Murray, the late Thomas E. Murray, and Prof. William V. O'Brien. As stated, the two principles already given are very abstract, and one could well wonder if they are not too remote for any practical application by the individual. To bring these closer to the concrete situation, they are supplemented in this book by a series of conditions under which they would seem to apply, thereby rendering a thermonuclear war morally justifiable. These conditions may be enumerated summarily as follows: (1) the war must be imposed by an obvious and extremely grave injustice; (2) it can only be entered upon as a last resort, when all other means for remedying the grave disorder have failed; (3) there must be a proportion between the damages that are being suffered through the perpetration of the grave injustice, and the damages that would be let loose by a war to repress the injustice; (4) there must be a solid probability of success in the violent repression of unjust action; and (5) the defensive warfare thus initiated must not escape entirely from the control of man. To these conditions are further appended two general propositions of the practical order, one affirming the legitimacy of defense preparations on the part of individual states, and the other disallowing the validity of conscientious objection to military service by the individual on the basis of his subjective conscience.

Such principles and conditions, it should be understood are not proposed as themselves furnishing practical truth about the morality of modern warfare. Rather they pretend to offer only what the Germans call a *Grenzmoral,* a limiting moral basis for reasonable action, which in every event must be implemented and complemented by a prudential decision for any actual situation that may arise. Whether or not such a prudential decision would actually be made by political or military leaders is a matter of some concern even to those who propose these moral principles. For one, such principles presuppose that the one making the decision have a refined notion of social justice and understand well all that the term "grave injustice" entails; again, they presuppose a sense of values in which "damages" are looked upon not merely in a material or economic way, but also in terms of spiritual and psychological realities. They further presuppose that the aim of modern warfare would be the establishment of a truly peaceful world order, all the demands of excessive nationalism aside—as, for example, is frequently implicit when one nation insists on "unconditional surrender" as the normal termination of any conflict. In a word, the person imperating the final decision to use nuclear weapons must be motivated by a sincere will to peace, which is a will to enforce the precept of peace by arms, which is basically a will to justice itself formed under the judgment of right reason. And under the particular conditions in which the world now finds itself, it would appear that this can never be more than a will to "limited war," with the principle of limitation being the exigencies of legitimate defense against patent injustice.

Granted all these conditions, and assuming these dispositions on the part of the one making the prudential military decision to employ nuclear weapons, moral science reinforces the judgment of the individual by supplying general principles under which he can act. Like medical science, it does not automatically ensure that the patient will get well. Like astronautical engineering, it does not automatically ensure that the satellite will go into orbit. But it does go as far as practical science can go, and furnishes a reasonable norm for action that can greatly assist the responsible person in making his decision.

Ethics and Moral Theology

Thus far I have written about ethics or moral science, and prudence (be it personal, or political, or military), but have made no mention of moral theology. Some might wonder whether what I have said so far represents the "Catholic position" on nuclear warfare, or whether I have taken a truly "Christian attitude" towards the subject. This immediately raises the question of the theology of modern warfare, to which we can now turn our attention.

Moral theology has much in common with ethics or moral science, but it differs in one significant respect from the latter discipline: it admits an argumentation from authority. The particular authority involved is that assented to by divine faith, and thus the theological argument proceeds at two levels, one requiring divine faith for its assent, the other requiring the use of human reason. Since little is contained in Sacred Scripture that is directly relevant to nuclear warfare, the practical import of the argument from authority (or divine faith) for the practicing Catholic is his belief in the teaching authority of the Pope. Thus to complete a theological analysis of the problem of nuclear warfare, we should have to analyze all the documents of Pope Pius XII and Pope John XXIII bearing on this problem, to see if this would alter the principles already proposed. The details of such an analysis are too lengthly to be treated here. Suffice it to say that it yields results completely consonant with what I have already said.

American Catholic theologians generally support the views I have presented. English Catholic theologians, on the other hand, have more frequently adopted a position that favors pacificism and is opposed to the use of nuclear weapons under the conditions I have listed. The English arguments are likewise presented in a book, edited by C. S. Thompson, and entitled *Morals and Missiles* (London: James Clarke, 1959). The resulting diversity of opinion among Catholics has naturally led to considerable debate in theological journals. Father John J. Farraher in the December,

1960 issue of *Theological Studies* gives a recapitulation of the principal arguments and issues involved. What he refers to as "pacifist" is the English position; the opposing position is the American one. He writes:

In this great debate (on nuclear warfare) all Catholic writers are agreed on the obvious points: (1) that nuclear war would be an extremely grave physical evil; (2) that it is to be avoided by any honorable and just means available, and especially by United Nations action; (3) that an aggressive nuclear war could not be justified; (4) that the use of nuclear weapons in a defensive war or a U.N. police action would be immoral if the same military ends could be achieved just as effectively and safely with lesser weapons. In other words, the extreme position of favoring a war merely to help the economy at home or simply to kill off all Communists cannot be a legitimate Catholic opinion. It would seem, further, that the extreme pacificist position, that all killing in any war is immoral and sinful, is also irreconcilable with Catholic theology.

That leaves two possible positions for pacifists: (1) that non-violence is the better way, even to the point of allowing Communist domination of the world; (2) that nuclear warfare is necessarily immoral, because the evils entailed are too great to be justified by any reason, even the avoidance of Communist domination.

It is on this second point that the issue exists between Catholics who are consistent with the traditional teaching of the Church. It is the question of which is the greater evil: the physical destruction and suffering of nuclear war, or communist domination. I believe that the vast majority of authorities on moral theology agree with what seemed to be the opinion of Pius XII and John XXIII, i.e., that Communist domination is definitely the greater evil. But certainly both are great evils and so to be avoided by whatever just means are possible.

In the meantime, since the issue is based on a weighing of evils and the proportion can hardly be infallibly decided, the theoretical question may still be debatable. But in the practical order, for the ordinary citizen, it seems to me that Catholic theology demands obedience to legitimate civil authority, unless the command is certainly unjust; that in doubtful matters the presumption favors legitimate authority. Hence, to be a conscientious objector, a Catholic would have to believe not only in the pacifist side of the debate, but in the complete lack of solid probability in the opinion of Pius XII and most Catholic moral theologians.*

Father Farraher is obviously concerned with the practical moral problem as to how a confessor should advise a conscientious objector, in England or the United States, who objects to military service on the basis of weapons used in modern warfare. The tone of his summary indicates that he does not think there is much basis for a sincere Catholic to be a conscientious objector. I would merely point out that his principal argument for the rejection of the British position is the argument from papal authority, which is basically a theological argument. Thus, from the point of view of moral theology, he regards the position adopted in this article as more consistent with official Catholic teaching than its opposite, and thus to be looked upon as the more probable Catholic position.

The Future

By way of conclusion, I should like to stress the main point I have been trying to make, namely, that the character of ethics as a practical science precludes the type of answer to the question of the morality of nuclear warfare that most of us would like to have. Anyone who has studied mathematics or physics or biology or psychology has an ideal of science, and of truth and certitude, that completely satisfies the human mind, that leaves it at rest and undisturbed about any important possibilities having been neglected. The "practical truth" and "practical certitude" of which I have written falls far short of this ideal of speculative science. Yet, in this day and age where the practical science of engineering assumes such importance in our civilization, we ought to have some notions of what one *can* expect in a practical science. The engineer's ideal should not be that everything he ever undertakes will always work perfectly: if it is, no matter how promising this may make our future space program appear, I can say that he is doomed to early disappointment in his engineering career. Rather he should be zealous that his engineering will always be planned well, that it will always take reasonable account of every foreseeable eventuality, that it will employ materials that will be adequate to the task, and that the

---

* Notes on Moral Theology, *Theological Studies* 21 (1960), pp. 592-593.

technical skills of the men to whom he entrusts its execution will be equal to the practical difficulties they will have to overcome.

I can understand the grave concern over the future of our nation, and its moral responsibilities for the nuclear forces we have unleashed over mankind. But here we can learn from our engineers and scientists. Like them, we must be realistic in our expectations. We must avoid the extremes of being unduly pessimistic over the dire prospects before us, and of having a false optimism that "everything will turn out well" if we keep striving for materialistic prosperity. Above all we must exert public pressure on our political and military leaders, to assure that they "form their consciences" properly, that they become endowed with the measure of political and military prudence, consonant with Christian moral principles, that is necessary to assure the attainment of "practical truth" in the difficult world situation now confronting us.

Eighteen years ago the world situation was very different. To return to the scene with which I began this paper, the morality of nuclear warfare appeared differently to me as I stood in the operations room on Tinian than it appears to me now. I had no direct part in the military decisions to drop either of the atom bombs with which World War II was terminated, but I did have access to much of the secret intelligence and war plans information on which the decisions to drop these bombs were based. I must confess that, on the basis of this information and my own staff experience, I thought at the time that these decisions represented sound military prudence and that they were morally defensible. After the war was over, when additional information became available, and particularly when the pragmatic basis of our political and military policies were made more explicit through discussion and debate, I was not so sure that "practical truth" had *de facto* been arrived at in this matter. Of course, "Monday-morning-quarterbacks" always look better than their "Saturday-afternoon" counterparts, but then they are not the real ball-players: they neither win nor lose games, they just talk about them. Perhaps the men of my generation are to be censured for not having talked enough about the work in which they were engaged, and while it was in progress. Yet secrecy is an integral part of the strategy of war, which even a democracy must respect. More reprehensible, in my eyes, was the lack of moral depth and of the influence of Christian principles in our thinking as a nation. If our military men did make a mistake, as well they could have—even though they were acting prudently and ethically—it was not so much their mistake as the mistake of their political leaders, in turn traceable to the philosophers (and should I add: and theologians?) who framed (or failed to frame) our national policy during the thirties and early forties.

Pray God that our Catholic president not be called upon to make the next decision to employ nuclear weapons. But if he is, perhaps his conscience will rest easier in the knowledge that his countrymen have had the time to reflect on some of these issues, and—more to be desired—have helped to create a national political atmosphere in which moral principles are given greater weight than the pragmatic "values" that have thus far motivated us as a democratic nation.

ESSAY XIII:

BEING SCIENTIFIC IN A
PRACTICE DISCIPLINE

     With the exception of the previous essay, all of the essays in this book have been devoted to the problems of theoretical sciences, i.e., sciences whose task it is to investigate "what is the case" in the world of nature, and little attention has been devoted to the problems of practical sciences, i.e., sciences whose task it is to investigate "what is to be done" so as to make the world a better place to live in. It is the purpose of this essay to investigate some of the characteristics of these practical sciences, or practice disciplines, to show how they differ from theoretical sciences in their methods and in the results they attain. The basic ideas can be found in the writings of St. Thomas Aquinas, as may be seen by consulting Chapter Two of the author's *The Role of Demonstration in Moral Theology* (1962a), where detailed citations of the works of Aquinas are given. Since much of the subsequent development has occurred in conjunction with the author's courses in the School of Nursing of The Catholic University of America, the illustrations toward the end of the essay are drawn from the science of nursing. The general analysis, however, is applicable to all practice disciplines and not merely to those connected with the health professions.

     A basic distinction can be drawn between theoretical knowledge and practical knowledge on the basis of the goal or end toward which each is directed. Theoretical knowledge has for its end the attainment of truth and that alone, whereas practical knowledge seeks truth as a means to an end, so as to order it to practice or operation. As a consequence these two types of knowledge are concerned with different matters:

practical knowledge considers things that we can do, or "operables," while theoretical knowledge considers things we can know but cannot do, or "non-operables."

Additional differences may be noted as follows. Practical knowledge is causative of things, whereas theoretical knowledge is merely apprehensive of them. Again, the object of practical knowledge is not truth alone, but the performable good under the aspect of its being true. Practical knowledge must therefore have an order to operation or practice, but it must be so ordered in a proximate way, i.e., it must be knowledge that directly regulates some operation and so bears immediately on the performable and its causes. If knowledge is to be practical, then, it must be applicable to a particular operation at a particular time and in a particular way. Although it may have its beginnings in considering the same subjects as theoretical knowledge, what ultimately distinguishes it from theoretical knowledge is that it terminates differently from the latter, in such and such a specific thing to be done.

But theoretical and practical are not necessarily spoken of in a mutually exclusive way. The intellect that is perfected by these two types of knowledge is one and the same, and there are degrees of both theoretical and practical knowledge. So it is possible to differentiate between the actually practical and the formally practical, and between the completely theoretical and the formally theoretical. Likewise there can be some overlapping: we can have theoretical knowledge of something performable or doable, and we can even make our theories in some sense practical. In the former case, such theoretical knowledge is not of great value unless it is actually ordered to operation, and hence it is said to be primarily practical and only secondarily theoretical; in the latter case, the theoretical knowledge is worth having even if it is never ordered to operation, and thus it is said to be primarily theoretical and only secondarily practical. And even in purely practical knowledge we still theorize, which means that in a certain sense practical knowledge presupposes theoretical knowledge, although the reverse is not necessarily true.

From these brief considerations we can conclude that there are two basic ways of differentiating theoretical from practical knowledge, one taken from the subject matter with which the knowledge is concerned, the other from the end of the knowledge itself. Theo-

264

retical knowledge has for its object the knowable, whereas practical knowledge is concerned with the doable; the end of theoretical knowledge is truth, whereas that of practical knowledge is operation. Other bases of distinction are obviously implied also, but these will become clearer from the consideration of the special type of practical knowledge in which we are interested, namely, practical science.

Theoretical and Practical Sciences

Just as theoretical knowledge is different from practical knowledge, so theoretical science is distinct from practical science. As sciences, however, both share a common characteristic: they are equally knowledge through causes. So it is not the search for principles and causes that serves to differentiate theoretical from practical science: practical science must uncover causes too, and demonstrate through them, as already explained in Essay 7. Its distinctive note is that it is concerned with the principles and causes of things to be done. Still, insofar as it engages in causal analysis, it can theorize and use analytical procedures similar to those of the theoretical disciplines. This does not mean, again, that even the more theoretical parts of practical science should be regarded as theoretical science. Such parts are only called theoretical in the sense that they are more remote from performance or operation, which is the proper end of practical science, and so determines everything that will be included within the scope of the discipline.

An important consequence of this difference between theoretical and practical knowledge is that theoretical science seeks demonstrative knowledge of its subject, whereas practical science seeks actually to *construct* its subject, precisely as capable of being produced, and needs scientific knowledge to do so. This operational requirement demands of practical science an even more detailed knowledge of its subject matter than is required in theoretical science. It does not suffice in a practice discipline, for instance, to know merely the cause of an effect; the perfection of the science requires a knowledge of all the movements and operations necessary to assure that such an effect will actually follow from that cause in the order of production. Practical science therefore presupposes theoretical knowledge, as has already been said, but it extends further than theoretical know-

265

ledge, all the way to knowledge of how the singular subject can be produced and actually perfected in the order of being.

As a further consequence of the difference of subject matter, there are also differences in the modes of procedure of theoretical and practical sciences. Theoretical science is said to proceed *analytically* or resolutively, because its ultimate function is to analyze a conclusion back to its proper principles, or, as explained in Essay 7, to resolve it to a middle term in one or other order of causality. Practical science, on the other hand, is said to proceed *compositively*. It must analyze and discover causes too, but its ultimate function is to apply universal principles and simple causes to the construction of composite singular entities that can exist in the operational order. In this, practical science is imitative of nature, which likewise produces complex singulars from simple causes and therefore proceeds compositively in the order of generation.

Finally, there are other ways in which we can speak of sciences being theoretical or practical. One such arises from the intention of the one who is acquiring the particular knowledge. So it is possible to make a distinction between the end of the science, as such, and the goal or end that is sought by the one acquiring the science, apart from the science's own intrinsic orientation. For example, there can be knowledge that is orderable to action of itself, but which the knower does not intend to so use, and which on this account can be said to be partly theoretical and partly practical. And conversely, although knowledge that is in no way orderable to action is simply theoretical, there are truths of theoretical science that can be used by the knower to guide his or her action remotely, and therefore these can be said to be at least remotely practical.

When all of these ways of speaking about science are taken into account, it is possible to chart the differences between theoretical and practical science and so explain the various senses in which disciplines can be said to be both practical and scientific. Knowledge itself, as we have seen, is either practical or theoretical according as it considers either what is to be done or what is to be known, and according as its end is either performance or truth. We have said that science is either practical or theoretical according as its mode of procedure is either compositive or analytical. And now we have the further basis of distinction that sciences are said to be practical because their knower intends operation, while they are also said to be theoretical because their knower intends truth and proceeds analytically, even though the science as such is concerned with something doable. All of these distinguishing notes may now be combined to yield at least five different categories of knowledge that can be termed theoretical or practical in various ways, and that are illustrated in the schema on the following page.

The first two categories are those of knowledge whose object is theory considered precisely as such, whose end as a consequence is knowledge, and whose mode is therefore analytical. The first category is constituted when the knower intends simply to know; in such a case his knowledge is in no way practical, and can be said to be completely theoretical. The second category is constituted when the knower does not aim directly at truth but rather at operation; in such a case his knowledge can be said to be primarily theoretical, insofar as the subject matter, end, and mode are those of theoretical knowledge, and only secondarily practical, because it is merely the intention of the knower that confers a practical character on the knowledge attained.

The third category is that of knowledge whose object is practice viewed precisely as theorizable, whose end as a consequence is knowing, and whose mode is hence analytical; there the knower can only intend truth, since he is abstracting from the fact that what he is considering is something performable or doable, and his knowledge may be spoken of as equally theoretical and equally practical.

The fourth and fifth categories are those of knowledge whose object is practice considered precisely as such, whose proximate end is performance or operation, and whose mode is therefore compositive. The fourth category is constituted when the knower does not intend operation, but rather truth; in such a case his knowledge can be said to be primarily practical, insofar as the object, end, and mode are those of practical knowledge, and only secondarily theoretical, because it is merely the knower's intention that confers a theoretical character on his knowledge. The fifth category, finally, is constituted when the knower actually aims at practice or operation; in such a case his knowledge

THEORETICAL VS. PRACTICAL KNOWLEDGE

Cate-gory	KNOWLEDGE				is called	
	whose OBJECT is	whose METHOD is	whose END is	whose KNOWER intends	*THEORETICAL*	*PRACTICAL*
I	theory as such	analytical	knowledge	knowledge	*completely*	---
II	theory as applicable	analytical	knowledge	practice	*primarily*	*secondarily*
III	practice as theorizable	analytical	knowledge	knowledge	*equally*	*equally*
IV	practice as such	compositive	practice	knowledge	*secondarily*	*primarily*
V	practice as such	compositive	practice	practice	---	*completely*

is in no way theoretical and can be said to be completely practical.

Reflection on this schema will show that practical science obviously does not pertain to the first two
categories, for these have all the characteristics of
theoretical science, which we are here attempting to
differentiate from practical science. Nor does practical science pertain to the fifth category, for the
latter is characteristic of the habits of prudence and
art. The reason for this can be seen in the distinction between the fourth and fifth categories just indicated. In the fifth category, the knower actually intends to perform a singular existent operation, and
this is characteristic of prudence or art, which are
concerned with singular actions that allow considerable
latitude in their performance. In the fourth category,
on the other hand, the knower immediately aims at the
truth about something doable or performable at a more
general level, abstracting from the direct intention to
do anything at the moment, and this is characteristic
of the human intellect, which can thus be perfected by
the habit of practical science.

Practical science, therefore, will have to be
placed in the third or fourth categories. It is not
completely practical knowledge, and in this it is distinguished from prudence, and at the same time it is
not completely theoretical knowledge, nor is it even
primarily theoretical and only secondarily practical,
and in these characteristics it is distinguished from
theoretical science. In itself, it is partly theoretical and partly practical. According to one way of
speaking, it perhaps can be said to be primarily practical and only secondarily theoretical, insofar as it
is concerned with practice as such, proceeds in a compositive mode, has operation as its end, but the knower
immediately intends only the truth about what is to be
done and abstracts from the direct intention to do it.
According to another way of speaking, it perhaps can be
said to be equally practical and equally theoretical,
insofar as it is concerned with practice considered
precisely as theorizable, proceeds in an analytical
mode, and has knowledge for its end, which is also the
immediate goal of the knower.

Analysis and Composition

Thus far only a brief indication has been given
of the modes of procedure that usually serve to differ-

269

entiate theoretical from practical science, namely, the analytical and compositive respectively. Since it has now been suggested that a practical science can proceed in either a compositive or an analytical mode, it becomes necessary to explain more fully what these two modes entail, and how they can both be employed in one and the same science without affecting its essentially practical character. Since the compositive mode is most distinctive of practical science, moreover, we shall start with that and then explain the sense in which such science employs analytical procedures as well.

The compositive process that is proper to a practical science can be illustrated by examples drawn from particular sciences. It is noteworthy, however, that there are differences among the practical sciences, for not all are concerned with practice or performance in exactly the same way. The biggest difference is between the practical science that deals with human action under the characteristic of being human or moral, known as ethics or moral science, and those that deal with objects that are the result of man's making or production, known to Aquinas as *scientiae factivae* and in our own day as the mechanical or engineering sciences. Intermediate between these two groups are the health sciences, those that are *factiva sanitatis* or "productive of health," of which medicine is the traditional example. The mechanical sciences are concerned with artifacts, whereas both moral science and medical science are concerned with natural entities -- man and living organisms that are to be restored to health. Because of this concern with nature the latter are more similar to each other in their modes of procedure, as will be explained presently.

Beginning with engineering science, however, one should note that before the engineer can proceed to build anything he must first understand its defining characteristics in full detail. Not only must he know these, but he must have analyzed the final product back to all the intermediate constructions that are necessary to produce it and all the operations that they in turn will require. It is only in this way that he can come to the first step in the compositive or constructive process, and also at the order he is to follow in the actual construction. Yet this knowledge, though essential, is really only a preliminary; the real work of engineering comes when such knowledge is applied to doing. Here there may have to be many variations in

270

the plans dictated by contingent circumstances, for
which an engineer is essential and in the effecting of
which he is most properly "engineering." In any event,
his knowledge must govern the actual process of construction, and this is the compositive procedure that
makes engineering a practical science. Even here,
moreover, the engineering science of itself does not
produce the completed structure. The engineer's universal knowledge as to how to produce a structure of
this kind must be complemented by the mechanical arts
of the workmen to produce the singular existent structure from the matter that happens to be available to
them.

Medical science, somewhat like engineering but
closer to moral science in its procedures, makes more
intimate use of nature in the effecting of its goal,
namely, health. The doctor, like the engineer, first
reasons back from the notion of health until he comes
to the first action with which he can initiate a return to health in the sick person, say, a particular
type of medicine that will normally overcome a particular type of infection. This requires a technical
knowledge of all the requirements for health in various organs, the distinctive characteristics of various
diseases, the interventions or causative factors that
can overcome abnormalities and restore normal operation, etc. But again, this is knowledge preparatory
to action; the doctor cannot give a prescription to
the patient and never see him again. He is actually
"doctoring" when he applies the causes to the actual
return to health, checks the progress and effects of
the medication, revises the dosage, etc. Here too his
universal knowledge is not enough. He is dependent on
the art of the pharmicist and of medical technicians,
and on the individual natural dispositions of the patient, as efficient causes, to achieve the ultimate effect: the concrete health of this individual.

These examples may serve to bring out the way in
which any practical science is characterized by a compositive process. Before something can be performed
or done in a scientific way, the action to be performed or the object to be made must be analyzed or broken
down into its components and into the various causative factors that can bring them about, all the way to
the first action to be initiated. When this is known,
then the compositive process proper to a practical
science begins. This proceeds in the order of being
or of practice and applies the causes to the construc-

271

tion of the object intended. Throughout the entire
process the practical scientist is not interested in
contemplating the truth, nor is he interested in knowledge for its own sake; his concern with knowing is
dominated by the use his knowledge may have for achieving his goal in the best possible way. And since what
he finally produces is a singular existent thing, and
not some universal about which he may have the greatest
certitude, his practical science must be complemented
by some type of prudence or art that assures him or his
collaborators that this is the best procedure to follow
in these particular circumstances, with these specific
materials at hand, with this individual, etc., so as
to achieve the desired result.

From what has been said thus far, it should be
obvious that a practical science initially requires a
certain amount of analysis or of resolution before it
can embark on the compositive process just described.
It is in this analytical procedure that the practical
sciences most resemble the theoretical sciences, and
in which they get involved in the research methods employed by the theoretical scientist whenever they attempt to learn more about their own subject matters.
To explain this aspect of a practical science it will
be helpful to compare medical science and moral science
with the theoretical sciences to which they most closely correspond, say, with vertebrate zoology and philosophical psychology respectively.

Medical science, by way of example, is interested in tumors that grow regularly in the intestinal
tract. To do research on tumors it employs essentially
the same investigative techniques as are used by the
zoologist when studying the intestines or any other
organ, and in this sense it uses an analytical procedure that corresponds to that of its related theoretical
discipline. Since it does so, one may ask why medical
research is not the same as biological research, or
why tumors are studied in medical science and not in
zoology. The obvious answer is that the goals or ends
of the sciences are different, and this difference dictates the relative importance assigned to their subject
matters. As the zoologist sees it, for instance, the
intestine is an integral part of the animal organism
and worthy of consideration in its own right; the tum-
or, on the other hand, is only an incidental thing, an
abnormality, which disrupts the normal functioning of
nature. For the medical doctor, on the other hand,
the situation is reversed: his proper concern is
health, and with reference to health a tumor assumes

272

great importance. He must know about the normal functioning of an intestine, but in a sense he can learn that from the zoologist. The special knowledge that the doctor requires respects the abnormality in the intestine, for it is only when he knows about this that he can proceed in the order of operation to restore his patient to health. Apart from that, his methods of investigation and research parallel those used by the zoologist, and these are in the analytical mode that is otherwise characteristic of the theoretical disciplines. But the entire reason for such research is that he be able to proceed in the order of composition, which is distinctive of his own science precisely as practical.

An analogous situation obtains between moral science and philosophical psychology, as can be seen by considering some of the matters that have already been discussed in Essay 11. The philosopher can study the powers of the soul and the habits with which they are endowed, and yet have little to say about virtues and vices and the way in which the latter will affect an individual's perfection as man. The moralist, on the other hand, will investigate virtues and vices in great detail, try to delineate their differentiating characteristics, how they are acquired and lost, and so forth. One might ask whether the knowledge the moralist seeks is important in itself, and if so, whether the specialist in philosophical psychology might not also wish to conduct a parallel investigation. Again the answer is no. In itself the knowledge of how any particular individual is habituated is trivial; it is only because such knowledge can be useful for directing human action, which is the goal of moral science as practical, that it is worth acquiring in the first place. But in order to acquire it, the moralist must employ the theoretical procedures that are characteristic of psychology, and in so doing he must seek causes and employ the methods of analysis that are requisite for any demonstrative science. Thus he uses the analytical techniques that are proper to theoretical discourse, although this is for him only a preliminary to his proper work of composition in the actual direction of human action to its ultimate goal, the perfection of an individual existing here and now under all the circumstances in which he may happen to find himself.

Here it may be remarked parenthetically that one and the same type of activity may be studied concurrently by the doctor and the moralist to ascertain, respectively, whether it will be productive of health in the individual, and whether it will advance the moral integrity of the doctor or the patient or both in achieving this result. It is this type of problem that has given rise to the interdisciplinary field of study known as bioethics or medical ethics, a field of study whose complexity is matched only by its importance, as each day more and more difficult problems face those who must make responsible decisions in the health sciences.

However this may be, it seems safe to conclude that analytical procedures are involved in the practical sciences we have been discussing. They proceed in the analytical or resolutive mode, examining their subject matter and breaking it down into all the causative factors that can serve to explain it in a universal or general way. But this is merely an intermediate stage in such sciences, because in the final result, as practical, they must be compositive in mode. Their composition, it should now be clear, is one that depends on analysis that is not essentially different from that of the theoretical sciences. Thus their method is not one that is opposed to the analytical mode, but rather one that presupposes and complements this mode for the case where the object of the science is practice as such, and not merely knowledge or the contemplation of truth.

Nursing as a Science

As a further illustration of the matters being treated in this essay, it may now be helpful to examine how nursing, as one of the disciplines usually counted among the health sciences, can be viewed as a practical science. The question is often asked whether nursing is an art or a science, whether or not it is possible to do research in nursing, and so on. Such questions are not easy to answer, but perhaps something will be gained by attempting to answer them in terms of the five categories of theoretical-practical knowledge that have already been sketched in this essay. What is usually referred to simply as "nursing," it may now be seen, is actually a composite of three different categories of knowledge. And depending on which aspect of the discipline is being considered, it is possible to answer truthfully that nursing is an art, that it is also a science, and that it is a science that has its own proper methods of research

274

that serve to distinguish it from other disciplines.

To see how this may be an appropriate answer let us consider the complex of disciplines represented on the diagram on the following page. Here a variety of subjects are listed in five different columns, each column corresponding to one of the five categories of theoretical and practical knowledge shown in the schema on p. 268 above. The disciplines in the first column are referred to as "pure sciences," with mathematics heading the list and other disciplines dealing with more complex subject matters following below them in order of increasing complexity. Column two contains a few disciplines that are labelled as "applied sciences:" these differ from those in the first column mainly in the goal that the scientist has in mind when studying them, namely, to put his knowledge to some practical application. The disciplines listed in the remaining three columns all have practice as their immediate object, and thus they may be referred to generically as practice disciplines. The examples of engineering and medical science already discussed are shown at the top of columns three and four, with those in column three differing from those in column four only in their methodology: in column three analytical or research methodology predominates, whereas in column four compositive or operational methodology is the central concern. Column five, finally, lists the art or technical "know-how" associated with the respective disciplines, all of which are necessary if proper results are to be achieved in actual practice.

The three aspects of nursing as a practice discipline already referred to are listed in the last three columns of the schema as nursing research, nursing science, and nursing art, respectively. Precisely as nursing, all three have health as their immediate concern, but they differ collectively from all the other health sciences in the aspect under which they are restorative of health, namely, that of continuous care. This being so, the concepts of health and of care are pivotal for the nursing profession, and more will be said about them presently. Assuming a general acquaintance with these concepts, however, one can differentiate the three aspects of nursing as follows.

Nursing art represents the practical "know-how" of a nurse who knows what to do in a particular situation, considering all of the attendant circumstances, so as to achieve the best possible result. It presup-

TYPOLOGY OF THEORETICAL AND PRACTICAL DISCIPLINES

I PURE SCIENCE	II APPLIED SCIENCE	III PRACTICAL RESEARCH	IV PRACTICAL SCIENCE	V ART OR TECHNĒ
Mathematics	Applied Mathematics			
Physical Sciences Astronomy Physics Chemistry	Applied Physics Chemistry	Research Engineering Physical Chemical	Engineering Mechanical Electrical Chemical	Technical Crafts Mechanic Electrician Computer, etc.
Life and Human Sciences Biology		Medical Research	Medicine Psychiatry	Paramedical Technicians
Psychology	Clinical Psychology	Nursing Research	Nursing Science	Nursing Art
Sociology				
Political Science		Jurisprudence	Law	Art of Politics
Philosophy		Metaethics	Ethics	Prudence
Theology		Moral Theology	Pastoral Theology Canon Law	Church Administration

poses some knowledge of the rules or principles of nursing practice, but these need not be known in a scientific way; frequently it suffices for the one acquiring the art to serve an apprenticeship and so learn by doing. The better one possesses the art the more prudence she or he will manifest in making nursing decisions, in knowing what rules to apply, what exceptions to make, and so on. Nursing art will always be necessary if there is to be good nursing care, but perhaps it should be noted that in the early days of nursing this was the only type of practical knowledge that was sought or expected in a nurse.

Nursing science differs from nursing art in that it presupposes a certain amount of analytical knowledge in the one possessing it, which is usually formulated in principles that define proper procedures to follow in the general case. Such principles are arrived at by causal analysis, but they are not merely theoretical principles: rather they are directed toward practice and toward intelligent application in all the circumstances that can be generally envisaged. The methodology that characterizes this aspect of nursing is compositive, just as is that of engineering or doctoring when a structure is being built or a patient is being cured. Such compositive method requires a plan based on analysis, but it continually invokes scientific principles to make adjustments in the execution of that plan, to assure that the most knowledgable and proven techniques are used whenever difficulties are encountered. Nursing science of this type is usually communicated in undergraduate programs, where students are taught the most up-to-date principles and methods on which to base sound nursing practice. To be effective, of course, it must be complemented by the prudent application of nursing art, and it is perhaps noteworthy that the science and the art need not be found in the same individual, though usually this is the case.

Nursing research differs from nursing science in that it attempts, by continued investigation and the systematic use of analytical techniques, to go beyond the present state of nursing science to formulate new principles and new procedures that will be more effective in restoring patients to health by the techniques of continuous care. It does this by formulating hypotheses and constructing theories and models that can be tested in practice and so lead to new ways of doing things. More will be said about research methods in the following section, so as to relate them to the contents of previous essays in this book. For now, it may simply be noted that this aspect of nursing is usually reserved to graduate programs, and that the resulting research and publication is continually being incorporated into the courses and textbooks used in undergraduate teaching, thus contributing to the cumulative growth of knowledge within the profession.

Concepts of Health and Care

To return now to the concept of health, it should be noted that this concept has been regulative of the medical profession since classical antiquity, for it has always been regarded as the task of the doctor to eliminate disease and so restore the human organism to good health. The concept of health has undergone an evolution in recent years, however, largely because of the great strides made in the elimination of infectious disease in the early part of the twentieth century. The greatest change would appear to be the idea that medicine should treat the whole individual, and not merely his disease; from this it was a simple step to include also the individual's social relationships -- his family, his work, his way of life, and his reactions to people and things about him. As a consequence health professionals have been called upon to explore and cure not only organic diseases but also all forms of human misery, psychic as well as social. The World Health Organization now defines health as "a state of complete physical, mental, and social well-being and not merely the absence of disease and infirmity." Similarly, the public health movement, focusing on man's integrity as a biopsychosocial organism, tends to identify his health with his happiness and his total welfare.

A slightly different emphasis is that of René Dubos, who also espouses a comprehensive concept of health but adopts what might be termed an ecological perspective in so doing. Dubos holds that health is a human phenomenon that must be viewed not only in the context of the whole man but also in relation to the total environment. He defines health as that state which expresses the success of the organism's efforts to respond adaptively to environmental change. Thus Dubos's emphasis is on adaptation, not on a state achieved. In his view the definition of the World Health Organization is too utopian: it misses the point that moderate stress and tension are necessary conditions of health. Perfect health can never be reached because man will never be perfectly adjusted to his environment.

These and other definitions of health have been examined critically by Ann Neale in an article entitled "An Analysis of Health" (*The Kennedy Institute Quarterly Report*, Vol. 1, No. 1, Autumn 1975, pp. 1-9), which should be consulted for fuller details. Neale herself argues that health's primary referent used to be, and should continue to be, a condition of the body. One may speak of social health, but this is an analogous use of the term that unfortunately can lead to assigning all deviance predicates to the categories of health and illness. For her, recognition of the fact that man is a biopsychosocial being whose well-being in any one of these realms (i.e., the bio-, psycho-, or social) is influenced by the others, and whose total well-being must take account of all these factors, does not mean that each of these aspects, or their sum, constitutes health. It is sufficient to adopt an organismic focus as the basis for understanding man as a biopsychosocial unity. A concept of health restricted to organic well-being, she argues, avoids the medicalizing of all human experience. It also recognizes human goods other than health. And most important of all, defining health as the well-being of a living organism makes it amenable to the investigation of the natural and human sciences: the norm or standard of a person's health is not precisely determined, for there is always more to learn about one's organs, organic processes, structures, and functions, and how these can be restored most expeditiously to their proper state.

Neale's ideas find confirmation and support in an essay by L. R. Kass entitled "Regarding the End of Medicine and the Pursuit of Health" (*The Great Ideas Today 1978*, Chicago: Encyclopaedia Britannica, Inc., 1978, pp. 72-103). According to Kass,

> health is a natural standard or norm -- not a moral norm, not a 'value' as opposed to a 'fact,' not an obligation, but a state of being that reveals itself in activity as a standard of bodily excellence or fitness, relative to each species and to some extent of individuals, recognizable if not definable, and to some extent attainable. If you prefer a simple

formulation, I would say that health is 'the well-working of the organism as a whole,' or again, 'an activity of the living body in accordance with its specific excellences.' [pp. 90-91]

Earlier in the essay he had pointed out that "health is different from pleasure, happiness, civil peace and order, virtue, wisdom, and truth." [p. 82] It is also something that is quite different from the preservation of life, and thus the concepts of health and longevity (or immortality) should not be confused: "Health is possible only for mortal beings, and we must seek it knowing and accepting, as much as we are able to know and accept, the transience of health and of the beings who are healthy" [*ibid.*]

What should emerge from these attempts to define health is a recognition that the concept itself is not something highly theoretical, nor is it capable of precise quantitative analysis as one might expect of a metrical concept. To refer to the types of concepts already explained in Essay 3, health is a natural or physical concept that pertains to the observational order and that can be recognized in a general way for the various types of living species. When one attempts to do scientific research in the health professions, then health as so understood is the goal at which she or he aims. The theoretical investigation is then undertaken in the context of a conceptual framework that embraces a wide variety of interrelated concepts or terms, all logically coherent, ranging from the observational concept through the metrical to the theoretical concept, each of which is explained above on pp. 49-61. To be more specific:

Observational concepts or terms, such as health, are those that fall directly under sense experience or can be grasped intuitively on the basis of that experience. With regard to the conceptual framework as a whole they are primitive and need not be defined in terms of other components of the framework or theory.

Metrical concepts or terms, on the other hand, are defined through a process of measurement or other operational procedure, and in this sense may be said to have stipulated definitions. Usually they are directly related to observational terms, in that the latter specify what one is attempting to measure or define operationally. Some element of convention is always involved in metrical concepts, and they are frequently formulated in such a way that they can be used to test one or other hypothesis.

Theoretical concepts or terms are those that do not fall under sense experience or observation directly, but are used to explain statements or generalizations involving observational or metrical concepts. Usually they are not defined directly, but rather provisionally and in terms of their consequences. The entities they refer to may or may not have extramental existence, but at least they may be thought of as "candidates for existence," as suggested in Essay 3, and they provide models in terms of which real existents can be analogously understood (Essay 10). It may be noted, however, that in a practical science it is not so important to decide the ontological status of theoretical entities as it is in a theoretical science. The reason for this is that knowledge or truth is not of primary concern in the former, because of its ordination to practice or to operation, whereas it is quite important in the latter, because of its interest in what is actually the case in the world of nature.

The special value of a conceptual system in a practice discipline is that it can be used to suggest and formulate hypotheses that then function in the hypothetico-deductive methodology outlined in Essay 3. Nursing hypotheses usually take the form of predictions based on theoretical concepts; they express relationships or correlations between metrical concepts that can be subjected to some kind of experiment or test. Any factors that play a role in an experiment or test, and particularly those that can be measured and brought under control in some way, are referred to as variables. A hypothesis, as used in nursing research, generally attempts to answer some question as to how particular variables will be related when the projected tests or experiments are carried out. Should the results turn out as predicted, the hypothesis is said to be verified or confirmed; should they not, it is said to be falsified or disconfirmed. Verification gives the hypothesis some degree of verisimilitude, whereas falsification can lead to its rejection, but more usually it suggests a revision or reformulation of the hypothesis so as to give it greater predictive power.

As it turns out, care is the central concept that underlies most nursing research. It is an observational concept in the sense just described; effect-

281

ively it describes a quality that can be grasped intuitively and is easy enough to recognize. Because it
is a qualitative concept it is difficult to quantify
and to measure, and yet it has metrical concepts associated with it, the same as do other qualities.
Measurements of the quality of nursing care are usually made on the basis of structure, or of process, or
of outcome. The more highly developed scales are those
based on the nursing process (Dunn Scale, Nursing Aud-
it, Slater Scale, Qualpacs). The scale or inventory
is itself directly related to a theory or conceptual
framework that identifies factors or variables in some
way measurable. These differ from one system to another depending on how one identifies the goal of nursing and the activities or processes by which this goal
is to be achieved. Examples may be found in the works
of Peplau, Henderson, Orlando, Wiedenback, Travelbee,
Johnson, Rogers, King, Orem, and Roy; for details, see
Sr. Callista Roy, *Introduction to Nursing: An Adaptation Model*, Englewood Cliffs, N.J.: Prentice Hall,
1976.

This, then, is a brief survey of the way in which
the analytical procedures of the more theoretical disciplines can be applied in a practice discipline such
as nursing to generate new knowledge. Sometimes the
research procedures here sketched will turn up causal
mechanisms that give a clear insight into new principles and procedures, but more usually the findings have
a provisional cast to them that render their general
acceptance within the profession problematical at best.
In any event, the concepts of health and of care are
central to nursing research, as they are for all other
aspects of nursing as a practice discipline.

As a final observation, it may be noted that the
place of the three components of nursing in the schema
on p. 276 providing a topology of disciplines gives
some indication of the many arts and sciences that influence nursing practice. Nursing art is obviously
closely related to the paramedical arts and to prudence, to say nothing of the art of dealing with people
in a political way. Nursing science has manifest affinity with medicine and psychiatry, and also with
ethics and law, as these are pursued by their various
practitioners. Nursing research in its more clinical
aspect is very closely aligned with medical and psychi-
atric research: it also draws heavily on pure and applied disciplines in the domain of the life and human
sciences, especially biology, psychology, and sociolo-

gy. The last two are particularly important, for the research methods developed in these disciplines prove most fruitful when applied to the concepts of health and care as these delineate the special subject matter of nursing research. And finally there is philosophy, the mother of all rational inquiry, which supplies the basic concepts on which any reasonable study must be based, and to which all scientific investigation must ultimately turn for reflection on its methodology and the validity of its results. Perhaps it is not too much to claim, therefore, as does M. C. Silva, that "ultimately, all nursing theory and research is derived from or leads to philosophy" ("Philosophy, Science, Theory: Interrelationships and Implications for Nursing Research," in the Sigma Theta Tau *Image*, 1977, Vol. 9, No. 3, p. 61).

PART V

ULTIMATE EXPLANATION

IMMATERIALITY AND ITS SURROGATES
IN MODERN SCIENCE

The word matter, it has been remarked, has passed out of the language of science, while more technical terms such as mass have largely taken its place.[1] This being so, one should not be surprised if other words with long histories and profound philosophical significance, such as substance, nature, and cause, have had similar fates in the scientific vocabulary. Nor should one be surprised if the concept that is the major interest of this convention, that of immateriality, should appear foreign to the concerns of scientist and philosopher of science alike. Now admittedly the word immateriality is of rare occurrence in scientific discourse, but this is no clear indication that the concept itself has been eliminated, or that its meaning is not reflected in other terms that enjoy greater currency. The subtle difference, in fact, between the meaning of immateriality and its verbal expression, long recognized by philosophers in our tradition, is the focal point of this essay. In our title we refer to these alternate expressions that capture the notion of immateriality in whole or in part as its surrogates. Here we adapt the Latin *subrogare*, "to seek in place of," to our particular purpose. For whatever reason, but most probably because of the empiricist bent of their discipline, scientists have sought to replace, or find a substitute for, the immaterial whenever this intrudes itself into their consideration. The surrogates obviously do not dispense with the concept; they merely attest to its pervasive character and to its radical uneliminability from scientific discourse.

In his *Philosophy of Natural Science*, a distinguished empiricist philosopher of science, Carl Hempel, gives witness to the type of subrogation I have in mind. When discussing theoretical explanation Hempel speaks of entities and processes that lie beneath or

behind the phenomena; he is willing to admit these into scientific discourse, he says, if they have specific
implications concerning the phenomena they are offered
to explain. This requirement does not entail, in his
view, the automatic rejection of what he refers to as
"non-material agencies," provided these have some empirical import.[2] The examples he gives of such non-
material agencies are revealing: vital forces, as
these are used to explain teleological processes in
nature; and gravitational forces, as these are used to
explain the regularity of planetary motions in Newton's
theory of the solar system. Here the concept of force,
in Hempel's mind, is non-material. Its status is somewhat ambiguous, for he sees gravitational force as having empirical import, but vital force as not. Should
we restrict ourselves to the physical sciences, however, we need no great jump of the imagination to include the concept of field, of energy, and even of
mass-energy under his general rubric of non-material
entities.

Immateriality, in this sense, is opposed to the
material in things, to the matter within them, as this
is conceived in a common-sense way. To use Michael
Farady's apt expression, "matter cannot act where it is
not,"[3] and since a body's gravitational force appears
to do just that, it is patently non-material. A fuller
delineation of the characteristics of matter that are
negated when one ordinarily speaks of the non-material
would, of course, have to include more than this. I
propose the following notes.

Matter somehow refers to the stuff of which a
thing is made, to its parts or components, without regard to the particular structure or arrangement that
might be imposed upon them. Structure or arrangement
is more frequently regarded as the correlative of matter, namely, form, and this is seen as apt to be shared
in a large number of things with the same form, whereas
the matter of a thing is thought to be peculiarly its
own. This suggests another characteristic of matter,
namely, that it is a type of individuating principle:
it separates one thing off from another, makes it different in number if not in kind, and serves to localize
it in space and in time. Yet another characteristic of
the stuff we call matter is its tendency to persist
throughout change. Whereas things that contain matter
have a transient mode of existence, in the sense that
they take on new appearances or actualities, the stuff
within them persists, and is thought of as a more or

less permanent substratum that endures beneath the changing appearances. And finally, possibly because of the note of emergence or actualization that is associated with a new appearance, matter is usually thought of as potential and inert, as the passive or sluggish component of things that makes them determinable in various ways, but does not actively contribute to this determination.[4]

Each of these characteristics of matter, we shall argue, is negated by one or other concept that plays a significant role in the thinking of modern scientists. The reasons for such negations become clear from a survey of science's history, and we propose that they can all be associated with the more or less thorough-going mathematization of nature that was instituted as part of the Scientific Revolution of the seventeenth century. As a consequence, moreover, it would appear that immateriality continues to reassert itself in new guise with each scientific advance. This may be regarded as a desirable outcome, but it is not an unmixed blessing, for many of the non-material concepts employed in the natural sciences seem to impede our understanding of vital and mental processes, to say nothing of evidence of God's existence that may be discernible from a study of the cosmos. It is to these problems that we would direct attention in the latter part of the essay, after first having traced the evolution and significance of concepts that serve as present-day surrogates for immateriality.

The Force Concept

To start with the concept already mentioned, that of force, this has a history almost as long as that of matter, which need not be traced here in any detail. For our purposes it may suffice to enumerate some of the uses of the medieval term for force, *vis*, as these have been documented by Annaliese Maier and other historians of science.[5] The term first of all could apply to compulsion or violence, the force imposed on a person or a thing from without, contrary to their proper inclinations. The second widespread use could designate a power of the soul, and thus one would recognize in living things a *vis formativa*, a *vis augmentiva*, a *vis generativa*, a *vis cogitativa*, and so on, to account for their various vital functions. And finally, the term *vis* could be applied to the natural powers of a non-living body, accounting for the actions and reactions that appear to originate within it, such

289

as its *vis motiva* and *vis resistiva*.[6] The force of
gravity, *vis gravitatis*, would pertain to the last
type, and it is noteworthy that the notion was already
known to Aristotle, although he did not use the Greek
equivalent of the Latin expression. The earliest mathematical treatment of such forces for analyzing the
fall of bodies in resistive media was likewise proposed by Aristotle, and was brought to considerable so-
phistication by Thomas Bradwardine and his disciples
at Merton College in fourteenth-century England.[7]

The more complete mathematization of nature is
commonly thought to have been initiated by Galileo,
whose statement that "the book of nature is written in
the language of mathematics" was taken by E. A. Burtt
and Alexandre Koyré to reflect a Neopythagorean or
Neoplatonist preoccupation on the part of the great
Pisan physicist.[8] Recent research, my own included,
would suggest that Galileo was not the pure-minded
rationalist that this characterization implies; it
would see him more as an empiricist working within an
Aristotelian framework, though with some Platonic
overtones.[9] But whichever view one adopts, there seems
little doubt that in his greatest work, the *Two New
Sciences*, Galileo conceived nature as an internal cause
or force that explains why bodies falling through non-
resistive media naturally accelerate, and do so in such
a way that their distances of travel are proportional
to the squares of their times of fall.[10]

Such a conviction on Galileo's part has a scholastic basis, as I have argued elsewhere, and this is
traceable to his early notebooks, including those dealing with motion, his *De motu antiquiora*.[11] In these
writings, which are based mostly on *reportationes* of
lectures given by Jesuit professors at the Collegio
Romano, Galileo shows himself well acquainted with
fourteenth-century developments at Oxford and at Paris,
and also with other accretions to the medieval doctrine
of forces that came about through the Italian Renaissance. Principal among the latter, in my view, was the
translation into Latin of John Philoponus's Greek commentary on the first four books of Aristotle's *Physics*,
which was not known to the Latin West during the Middle
Ages. Here Philoponus proposes a curious emendation of
the account in the medieval tradition, wherein nature
was defined, following Aristotle, as "a principle and
cause of motion and rest in that in which it is primary
and immediate, and not merely incidental."[12] In Philoponus's version, the foregoing definition is expanded

to read as follows: "Nature is a kind of life or force that is diffused through bodies, that is formative of them, and that governs them; it is the principle of motion and rest in things, and in such things alone, in which it inheres primarily and not incidentally."[13] The Latin translation of this -- *natura est quaedam vita sive vis*, etc., -- became available at Venice in 1539, and quickly came to be incorporated into the commentaries and notes that were studied by all natural philosophers, Galileo included, until the end of the sixteenth century. Now notice what happens when Philoponus's Neoplatonic interpretation of nature is superimposed on Aristotle's classic definition. Immediately nature itself is conceived as an *anima mundi*, an enlivening force that is operative throughout all of creation, within animate and inanimate objects alike, and that can account for their spontaneous movements. It has often been remarked that Galileo abandoned a search for the causes of falling motion, regarding this as "not really worthwhile."[14] Such may be true of his search for extrinsic agents that might influence a body's fall, but there can be no doubt that Galileo was quite convinced that he knew the internal cause of their motion, for this was a force implanted in them by nature.[15]

The consequences of this view of nature and its forces had important consequences for the development of modern mechanics, and especially for its mathematical formulation. Max Jammer gives abundant documentation, in his *Concepts of Force*, of how the *anima mundi* tradition otherwise influenced the thinking of Geronimo Fracastoro, Antonius Ludovicus, Bernardino Telesio, and William Gilbert.[16] Soon the force concept had such appeal and such flexibility that it could displace the concept of cause itself. It would be difficult, for example, to find a fuller account of the forces influencing motion than that given by Michael Varro in his *Tractatus de motu* published at Geneva in 1584, for practically every proposition of this work contains the term *vis* in one or other of its inflected forms. But it remained for the better known Johannes Kepler to propose a consistent mathematical view of the concept of force, and this when seeking a causal explanation of the fact that the planets move in elliptical orbits with velocities that vary with their distance from the sun. Such velocities are the effect of a regulative force, in Kepler's view, that also varies with the distance. So he could write in the *Astronomia nova*:

> For we see that these motions take place in
> space and time and this force emanates and
> diffuses through the space of the universe,
> which are all mathematical conceptions. From
> this it follows that this force is subject
> also to other mathematical necessities.[17]

As Collingwood puts it nicely, it was Kepler who "took
the momentous step of proposing that in treating of
physics the word *anima* should be replaced by the word
vis; in other words, that the conception of vital energy producing qualitative changes should be replaced
by that of a mechanical energy. . .producing quantitative changes."[18] And that step was graphically recorded when Kepler himself substituted the word *vis* for *anima motrix* in his notes to the 1621 edition of the *Mys-
terium cosmographicum*, thus acquiescing to the interchangeability of *vita* and *vis* that Philoponus had introduced a millenium earlier in his revised definition
of nature.[19]

By the time we reach Isaac Newton, it goes without saying that forces are pervasive in the universe,
they are characteristic of matter -- the *vis insita*,
the *vis inertiae*, the *vis gravitatis*. Such forces conceived mathematically provide the basis for all the
mechanical properties of the universe. They are for
Newton nature's causes, its *verae causae*, even though
we must remain agnostic as to their more ultimate
causes and seats. In virtue of them, matter is endowed
with an order and an activity that reflects the intelligence and dominion of a Supreme Being.[20] No longer
passive and inert, no longer the sluggish earth of the
Aristotelians, matter finds its way unerringly to a
center of gravity according to the most complex of mathematical calculations. We need not push on to modern
developments, where force is regarded as a vector quantity or as a parameter that can be translated into
space-time curvature with the aid of tensor mechanics,
to see all that the Newtonian achievement implies.
Henceforth matter is no longer delimited and localized:
every particle in the universe influences every other,
and its very materiality is the means whereby it reaches beyond itself to the farthest bounds of the universe.

The Field Concept

These considerations lead us naturally to the
next concept devised by modern science to explain the
strange immateriality whereby matter comes to act where

it is not. I refer to the concept of field, a concept invented precisely to rid science of embarrassing problems associated with action at a distance.[21] Aristotle, as is well known, did not countenance the possibility of one material body acting on another across empty space, i.e., without the two bodies being in contact or without the presence of a third body or medium between them. Nor did Aristotle countenance the existence of a physical void, an absolutely empty space, containing no matter whatever. Nonetheless, from earliest times, men were aware that bodies remote from each other, such as the magnet and the iron it attracts, or the moon and the ocean tides it apparently influences, somehow act on one another. Mathematical astronomers from Ptolemy to Kepler correlated many events in the celestial orbs with those in the sublunary regions, and to account for them they simply postulated *influentiae*, or influences, that were transmitted through the intermediary regions.[22] Since these were not apparent to the senses, medievals referred to such influences as *qualitates occultae*, and later, when the force concept came into general use, as *vires occultae*.[23] An occult quality or an occult force posed no scandal for them, as they were never committed to an ontology that took the observable as the only index of the real. Since a void is impossible in nature, they reasoned, matter must be ubiquitous; matter, moreover, is a substrate, and in its ultimate understanding it must be without sensible qualities; therefore it requires no particular observable properties in order to exist.

All of this changed, as Newton's "system of the world" accounted for more and more dynamical phenomena, and Cartesian vortices operating in a plenum turned out to have no empirical support or predictive success whatever. Atomistic theories deriving from Greek antiquity were revived, and the success of the vacuum pump led the English to speculate that void space might exist after all. But on the Continent Newton's force of gravity was viewed with suspicion, for it too was an occult force, an occult quality, an apparent return to the type of explanation advanced for so long by the peripatetics. The ensuing debates, of which those between Leibniz and Samuel Clarke are the most notorious, gave new food for thought on the subject of immateriality.[24] Both of these thinkers, I remind you, were God-fearing men; they believed in the existence of spirit as well as matter. The focal point of their difference was precisely how they conceived the immaterial as acting on the material. Stymied by the prospect of action

293

at a distance, Clarke had to speak of "immaterial rays" that penetrate to the interiors of bodies and so influence them; he saw nothing incongruous in holding that something "immaterial" can act on matter and produce effects in a physical way. Leibniz surely believed in God's causality on the universe, but for him God's action was something metaphysical, and it could not be counted as acting in a physical way. He had already worked out an energist concept, that of *vis viva*, and his *vis viva* could not be conserved if there were "immaterial" influences of the type advocated by Clarke.[25] The debate led to an impasse, but it is noteworthy that Leibniz's views had a profound influence on the Croatian Jesuit, Roger Boscovich, who attempted to renovate the material corpuscles of Newtonian natural philosophy by regarding them as immaterial centers of force. Rather than reject the void, as Leibniz was forced to do in the interests of continuity, Boscovich sought to achieve the same result by rejecting matter, as something possessing real spatio-temporal extension.[26]

Boscovich leads us naturally to the more famous "immaterialist" among physicists, Michael Faraday, under whose inspiration the force-field came to be regarded as more fundamental than matter.[27] Now a field, like a force, is much easier to conceive mathematically than it is to understand physically. A mathematical physicist would describe it as defining a region of space wherein all or most points have associated with them some variable quantity that is itself a function of space and time. Here mathematical abstraction proves most helpful, for one can stipulate a definition of this type by ignoring completely (i.e., by abstracting from) the physical nature of the entities being quantified. And the resulting concept proves remarkably helpful in its applications to a wide variety of phenomena -- observable, but also occult. Those of us who have studied physics know the broad range of subjects subsumable under field concepts: fluid dynamics, electrodynamics, electromagetism generally, gravitation, the many types of interactions now associated with elementary particles.

The concept of field, as already remarked, enables one to finesse most of the difficulties posed by action at a distance. The phenomena to which it applies invariably show field strength to depend on the distance between agent and recipient; so, for example, the magnitude of the gravitational force between bodies

294

varies inversely as the square of the distance between them. Again, in the case of electric and magnetic phenomena, intermediary bodies are known to exercise influence, as in shielding effects. Moreover, such actions are propagated with a finite velocity, and the implied dependence on space and time is incompatible with action at a distance, which should be instantaneous. Finally, fields have properties that differ from point to point, and that are describable in terms of potentials; thus they function as operational media, and have a degree of reality corresponding to the action they transmit. Whatever phenomena urge scientists to admit the action of a field, also urge the acceptance of a medium that supports such activity.[28]

But the price of accepting field concepts turns out to be high. In the ultimate analysis, practically all properties of bodies become reducible to the forces that are the manifestations of field activity. The substrate of this activity, from which abstraction had been made in an earlier stage of the process, now returns to haunt those who utilize it. If the substrate is not a material ether, and the null result of the Michelson-Morley experiment gives one pause here, then what is this medium in which fields come to exist? The more one questions, the more one wonders about the properties to be assigned to such a substrate. What happens, in effect, is that the "material" becomes more and more "immaterial," and practically all of the characteristics ascribed to matter at the outset of this essay come to be negated, with the sole exception of its being a substrate bereft of all definable form and best thought of as a mathematical entity alone.

Energy and Mass

In discussing fields we mentioned the potential associated with them; to state this in another way, one could say that fields, for the modern scientist, are carriers of energy, and this brings us to a third concept we must discuss, the concept of energy, and finally to another concept that has recently come to be closely associated with energy, that of mass.

The Greek equivalent of our English term, *energeia*, was again known to Aristotle, who used it to denote actuality, the very opposite of the term *dunamis*, or potentiality, that he had associated with matter. The Greek word is a composite of two others, *en* and *ergon*, meaning "in work," and the modern significance seems to date from the year 1717, when Jean Bernoulli

295

again put these together to designate virtual work --
a concept related to energy, yet with a long history
that can be traced back through the medievals to the
pseudo-Aristotelian *Quaestiones mechanicae*.[29]   But
Leibniz's *vis viva* has already been mentioned, and this
is the proximate forerunner of the energy concept.   It
was adumbrated too by Descartes' "quantity of motion,"
which we now call momentum.   Both Leibniz and Descartes
were searching for a measure of motion that would be
conserved in collisions and on impact, and so could
function as a principle for developing the science of
mechanics.   From their proposals, and throughout the
eighteenth century and beyond, physicists gradually refined this measure and so gave energy its modern significance.   The steps involved the transition from *vis
viva* or "living force" to "latent living force," the
resulting identification of some energy as kinetic and
other as potential, and ultimately the proposal that
most physical processes involve transformations from
one type to the other.

The flowering of the energy concept, and especially the focusing on it as something "immaterial," came
in the nineteenth century, when applications were
sought outside the field of mechanics; from this a generalized notion was developed that could be seen operating throughout all of nature.   The earliest studies
were those concentrating on the nature of heat and its
connection with motion, and these quickly established
the interchangeability of the two, usually expressed in
terms of what is called the mechanical equivalent of
heat.   A more challenging line of research was suggested when the organic compound urea was first synthesized
in the laboratory, and the hypothesis was advanced that
the mechanical energy of animals, as well as their body
heat, derived from the chemical energy of their food.
Other studies on the human blood in tropical climates
generally confirmed these speculations.   It was not
long before the suspicion was voiced that the various
forces of nature were convertible -- mechanical, thermal, electrical, magnetic, and elastic.   All appeared
to be one or other manifestation of some underlying
principle that was conserved throughout all of nature's
operations.

Two movements that were essentially philosophical
grew out of this concern with the energy concept, namely, *Naturphilosophie* and energetics.   The first is usually associated with the name of Schelling, who sounded
the romantic expectation that "magnetic, electrical,

296

chemical, and even organic phenomena would be interwo-
ven into one great association. . .[which] extends over
the whole of nature."[30]   What is most striking about
Schelling's followers, the *Naturphilosophen*, is that
they conceived the roots of this association to lie in
spiritual and immaterial entities.   A pupil of the
Danish physicist Oersted, Ludwig August Colding, perhaps gave the clearest expression of this conviction,
for he spoke of the forces of nature as

> spiritual and immaterial, entities whereof we
> are cognizant only by their mastery over na-
> ture. . ., powers which must evidently be in
> relationship to the spiritual, immaterial, and
> intellectual power itself that guides nature
> in its progress; but if such is the case, it
> is consequently quite impossible to conceive
> of these forces as anything mortal or perish-
> able.[31]

A similar thought was voiced by the Englishman James
Joule, who avowed that "the grand agents of nature are
by the Creator's *fiat* indestructible."[32]

A second movement, the "school of energetics,"
reacted against the materialism and mechanism that had
earlier characterized the thought of scientists, and
seized on the concept of energy as their obvious re-
placement.   Its foremost spokesman, Wilhelm Ostwald,
wished to be rid of matter entirely, seeing it as a
useless hypothesis rather than the supposed vehicle
and supporter of energy.   In his view, energy itself
is *the* actuality of nature, and all physical phenomena
are nothing more than its manifestations.   Others ques-
tioned the metaphysical demand that energy have a material medium in which to exist.   Before long a substantial literature had developed, mainly in Germany
and Scotland, which showed that nineteenth-century
scientists were preparing to reject the matter concept
not only as useless in their discipline but as lacking
in any validity whatever, even at the deepest levels of
metaphysics.

This rejection of matter in favor of energy would
not have been serious in itself, if there had not been
a corresponding evolution in the concept of mass, enabling the latter to be linked with energy by Albert
Einstein in a famous paper written at the beginning of
the twentieth century.[33]   Energy had gotten its start as
a measure concept, a way of reckoning the quantity of

motion, and mass had a similar origin, though closer to
our purposes, for it was to designate the quantity of
matter conserved in various changes. Now the expression *quantitas materiae* was not foreign to medievals,
for it had entered into their discussions of transsubstantiation, and had even been proposed by Jean Buridan
as useful for the quantification of impetus. It was
Kepler's work with an allied concept, however, that of
inertia, that led to the modern notion of mass. Kepler
thought of matter as sluggish and lazy, as "too plump
and clumsy to move itself from one place to another."[34]
And he found in this characterization a way to explain
dynamically his newly discovered elliptical orbit for
the planet Mars. Already convinced that the planet was
moved by a force emanating from the sun, he sought
something within the planet's matter that would oppose
this moving force, and so cause departures from the
ideal circular paths he had been seeking. This led him
to a concept we recognize today as that of inertial
mass, described by him in the following words: "Inertia, or opposition to motion, is a characteristic property of matter; it is stronger the greater the quantity
of matter in a given volume."[35] His formulation was
taken up by Sir Isaac Newton, who proposed to use the
Latin *massa* to designate this *quantitas materiae*.[36] The
Latin term was then translated into English as mass,
which Max Jammer sees as connected etymologically with
our liturgical term, *via* the transsubstantiation that
had entered into theological explanations of the Eu-
charist.[37]

    Thus far the mass concept was as material as one
could wish. But then it turned out to be very useful
for computing the force of gravity, and it was seen to
enter into the equations determining what would constitute a gravitational field. On this basis, mass came
to be regarded as determining a body's response to
gravitational attraction, and even as being the quantifiable source of the attraction one body exerts on
others. Thus all the problems we have already seen associated with the immaterialization of force and field
were inadvertently transferred to the concept of mass
itself.

    While physicists were pondering these problems,
Albert Einstein made a discovery in 1905 that connected the concept of mass in a very fundamental way with
that of energy, and this had the most unexpected consequences, leading ultimately, as you all know, to the
invention of the atomic bomb. The paper in which he

298

proposed this had the simple enough title, "Does the Inertia of a Body Depend upon Its Energy Content?"[38] In the course of the paper he produced some calculations that showed, as he put it, "if a body gives off the energy E in the form of radiation, its mass diminishes by E/c^2," where c designates the velocity of light. [39] He concluded rather casually with the remark that the mass of a body is a measure of its energy content, from which the famous equation $E = mc^2$ follows directly. [40] The equivalence of mass and energy that this equation suggests was later put to experimental test, and it was found not only that the entire mass of a subatomic particle could be transformed into radiant energy, but also that such energy could be converted back into mass. And finally, in 1945, only forty years after the formulation of the equivalence relationship, its applicability even to the bodies of ordinary experience was demonstrated most graphically at Almagordo, Hiroshima, and Nagasaki.

At this point we come to some of the most profound philosophical problems facing the modern scientist, particularly in his flirtations with the notion of immateriality. Energy itself has a somewhat evanescent and rootless character, and now mass, initially conceived to designate the measure of matter in all its sluggishness, is found to be hyperactive and just as ephemeral as energy. The two, linked together, become the conservation principle that governs all interactions, from those between elementary particles to those occurring within exploding galaxies in the remote depths of space. The character of the substrate or matrix that provides the extramental basis for such activity, from which new entities in their bewildering variety emerge and into which they again disappear, is not known. Werner Heisenberg has proposed that this protomatter is like the *potentia*, the *hulē*, of Aristotle, but most physicists are disinclined even to discuss its ontological status. [41] They ascribe to their elementary particles, moreover, some very peculiar properties, unlike those of the objects of ordinary experience, which they describe variously as atomic number, hypercharge, strangeness, and isotopic spin. And throughout all this probing into the microstructure of the real, as the late Norwood Russell Hanson reported it, matter has been dematerialized: no longer observable, not even picturable, bereft even of the normal kinematic and geometrical properties we assign to the bodies with which we daily come in contact. [42] So we have gone from immateriality to dematerialization, and I suppose my remarks would not be complete if I did not mention current speculation about anti-matter, the polar opposite of the dematerialized stuff at which we have finally arrived, and endowed with God-knows-what kinds of characteristics. The matter that has disappeared from the scientist's vocabulary, as we said earlier, again reappears, but now with the prefix "anti-," to designate yet another way in which matter can be negated, and yet still employed, in the speculations of the modern physicist.

Philosophical Reflections

A host of problems can here engage the Catholic philosopher, particularly one interested in the concept of immateriality. One might expect, of course, that philosophers of science would have dealt with these problems in great depth, and so would have much to contribute toward their solution. As it turns out, however, not much assistance can be expected from them, particularly by way of clarifying the ontological import of scientific concepts in which we might be interested. Like much recent philosophy, philosophy of science is heavily influenced by the analytical tradition, and its practitioners see themselves as filling a therapeutic function, dissolving traditional puzzles and paradoxes by showing how they arise from a misuse of language -- in their case scientific, as opposed to ordinary, language. As a consequence few philosophers of science on the current scene would take on the task of specifying any ontological basis for concepts such as force, field, mass, and energy. Their preference would rather be to treat these after the fashion of theoretical terms, as terms that have no independent meaning but require interpretation through the entire conceptual system of which they form a part.[43] And when such concepts are left thus embedded in a logical superstructure, as it were, they can be safely used in an instrumentalist way without calling for any realist interpretation whatever. This saves the average philosopher of science from much embarrassment, for in all probability he has no philosophy of nature to provide a backdrop for his philosophizing about science. Lacking the basic tools for a realist account of nature in all its complexity, he perforce cannot make connections between such an account and current scientific terminology. The only avenue for doing so that might lie open to him would be the route through history, but this again often proves to be *terra incognita* for those trained in his specialty.[44]

300

The magnitude of the problem this creates for the Catholic philosopher is accented when one considers how matter has hitherto functioned in Aristotelian Thomism to reveal the bases for its own transcendence. One could delineate at least three areas where immateriality has traditionally been cognizable from a study of nature, wherein the examination of material beings provides a clue for one's rising above the limitations of matter. The first is in the study of the living, where the concept of soul is initially encountered, and where some degree of eminence over the passivity and inertness of matter itself is readily experienced. The second area is the study of knowledge, where one becomes aware of the presence of forms that are not physically united to matter, but somehow exist in it in an intentional or immaterial way. And the third area is the study of the first cause of motion or change in the world of nature, which leads one to an awareness of incorporeal or immaterial being, and ultimately to the Author of Nature, God himself.

My theme thus far has been that the concept of immateriality has not been eliminated from scientific thought, even though the word itself may rarely appear in its literature. Now I should like to stress that the ways in which immateriality reenters into the thought of scientists are not particularly helpful for advancing any of the three moves toward transcendence I have just mentioned, and indeed can more often prove to be a hindrance rather than a help in their direction. The point may be illustrated by a brief appraisal of each of these levels of immateriality, to show how opaque they become to our understanding when we attempt to reach them from their surrogates in modern scientific discourse.

Beginning with the last, the argument for the existence of an incorporeal or immaterial being based on a study of the cosmos, usually referred to as the cosmological argument, I need only refer to my address to this association in 1972, which focused precisely on this problem.[45] Aquinas's clearest proof for the motor causality principle, "Whatever is moved is moved by another," was based on the divisibility of the material body that is in motion, and was seen by him as a *propter quid* demonstration. In the paper just noted I sketched the history of this proof from the earliest Greek commentators down to Agostino Nifo. I further showed how the ontological thrust of the proof is still intelligible to us in the present day, except that we interpret the motor causality that it implies in terms

301

of the concepts of force, mass, and energy. Now, when
we have understood Aquinas's proof of the motor principle through material causality, we gain a full appreciation of the sheer inertness and passivity of the
material object as such. Moreover, when we discourse
about such an object in terms of force, mass, and energy, we are able to introduce an element of efficiency
and activity into the corporeal substrate, and, as I
mentioned in that paper, we already have grounds for
suspecting that elements of the divine may actually
be found in matter.[46] But when we totally absorb motor
causality into these scientific terms, and allow them
to be regarded as technical constructs that have no
reference to the real world apart from some theoretical
system of which they are a part, then we effectively
squelch whatever intimations of transcendence are to be
found in the movements of material objects. That is
why, for many of our contemporaries, the cosmological
argument can be terminated before it is started, or can
be so insulated from philosophical inquiry as to nullify its value as a starting point in any search for
transcendence.[47]

A somewhat similar fate awaits the approach to
immateriality through intentionality, that is, through
an analysis of the requirements for knowledge. All I
need do is refer you to the extensive literature on the
mind-body problem, and there you will see that many
philosophers who identify themselves as realists --
Wilfred Sellars and J. J. C. Smart, for example -- feel
that mind states are adequately explained in terms of
neurons and other forms of biophysical and biochemical
energy.[48] The development of transistors, solid-state
circuitry, the entire computer industry, has done much
to buttress this conviction. Knowledge is now proposed
as equivalent to information, and this can be transmitted by energy pulses of various types, then stored,
classified, translated, and disseminated, all by the
operation of computers. So activities that at one time
seemed to require a peculiar type of soul, or power of
the soul, to transcend matter, now seem explicable in
terms of the material substrate alone, endowed as it
is with new and hidden sources of energy.[49]

At the level of life, or of soul, the pattern is
the same. Here the growth of molecular biology, particularly research on the DNA molecule and its modes of
replication, seems to provide the biologist with all
the principles he needs to explain his subject matter.
Many philosphers of science think that they can now
dispense with teleology and replace it by teleonomy,

which effectively would explain all goal-directed behavior in terms of programming that has been engrained
in the organism's genetic material.[50] So again the
sources of vitality, of immanent activities that were
once seen to transcend the inorganic, are now apparently reducible to biochemistry, and matter seems sufficient of itself to explain them, without recourse to any
life principle.

Concluding Programmatic Postscript

Earlier I remarked that philosophers of science
are not particularly helpful for restoring matter to
its rightful place in a realist philosophy. When saying this I had in mind the mainstream of thought in the
movement that developed in the United States under the
influence of Rudolf Carnap, Hans Reichenbach, and the
members of the *Wiener Kreis* who emigrated to this coun-
try in the 1930's.[51] In conclusion I should like now
to hint at a direction this discipline might take to
bring itself more in line with a philosophy of nature.
Such a move, in my view, would offer promise for a reinstatement of helpful realist categories, and it would
also make the concept of immateriality more accessible
from within the framework of the philosophy of science.
In essence, the development I suggest would capitalize
on recent discussions of the inadequacy of the "observational-theoretical" dichotomy by showing that many
so-called theoretical terms are reducible to the observational, and thus have at least indirect ontological
significance.[52] In effect, therefore, I advocate that
we go about a systematic "unpacking" of the concepts
discussed in this essay, to reveal the constructional
aspect that is associated with their mathematical formulation, and to disengage this aspect from the reference they inevitably entail to such traditional concepts as power, nature, matter, and substance.[53]

A convenient starting point is the concept of
force, particularly when this is seen as related to
nature as intimated by Galileo and earlier as incorporated into the definition of nature by John Philoponus.
The history of the use of force concepts shows that
they can be applied indifferently to the force imposed
on a material object to move it from without and to the
force exerted by a heavy object as it tends downward
toward the earth. Both of these instantiations of
force can be sensed directly, and thus pertain to the
order of observation. The empirical concept of force
builds on this observational base by specifying a met-

ric, or a process of measurement, that permits a quantity to be assigned, say, to the *vis gravitatis*. The important thing to note in such a transition from the observational term to the metrical term, however, is that what is being measured is effectively a power, a *vis* or *virtus* associated with the nature of the real entity that is subjected to measurement. And this leads to an obvious corollary, namely, that it is only when the concept of causal power is reintroduced into the philosophy of science, along lines recently suggested by Rom Harré and Edward Madden, that contact can be re-established with the natural necessities of the real world on which scientific thinking is ultimately based.[54]

The procedures to be employed in this project have been outlined by me elsewhere for the measurement and definition of sensible qualities.[55] The key problem is one of assigning dimensional units to qualities of various types, and by this I mean motive and resistive powers as well as qualities that are directly sensible to sight and hearing. The technique I advocate uses the concept of weight as a bridge between the concept of force and that of mass. As already intimated, there are many problems associated with mass as it is employed in recent physics, but the basic meanings of gravitational mass and inertial mass can readily be discerned from the history of their development, and these present no insuperable difficulties. Here we must take courage from Ernst Mach's reminder that "one can never lose one's way, or come into collision with facts, if one always keeps in view the path by which one has come."[56] Pursuing this path, it is possible to associate mass, no less than force, with the specific natures or substances of bodies, through the wide range of powers, activities, and reactivities that lend themselves to experimental inquiry.[57]

The concepts of energy and field present more difficulty, and in this area additional work needs to be done. As already suggested, the field concept may have more validity as a mathematical construct than as a physical entity, and thus in itself may lack direct physical reference.[58] The concept of energy, on the other hand, seems amenable to treatment along lines similar to those just indicated for the concept of mass. Paul Durbin has already made a promising start in this direction by building on earlier discussions that regard energy essentially as a theoretical construct, and linking it with the concept of nature,

304

thereby giving it an Aristotelian interpretation.[59]

If this program can be successfully implemented, and I see no reason why it cannot, a path will be re-opened for connecting what many regard as theoretical terms hopelessly embedded in formal systems[60] with the more readily validated concepts of the philosophy of nature, such as those of substance, nature, and cause. In the context of these latter concepts, of course, matter can be understood in its ultimate reality, and ways can be indicated for its authentic transcendence.[61] What we have attempted to show in this essay is that scientists themselves have already provided many clues for such a project. Those who work unceasingly with matter sooner or later seem to see that it cannot serve as an adequate explanatory principle even for the range of phenomena that come under their scientific purview -- to say nothing of man's total experience of the fully human and the divine. But much remains to be done if we are to understand all that their surrogates imply, and use this to deepen and refine an acceptable content for the concept of immateriality.

NOTES

[1]For a lengthy discussion of this terminological usage, see Ernan McMullin's Introduction to *The Concept of Matter*, Notre Dame: University of Notre Dame Press, 1963.

[2]*Philosophy of Natural Science*, Englewood Cliffs, N.J.: Prentice Hall, 1966, p. 72.

[3]In a letter of 1844 published in the *Philosophical Magazine*, cited by Mary Hesse in her article in *The Concept of Matter* (n. 1 above), p. 379.

[4]This paragraph has been summarized from H. J. Johnson, "Changing Concepts of Matter from Antiquity to Newton," *Dictionary of the History of Ideas* 3 (1973), pp. 185-196.

[5]See Miss Maier's "Ursachen und Kräfte," in her *Vorläufer Galileis im 14. Jahrhundert*, Rome: Edizione di Storia e Letteratura, 1949, pp. 53-78; also my "Causes and Forces in Sixteenth-Century Physics," *Isis* 69 (1978), pp. 400-412.

[6]Some idea of the range of uses of the term *vis* in Aquinas's vast literary output can be gleaned from the *Index Thomisticus*, ed. R. Busa, Stuttgart: Friedrich Frommann Verlag, 1975, Vol. 23, pp. 348-374, which records this word in its various inflected forms over 2540 times.

[7]Some of the more important texts tracing this development, all in English translation, are given in *A Source Book in Medieval Science*, ed. E. Grant, Cambridge, Mass.: Harvard University Press, 1974, pp. 253-367.

[8]For details, see Burtt's *The Metaphysical Foundations of Modern Science*, 2nd rev. ed., New York: Humanities Press, 1932, and Koyré's *Metaphysics and Measurement*, Cambridge, Mass.: Harvard University Press, 1968.

[9]See my "Galileo and Reasoning *Ex suppositione:*
The Methodology of the *Two New Sciences*," in *Proceedings of the 1974 Biennial Meeting of the Philosophy of
Science Association*, ed R. S. Cohen et al., Dordrecht-
Boston: D. Reidel Publishing Co., 1976, pp. 79-104.

[10]Galileo Galilei, *Two New Sciences*, tr. Stillman
Drake, Madison: The University of Wisconsin Press,
1974, p. 153.

[11]Some details are given in my *Galileo's Early
Notebooks: The Physical Questions*, Notre Dame: The University of Notre Dame Press, 1977, and "Galileo Galilei and the *Doctores Parisienses*," in *New Perspectives
on Galileo*, eds. R. E. Butts and J. C. Pitt, Dordrecht:
D. Reidel Publishing Co., 1978, pp. 87-138.

[12]Thus Thomas Aquinas gives the definition in Latin as "principium et causa motus et quietis in eo in
quo est primo et per se et non secundum accidens" --
In II Physicorum, lect. 1, n. 5.

[13]Natura est quaedam vita sive vis quae per corpora diffunditur, eorum formatrix et gubernatrix, principium motus et quietis, in eo cui inest per se primo
et non secundum accidens -- Aristoteles, *Physicorum
libri quatuor*, cum Ioannis Grammatici cognomento Philoponi commentariis, quos. . .restituit Ioannes Baptista Rosarius, Venice: Hieronymus Scotus, 1558, p. 67,
col. b.

[14]*Two New Sciences*, tr. Drake, p. 159, n. 12, as
well as Drake's introduction, esp. pp. xxvi-xxx; the
expression "not really worthwhile" is from the older
translation of Crew and De Salvio.

[15]See my "Some Sixteenth-Century Views of Nature
and Its Causality," to appear in *Nature in the Middle
Ages*, State University of New York, Binghamton.

[16]Cambridge, Mass.: Harvard University Press,
1957, esp. pp. 71-80.

[17]Cited by Jammer, *Concepts of Force*, p. 87.

307

[18]R. G. Collingwood, *The Idea of Nature*, Oxford: Oxford University Press, 1945, pp. 101-102.

[19]On the factors inducing Kepler to make this change, see M. B. Hesse, *Forces and Fields*, New York: The Philosophical Library, 1962, p. 101, n. 1.

[20]See Alexandre Koyré, *Newtonian Studies*, Cambridge, Mass.: Harvard University Press, 1965, *passim*; also my *Causality and Scientific Explanation*, Vol. 1, Ann Arbor: University of Michigan Press, 1972, pp. 205-210.

[21]Thus Mary Hesse subtitles her *Forces and Fields: The Concept of Action at a Distance in the History of Physics*.

[22]Galileo was aware of this teaching, as can be seen from his early notebooks; see my translation (n. 11 above), pp. 228, 297.

[23]For Aquinas's understanding of these "occult operations," see J. B. McAllister, *The Letter of Saint Thomas Aquinas De Occultis Operibus Naturae. . .*, Washington: The Catholic University of America Press, 1939.

[24]For details, see Alexandre Koyré, *From the Closed World to the Infinite Universe*, Baltimore: The Johns Hopkins Press, 1957, pp. 235-276.

[25]See Mary Hesse's essay, "Action at a Distance," in *Concepts of Matter* (n. 1 above), pp. 376-377.

[26]On Boscovich, see the article in the *Dictionary of Scientific Biography*, Vol. 2, New York: Charles Scribner's Sons, 1970, pp. 326-332.

[27]For a brief sketch of Faraday's life and work, see the *Dictionary of Scientific Biography*, Vol. 4, New York: Charles Scribner's Sons, 1971, pp. 527-540.

[28]This paragraph is abbreviated from my article on "Action at a Distance" in the *New Catholic Encyclopedia*, Vol. 1, New York: McGraw-Hill Book Co., 1967, pp. 96-97.

[29] See Max Jammer, "Energy," *New Catholic Encyclopedia*, Vol. 5, pp. 343-346, on which much of this section is based.

[30] Cited by Jammer, "Energy," p. 345.

[31] In an article published in the *Philosophical Magazine* of 1864, cited by Jammer, "Energy," p. 345.

[32] *Ibid.*

[33] The best treatment of this subject is Jammer's *Concepts of Mass*, Cambridge, Mass.: Harvard University Press, 1961.

[34] In his handwritten notes, cited by Jammer, *Concepts of Mass*, p. 36.

[35] In *De causis planetarum*, cited by Jammer, *ibid.*, p. 56.

[36] In the first definition of the Latin text of his *Philosophiae naturalis principia mathematica*, London: Royal Society, 1687.

[37] See Jammer's article on "Mass" in the *New Catholic Encyclopedia*, Vol. 9, pp. 412-413.

[38] The original paper is reprinted in a collection entitled *The Principle of Relativity*, by A. Einstein et al., New York: Dover Publications, n.d., pp. 67-71.

[39] *Ibid.*, p. 71, except that L is used by Einstein as the symbol for energy.

[40] *Ibid.*

[41] In his *Physics and Philosophy*, New York: Harper Torchbook, 1958, pp. 40-41.

[42] In an article entitled "The Dematerialization of Matter," in *Concepts of Matter* (n. 1 above), pp. 549-561.

[43]This is well explained by Ernan McMullin in his philosophical analysis of this concept in the *New Catholic Encyclopedia*, Vol. 5, pp. 346-349.

[44]Historians of science have made substantial contributions in this area. See, for example, M. P. Crosland, ed., *The Science of Matter*, Baltimore: Penguin Books, 1971; and S. Toulmin and J. Goodfield, *The Architecture of Matter*, London: Hutchinson, 1962.

[45]"The Cosmological Argument: A Reappraisal," *Proceedings of the American Catholic Philosophical Association* 46 (1972), pp. 43-57, reprinted as Essay 15 of this volume.

[46]*Ibid.*, p. 55.

[47]*Ibid.*, p. 51.

[48]Sellars adumbrated his position in his paper, "Being and Being Known," *Proceedings of the American Catholic Philosophical Association* 34 (1960), pp. 28-49, and has developed it in subsequent publications. See also J. J. C. Smart, *Philosophy and Scientific Realism*, New York: Humanities Press, 1963.

[49]It is perhaps noteworthy that the French Jesuit, Teilhard de Chardin, seized on the energy concept as being capable of bridging the gap between the noosphere, the biosphere, and the lithosphere, but his price for doing this was to insist that all energy is psychical in principle. For the appropriate references and a critique, see my "The Cosmogony of Teilhard de Chardin," *The New Scholasticism*, 36 (1962), pp. 361-376.

[50]For a brief discussion, see my *Causality and Scientific Explanation*, Vol. 2, Ann Arbor: The University of Michigan Press, 1974, pp. 312, 213, 204-205.

[51]Representative readings are given in B. A. Brody, ed., *Readings in the Philosophy of Science*, Englewood Cliffs, N.J.: Prentice Hall, 1970.

[52]See the selections in Brody, *Readings*, under "The Observational-Theoretical Distinction," pp. 224-250.

[53]The general background for this proposal is sketched in my "Philosophy of the Physical Sciences: Some New Perspectives," in *Philosophy and Contemporary Man*, ed. G. F. McLean, Washington: The Catholic University Press, 1968, pp. 50-64, reprinted as Essay 2 of this volume.

[54]See R. Harré and E. H. Madden, *Causal Powers: A Theory of Natural Necessity*, Oxford: Basil Blackwell, 1975; also Harré's *The Principles of Scientific Thinking*, Chicago: The University of Chicago Press, 1970.

[55]"The Measurement and Definition of Sensible Qualities," *The New Scholasticism* 39 (1965), pp. 1-25, reprinted as Essay 5 of this volume.

[56]*The History and Root of the Principle of the Conservation of Energy*, tr. P. E. Jourdain, Chicago: Open Court, 1911, p. 17.

[57]See "Measurement and Definition" (n. 55 above), pp. 11-14.

[58]Some thinkers, however, attribute a fundamental physical significance to the field concept; see Harré and Madden, *Causal Powers*, pp. 161-185, and Mendel Sachs, *The Field Concept in Contemporary Science*, Springfield, Ill.: Charles C. Thomas, 1973. For a benign interpretation of this position, see my *Causality and Scientific Explanation*, Vol. 2, pp. 303-307.

[59]In his *Philosophy of Science: An Introduction*, New York: McGraw-Hill Book Co., 1968, pp. 207-214.

[60]On theories as partially interpreted formal systems, see the essay by Rudolf Carnap reprinted in Brody, *Readings*, pp. 190-199, together with the essays immediately following, to p. 293.

[61]We would question, therefore, the attempts made by existential and transcendental metaphysicians to rely on the concept of *esse* so exclusively as to dispense with matter entirely in their search for transcendence. The German Jesuit, Karl Rahner, for example, sees material reality as conceivable "only and precisely as an essential aspect of spirit," or "simply as a

kind of restricted, in a certain sense, 'solidified,' spirit." Here he employs the term "spirit" as a translation of Aquinas's *esse* or existential act. (See his "The Unity of Spirit and Matter," in *Man Before God: Toward a Theology of Man,* by Juan Alfaro et al., New York: P. J. Kenedy and Sons, 1966, p. 41.) For Rahner, Aquinas's *materia prima* has no positive meaning in itself, but signifies real negativity and limitation alone (*ibid.*). Effectively, therefore, he denies the positive reality of matter and so uses spirit as the preferred starting point for his philosophizing. In our view, American Catholics, living as they do in a materialist culture that is heavily influenced by science, must face up to the reality of matter if they are ever to point the way to authentic transcendence.

COSMOLOGICAL ARGUMENTS
AND SCIENTIFIC CONCEPTS

Philosophers have always been interested in what may be referred to as "theistic proofs," i.e., rational arguments for the existence of God. This interest continues in the present day, but whereas in the past it was accompanied by an acceptance and, at times, by an energetic defense of the validity of such proofs, in the present the interest has turned to skeptical refutation, if not to morbid interment as a part of the "Death of God" ritual. Wallace Matson's *The Existence of God*[1] is such a vicious attack that one may well ponder over the militancy of his atheism, but Anthony Kenny's recent work, *The Five Ways*,[2] seems to have a different inspiration entirely. This is the work of a man who regards belief in a divine revelation as reasonable only if knowledge of God's existence is possible, who has sought such rational justification for faith in the five ways of Aquinas, but who rejects all of these as lacking in probative value. Kenny's argument is involved and worked out in detail for the five proofs individually, but in essence it reduces to this, that the proofs are too embedded in a cosmology that is medieval and cannot withstand modern critique.

In delineating my topic I have in mind precisely the difficulty that seems to have inspired Anthony Kenny's book. There are many usages of the term "cosmological argument," and I do not intend to discuss all of them here.[3] For one, I am not interested in the Kantian usage, which exhibits much the *a priori* character of an ontological argument. Rather I am concerned with demonstrations that purport to proceed *a posteriori,* from effects that are manifest or discernible in the cosmos, to a transcendent cause. Even here, however, I must be more limited in my approach, for of the five ways of

313

Aquinas only four are generally termed "cosmological," and of these the major part of what I say will be concerned with the first, or *prima via,* the argument, namely, from motion.

In the proof *ex motu,* the major difficulty is that offered by the motor causality principle, *omne quod movetur ab aliquo movetur,* on which a considerable literature has recently developed.[4] The more popular justification of this principle among scholastics is that used by Aquinas in his *Summa Theologiae,* where he employs the act-potency dichotomy in its proof.[5] While metaphysical in character, and of the widest possible extension for theological purposes, this particular proof does little to illumine the causality involved in local motion, a type of motion which perforce holds the greatest interest for cosmologists. Moreover, when philosophers of science permit themselves to speak of the causes of local motion, they commonly think in terms of forces, or energy, or mass-energy, and the ontological referents of these terms prove quite difficult to identify. Indeed, Max Jammer concludes his scholarly *Concepts of Force* on the note that force concepts are commonly employed in physics to cover up a basic ignorance of mechanical processes, that they are similar to logical entities, like the middle terms of syllogisms that cancel out in the final conclusion.[6] If one explains this difficulty of modern scientists with force concepts in terms of the Humean critique of causality, the *omne quod movetur* principle becomes even more difficult to justify, and the argument from motion appears quite untenable in the light of modern science.

The Argument in Physics VII, 1: There is, however, another move open to those who read Aquinas in search of a justification for the motor causality principle, particularly in the context of the need for a mover in cases involving local motion. This consists in examining Aquinas's commentary on the seventh book of Aristotle's *Physics,* where Aristotle gives his own cosmological proof of the motor causality principle—a proof that Aquinas employs explicitly in the *Summa contra Gentiles* and implicitly in the *Compendium theologiae,* with the understanding that this is the most obvious and efficacious, one that cannot be withstood.[7] And while he maintains that the overall thrust of the argument *ex motu* is still *a posteriori,* Aquinas asserts that Aristotle's proof in the seventh *Physics* of the disputed premise, *omne quod movetur,* is actually a demonstration *propter quid.* It is because of this remarkable statement that I will devote the major portion of this paper to an examination of this argument in *Physics* VII. I shall attempt to establish that Aquinas is correct in his assessment, that the demonstration is truly *propter quid,* and that oddly enough it is made not through efficient causality but rather through material causality. If these points can be established, some interesting consequences follow that shed light on the cosmological argument, and particularly on the criticisms that have been advanced in the light of modern science.

Aristotle's argument is deceptively simple and may be summarized as follows.[8] It seems obvious that everything in motion is necessarily moved by some thing. Yet there are cases where the source of motion seems to be within the object moved, and thus the possibility arises that the object moves itself. If it can be shown, however, that the object rests because some other thing rests, this will count as evidence that the object is not moved primarily and essentially by itself, but is being moved by another thing. So, let the object moved be a body, AB, and since as a body it is divisible, let it be divided at C. Now assume that the part CB rests, and then the whole AB must rest also. If AB does not rest, then assume that it is in motion. In this case, if part CB continues to rest it is possible that part AC be in motion. Should this be so, however, AB could not be in motion primarily and essentially, although it might be moved through a part or only accidentally. Since what is of concern here, however, is an object that is in motion primarily and essentially, in this respect it must be held that the whole AB rests at the rest of another, namely, its part CB. Therefore it is being moved by another. It should be noted that the argument is perfectly general, since every body that is in motion is divisible, and if a part is resting, then the whole must be resting too. Therefore, everything in local motion is necessarily moved by some thing.

This argument is analyzed briefly by Anthony Kenny, and he rejects it as having no probative force whatever.[9] He is not alone in this, however, since the argument has proved troublesome to practically all commentators and through the centuries has provoked a whole series of arguments and counter-arguments in its refutation and defense. Since these prove more illuminating than Kenny's somewhat abrupt dismissal of the demonstration, let us now turn to their examination.

Evaluations of the Early Commentators: The first to attack this Aristotelian proof was Galen of Pergamon, the great physician, who was generally sympathetic to Aristotle and his methodology but diverged from him on several important matters.[10] This particular proof is one. Galen agrees with Aristotle in considering the case of an object AB that is in motion essentially, where the source of motion is within the thing, and where it is not being moved by one part moving the other. Galen understands these conditions as applicable only to one of the first simple bodies, or elements, where all the parts are similar and not other than the whole.[11] In such an understanding, Aristotle's proof is based on an impossibility, since one cannot even conceive that the whole move and a part be at rest. This would be equivalent, for Galen, to the whole moving and not moving at the same time. Therefore, Galen concludes, the proof is to be rejected as "most ignorant and remote from what is correct to a degree unimaginable."[12]

The exact nature of this refutation by Galen has been unknown for centuries, but has recently come to light through the discovery of two Arabic manuscripts whose English translations became available in 1961 and 1969.[13] When pieced together, they enable us to reconstruct Galen's argument accurately, although not precisely in the form in which he first presented it. The source turns out to be a treatise composed by a man who studied Aristotle with Galen under a common teacher, Herminus, and who is no other than Alexander of Aphrodisias. The treatise seems not to be a part of Alexander's lost commentary on the *Physics* of Aristotle, but rather a polemical work directed specifically against Galen, and devoted to a lengthy discussion of the proof in question.[14] Alexander defends Aristotle's argumentation, although he presents it as dialectical and not as strictly demonstrative for all the cases to which it might be applied. In Alexander's analysis it is not Aristotle but Galen who is ignorant, because he failed to understand the argument in the first place.

An object *AB,* according to Alexander, can be in motion essentially (*per se*) whether it is moved by a source outside of it or by a source within itself. In the latter case, the source within may be viewed as a motive force, and then it is "something else" apart from the object moved. The two simplest cases are an elemental body, which is moved by an inclination within, its heaviness, and an animal, which is moved by its soul.[15]

In the broader context furnished by these examples, Alexander proceeds to explain the sense of Aristotle's dictum that everything in motion is necessarily moved by another thing. The understanding of "another thing" in this statement must be different for the various cases enumerated. When the source of motion is outside the object that moves, then the "another thing" is clearly the cause of the motion of the object, and if the object moves, both the whole object and all of its parts move with it; if it rests, both whole and parts rest at the same time. In the case where the source of motion is within, however, the "another thing" to which Aristotle has reference is the cause of the object's motion, correctly enough, but this is not the part that happens either to move or be at rest while the object itself moves. Galen is wrong in identifying the part with the whole or the whole with the part, and in trying to interpret the part as the active source, or cause, of the motion. Not every part of an animal stops when the animal stops essentially *(per se),* nor does every part move necessarily when the whole moves. Thus it is possible to speak of the whole stopping when some "other thing" stops, and to understand this "other thing" as a part of the whole. So understood, Aristotle's argument is quite valid. As long as an object has parts, it cannot be moved primarily and essentially by itself, but must be moved by another thing. The alternate motion and rest of its parts are not necessary concomitants of its own motion, but their very separability from the motion of the whole indicates to us that the object is not moved primarily and essentially by itself. The object *AB*, is moved by "another thing," which is not, as Galen thought, the part *CB*, but rather a "motive force" or a "soul," and this is not to be identified with either *CB* or *AB*.[16]

Alexander's point is made in the context of Aristotle's dictum, "Every thing in motion is necessarily moved by some thing," but it is more readily seen in his explanation of the principle Aristotle uses to manifest this, namely, "If an object stops because some other thing stops, it is being moved by another thing." In this latter statement, the two similar expressions, "other thing" and "another thing," have the same referent when the source of the motion is outside the object moved, and in this case it is the cause of the motion, whereas they have different referents when the source of the motion is within. Thus, in the cases just explained, "other thing" refers to a part of the whole, whereas "another thing" refers to the cause or source of the movement. For objects moved from within, therefore, Alexander understands this statement to mean that when a whole object comes to rest because a part comes to rest, the whole is being moved, not by the part, but by the soul in the case of an animal and by heaviness in the case of the elemental body. Therefore, for him, each of the following statements is true: (1) a whole is not moved essentially if it is moved by a part; (2) a whole can be moved essentially if the mover is not a part but is external to the body in some way; and (3) a whole stops essentially when a part stops, which is itself an indication that it is moved either by a soul or by a motive force such as gravity.[17].

Alexander's argument is diffuse and repetitive, and even when available to later commentators did not elicit complete assent. Themistius, for example, apparently found the argument difficult to understand and by-passed it completely. Simplicius, on the other hand, while noting Themistius's tactic, has too great a respect for both Aristotle and Alexander to gloss over their words without comment.[18] He does note, however, that for Alexander the argument is essentially dialectical, and with this he agrees, but because Alexander's argument is "obscure and involved," he proceeds to exhibit his own "understanding of this for those who are seekers after truth."[19] This attempt, however, proves disappointing, for while Simplicius is definitely opposed to "that wearisome man," Galen, he does little more than reformulate Alexander's argument in stricter logical form.[20]

The next commentator whose evaluation of the argument we shall consider is Avicenna, who treats it briefly in his *Sufficientia*.[21] More heterodox in his Aristotelianism that his predecessors, Avicenna favors Galen over his adversaries and stresses the element of impossibility involved in the conditions with which Aristotle surrounds his argument. In essence, as Avicenna understands it, Aristotle is using an impossible antecedent to deduce an impossible consequent. He himself feels that arguments of this type must be established from the way things actually are in nature, and therefore,

317

while conceding a logical force to the argument, denies it any physical validity in establishing the motor causality principle.[22]

At this point the score is evened up. Alexander of Aphrodisias and Simplicius regard Aristotle's proof as valid but dialectical, whereas Galen and Avicenna regard it as invalid altogether. With this state of affairs, it is somewhat surprising that the next three commentators we will consider, Averroës, Aquinas, and Nifo, all treating the argument at great length, come to the conclusion that it is a true demonstration, and in the case of Aquinas and Nifo, that it may even be regarded as a demonstration *propter quid*.

Demonstrative Character of the Proof: Averroës' commentary on this passage is important on two counts: first, it examines the modes of impossibility that are associated with the argument, extending the example to the more difficult case of celestial movements in addition to terrestial movements, and showing how even in this context Galen and Avicenna have missed the point of the proof; and second, it examines the probative force of the argument and concludes that it is a demonstration *signi* though not *simpliciter* and *propter quid*.[23] The significance of the move to the heavenly bodies, as noted in the first count, is that for Averroës the souls of animals are divisible, or have parts in a certain way, whereas the soul of the heavens, conceived after the fashion of Plato's *anima mundi,* is completely indivisible and thus has no parts whatsoever. When one applies to celestial movements Aristotle's argument that if the whole stops because some part stops it must be moved by another thing, and understands the term "whole" to refer to the heavens, then the argument is involved in a multitude of impossibilities. One cannot say that the heavenly body as a whole comes to rest, since for Aristotle this is impossible, nor can one speak of the "rest of a part," for this cannot be a part of the heavens, which as has just been said never rest, nor can it be a part of Plato's *anima mundi,* because this is indivisible and has no part. Nonetheless, even though antecedent and consequent are impossible, the consequence or illation between them is not impossible, and since this is what carries the burden of the argument in a hypothetical *reductio ad absurdum,* Aristotle's argument is still valid. As Averroës sees it, the consequence is similar to that in the statement, "If a stone flies, it has wings"; although it is impossible that a stone fly, or that it have wings, there is nothing wrong with the illation between these statements, being that of what we now call a counter-factual conditional.[24]

With regard to the second count, relating to the character of the proof, Averroes is not completely clear as to why the argument is only *signi,* but his reason is probably that pointed out by Nifo in his exposition of Averroës's text.[25] The argument proves a cause of motion from the rest of a part in the object moved, or conversely, it argues from the rest of the whole to the cause of the motion of a part. Now rest is not the cause of motion, nor is motion the cause of rest. Therefore the argument does not proceed on the basis of causal analysis, but rather on the basis of certain signs that indicate a cause being at work. In this understanding "cause" is taken to mean an efficient cause, and in this sense the argument is not even *a priori*, not to say *propter quid*.

Like Averroës, Thomas Aquinas has a lengthy commentary on this argument, where he manifests an acquaintance with the objections of Galen and Avicenna, and gives his own support to the resolutions offered by Averroës.[26] The latter, according to Aquinas, holds "that a conditional can be true when the antecedent is impossible and the consequent is impossible." This is correct, and Aquinas goes on to explain why:

> For example, if man is an ass he is an irrational animal. It must be granted, therefore, that if a mobile object moves itself, it is impossible for either the whole or a part to be at rest, just as it is impossible that fire is not hot because it is the cause of its own heat. Hence this conditional is true: "If a part of a mobile object that moves itself is at rest, then the whole is at rest." Moreover, if Aristotle's words are weighed carefully, he never uses the resting of a part except in an expression having the force of a conditional proposition. For he does not say, "*CB* is at rest." Rather he says, "If *CB* is at rest, then *AB* must be at rest." And again, "When a part is at rest, the whole is at rest." And from this true conditional, Aristotle demonstrates the proposition.[26]

While agreeing thus far with Averoës, Aquinas chooses to depart from the Commentator on his evaluation of the force of the argument. He continues:

> But Averroës says that this demonstration is not *simpliciter* but that it is a demonstration *signi* or demonstration *quia* wherein such conditionals are used. This answer is reliable insofar as Averroës is speaking about the truth of the conditional. But it seems that it must be said that the demonstration is not *quia* but *propter quid*. For it contains the reason why it is impossible for a mobile object to move itself.[28]

At this point Aquinas gives his own justification of the proof, which reads as follows:

> To see this it must be understood that a thing's moving of itself is nothing other than its being the cause of its own motion. That which is itself the cause of something must possess that something primarily. For that which is primary in any genus is the cause of the things that come afterward. Thus fire, which is the cause of heat for itself and for others, is the primary hot object. However, Aristotle has shown in Book

Six that there is no primary, or first, in motion, whether this be taken on the part of time, or of magnitude, or of the mobile object itself, because of their divisibility. Therefore there cannot be discovered anything primary whose motion does not depend on something prior. For the motion of a whole depends on the motion of its parts and is divided into them, as was proved in Book Six. Therefore, Aristotle thus shows the reason why no mobile object moves itself. For there cannot be a first mobile object whose motion does not depend on its parts; just as if I were to show that a divisible thing cannot be the first being because the being of whatever is divisible depends on its parts. And thus this conditional is true: "If a part is not moved, the whole is not moved," just as this conditional is true, "If a part is not, the whole is not."[29]

It is obvious from this text that Aquinas discerns in Aristotle's reasoning a causal argument, but this argument is not made through efficient causality. Rather it is based on a necessity that arises when the parts are considered in relation to the whole, and since in this case the parts are really the matter of the whole, the causality involved is that of a material cause.[30] This point, as we shall indicate shortly, is of some importance in evaluating present-day forms of the cosmological argument, for it seems to be completely overlooked in all contemporary analyses.

Before proceeding to this, however, brief notice should be given to the commentary of Agostino Nifo on this difficult passage in Aristotle.[31] As was his custom. Nifo comments not only on Aristotle but on Averroës's commentary as well, and takes into account also the commentaries of Aquinas and others. His, therefore, is one of the most complete expositions of this text, and worthy of close examination. Space does not permit that here, however, and thus we must be content with a single observation. Nifo notes that in the original text Aristotle first proposes a whole AB whose source of motion may be inside it or outside it, and that it is only the former case that presents difficulty, for here it seems that AB could move itself. To analyze this more troublesome case, Aristotle ceases to talk for the moment about a whole AB that is divided at C, and speaks instead of an another whole, presumably that of an animal, which he designates DEF. In this example, Nifo understands F to be the body of the animal, E to be its heart, and D to be its soul. Then the animal is moved by a part, i.e., the remainder of the body is moved by the heart, and that part is moved in turn by something else, i.e., by another part, the soul.[32] There is a difference, however, between part E (the heart) and part D (the soul), because while E is a quantitative part and thus is integrally involved in the movement of the whole, D is more properly said to be a qualitative part, and does not enter into the movement of the whole in the same fashion. This interpretation enables

Nifo to make sense out of Aristotle's statement, "If the whole stops because some other thing," namely, a part, "stops, it must be moved by some other thing," also a part, but not the same part. In other words, if the whole stops because a quantitative part stops, this can be an indication that the whole is moved by another part, i.e., a qualitative part such as a soul. In this case it cannot move itself primarily and essentially.[33]

Contemporary Applications: Recent authors, with one exception that I know of, either ignore or reject the line of reasoning we have been examining thus far, and so pass over this prototype of the cosmological argument or reject it as invalid in a modern thought context. The exception is Michael Buckley, who in his recent work, *Motion and Motion's God,*[34] correctly identifies the argument as the culmination of Aristotle's *Physics* and thus central to any cosmological argument worked out in an Aristotelian context. It is not the Aristotelian, however, but the modern thought context that offers difficulty, so let us now proceed to the contemporary application of the historical material we have just reviewed.

Why do we have difficulty in understanding the type of justification for the motor causality principle offered by Aristotle in Book Seven of the *Physics?* Is it merely because we are somewhat rusty on the materials covered in Books Five and Six of that same work? That may be part of the difficulty, but I suspect that its deeper root lies in the cosmology in which it is imbedded. And whether or not we have been able to supply an alternate cosmology that is more viable in the present day, we are prone to regard the problem as already solved in such a way as no longer to require a motor causality principle. We are disposed to do this, I maintain, because we absorb motor causality into technical terms such as force, mass, and energy, and thus effectively terminate the argument before it can be started or so insulate it from philosophical inquiry as to nullify its value as a starting point in any search for transcendence.

Let me illustrate this by taking object *AB,* a divisible body, and instantiating it in three different ways: (1) as a block of wood; (2) as a mechanical mouse; and (3) as a live mouse. In each case I am interested in the local motion of body *AB,* a translational motion from here to there. The first case, though the simplest to visualize, turns out to be conceptually the most difficult, for I wish to explain the motor causality involved when the block of wood moves, and again in three different ways: (a) when I push it; (b) when I throw it; and (c) when I allow it to fall to the ground. The instances of the mouse, whether mechanical or live, are less difficult, because the mouse rather obviously moves itself, whereas the block of wood's claim to being a self-mover is not at all obvious. Let us start, therefore with the mouse, and inquire into how its motion can enlighten us on the principle, "Every thing that is in motion, is moved by some thing."

The live mouse may be regarded as made up of parts *D, E,* and *F: F* denominates the part or parts that seem to move as a whole, and *E* the quantitative parts that do the moving when the whole moves. I do not intend to enter into the physiology of mice, and will be content to identify *E* as the brain, the heart, the muscles, and the legs, to all of which we ascribe the mouse's motor actively. Aside from these parts, however, followers of Aristotle will insist on yet another mover, identified by Nifo as a qualitative part, and in the case of the live mouse called the mouse's soul. To the extent that the soul is not a quantitative part, and to the extent that it is separable from the mouse's body, and upon separation results in a dead, or inert, or unmoved mouse, one can say in this instance that the soul is other than the mouse's body, and therefore that the body's movement illustrates the principle, "Whatever is in motion is moved by another thing."

For those who have difficulty with the soul concept, let us consider now the mechanical mouse, and for the sake of simplicity, let us conceive it as merely a block of wood, *AB,* moved by a wheel, which is itself made to rotate by a coiled spring or a stretched rubber band. Wind up this mechanical mouse, place it on a smooth surface, and it too seems to move itself. The case is not dissimilar to that of the live mouse, so let me label the moved part, the block of wood, *F,* and the moving part, the wheel, *E.* Perhaps I should include with the wheel the spring and the rubber band, for a further condition is needed for the wheel to move the block of wood. The spring must be coiled, or the rubber band must be stretched, and although coiling and stretching may introduce a quantitative change in the object coiled or stretched, the resulting modification is more qualitative than it is quantative. It is difficult to name this qualitative part, which I shall denominate *D,* but common parlance will probably countenance the terms force and energy. We say *D* moves *E* and *E* moves *F* in the sense that the force moves the wheel and the wheel moves the mouse, or we say that the mechanical mouse moves as long as there is energy in the spring or in the rubber band, and this energy moves the wheel, which in turn moves the mouse. Note how, in this explanation, the concepts of force and energy play the same role as the concept of soul, and if one were to inquire whether the case of the mechanical mouse instantiates the motor causality principle, he would have to reply that, to the extent that the force and the energy are different from the body *AB,* to that extent "Whatever is in motion is moved by another thing."

These cases have illustrative value, but it seems to me that neither is precisely what Aristotle has in mind when he speaks of a body *AB* moving primarily and essentially, for both can be traced down to motion "through a part," and *per partem* is usually opposed to *per se.* The simple block of wood, however, unadorned with wheel and spring, can move *primo* and *per se,* and so let us now turn our attention to the simple block.

Let us first imagine the block on a plane surface, and examine the case where it moves because I push it. In such a case there is no doubt that whatever is moved is moved by another, and I am that other. Note here, however, that even I can be replaced by the force concept, for we can conceive my push on the body as a mechanical force, and then we say the block of wood is moved by a force. Whether it is accelerated in its motion or uniform will, of course, require a different understanding of the force concept, but let us merely note this in passing and possibly return to it later.

Second case: instead of my merely pushing the block of wood along a surface, let me now throw it through the air. Consider the thrown block in simple translational motion, and then the whole block and each of its parts move with the same velocity. Now, does this case instantiate the motor causality principle? I threw the block—let there be no doubt about that—and thus it would seem that I am the mover. In a general way that suffices for an answer, but it does not seem to explain how I actually move the block after it has left my hand, and so various "other movers" are excogitated.[35] For example, I impressed a force, or an impetus, or a momentum on the block of wood, and these serve to explain its motion. Notice that, as in the case of the mechanical mouse, these explainers are essentially qualitative, although they are associated in some way with the quantitative parts of the wood. In the example, E and F, as quantitative parts, are differently conceived than D, the qualitative part, which we call force, energy, or more properly momentum (mathematically equivalent to mass times velocity). Some of you may feel comfortable thinking of me as the mover of the thrown block, but I suspect that more of you would prefer to say that it is being moved by a force, or by a momentum (something associated with its mass), and this is the only sense in which it can be said actually to be moved by some other thing.

Finally, let us consider the case where I do not throw the block of wood but simply drop it. The block of wood moves, and clearly I do not move it in any essential way, and so again it seems to move itself. But is this actually the case? Many educated people will answer "No," it is being moved by the force of gravity, or by potential energy. And if they think in terms of the motor causality principle, their explanation of its movement will not be appreciably different from the way in which they explain that of the mechanical mouse or the thrown object. On such a supposition, let us examine at this point the mechanism they may employ in the explanation.

To do this it will be convenient now to return to a problem discussed by Avicenna, Averroës, and Nifo in their commentaries on Aristotle's argument, but which I passed over in my historical exposition.[36] When a heavy object falls, are all parts of the object completely homogeneous with the whole, or are there some parts that are "first moveds," in virtue of whose moving the other parts are made to move? Averroës and Nifo identify such "first moveds" as the minimal parts of the object, usually referred to as *minima naturalia,* and their question makes sense in the Aristotelian context of whether the whole is moved by parts, on whose motion or rest the motion of the whole depends. To locate their query in a modern thought context, let us ask whether the block of wood falls because all of its parts are attracted to the earth, or because only certain parts, or parts of those parts, are so attracted? Is it only the massive nuclei of the constituent atoms and molecules that explain the fall of the block of wood, or does the block fall as a whole, and in equal virtue of each and every one of its parts? We cannot explore the answers to these questions now, but let me simply note that one who prefers an answer in terms of atomic and molecular nuclei has equivalently opted for a *DEF* type of explanation, where *F* are the remaining quantitative parts, *E* are the nuclei as moving quantitative parts, and *D* is what Nifo would call a qualitative part, now variously understood as force, mass, or energy. So even in this case we have justified Aristotle's motor causality principle, and it still remains true that "Whatever is in motion is moved by something else."

Efficient vs. Material Causality: It is not my intention, however, to dwell on this justification, but rather to draw attention to the extreme difficulty of tracing lines of efficient causality in directions indicated by terms such as force and energy, and the value, on the other hand, of concentrating on material causality in the early stages of the cosmological proof. Did we have space, it would be most interesting to trace in detail the way in which force concepts have baffled the greatest of classical philosophers in their attempts to account for efficient causality. I refer the reader to my forthcoming book, *Causality and Scientific Explanation,* for a full treatment of this fascinating topic.[37] Suffice it to mention here only the following highpoints.

Isaac Newton, the founder of classical mechanics, probably went deeper than any other man into an understanding of the concept of force, and particularly the so-called "force of gravity," and yet he ran into an impasse in every search for its efficient cause. His own personal view was that this had to be immaterial, that such an immaterial principle was necessary not only to explain gravitating motion but even the uniform motion of bodies, and that ultimately it must be identified with God. David Hume was more explicitly agnostic when dealing with causality, but his own positive exposition is so laden with inconsistencies as to have only suggestive value for other philosophers such as Berkeley and Kant. George Berkeley was quite willing to admit, with Hume, that the Newtonian scientist could not detect causes. His was the frontal attack on the force concept, for in his view it had the same ontological status as the epicycles of the medievals. Berkeley has been hailed on this account as the first instrumentalist among philosophers of science, but his own metaphysical views were not unlike that of Newton. If the physicist could not discover causes the metaphysician could, and these were nothing more than God's immediate operation in the physical universe. Leibniz changed the emphasis somewhat as he entered into the long debate with Newton via Samuel Clarke, but he too traced motion back to God, although his understanding of force was far different from that of Berkeley. And finally, Immanuel Kant, so convinced of the truth of Newtonian science that he would use it as a tribunal to condemn classical metaphysics as a transcendental illusion, jeopardizes his entire *Critique of Pure Reason* as he vainly sought to build his *Metaphysical Foundations of Natural Science* on the very concept of force.

My point is simply this: the cosmological argument needs reappraisal in the present day. The problems of local motion are not insoluble, but they require attack not only in terms of the principles of final and efficient causality, but according to the demands of formal and material causality as well.[38] The proof of motor causality through the material cause, as explained by Aquinas in his commentary on the seventh book of the *Physics*, leaves full room for an understanding of the sheer inertness and passivity of the material object as such. Discourse about such an object in terms of force, and mass, and energy brings efficiency and activity into the corporeal substrate, and already begins to intimate that elements of the divine may be found in matter. This is not to deny such elements; in fact, it is their very presence in matter that makes the cosmological argument so interesting to begin with. This is not to deny also that a full analysis of motion in terms of act and potency, and a careful metaphysical assessment of all facets of the infinite regress problem, are essential for the completion of the cosmological argument. But the starting point of the argument, more than anything else, requires reappraisal in the present day, and to this task the proof from the divisibility of the movable object can still make a distinctive and noteworthy contribution.

REFERENCES

[1](Ithaca: Cornell University Press, 1965).

[2](London: Routledge & Keegan Paul, 1969).

[3]For details, see Donald R. Burrill, ed., *The Cosmological Arguments:* A Spectrum of Opinion. (New York: Doubleday Anchor, 1967).

[4]See Solomon Pines, "Omne quod movetur necesse est ab aliquo moveri: A Refutation of Galen by Alexander of Aphrodisias and the Theory of Motion," *Isis*, 52 (1961), 21-54; J. A. Weisheipl, "The Principle *Omne quod movetur ab alio movetur* in Medieval Physics," *Isis*, 56 (1965), 26-45; Nikolaus Lobkowicz, 'Quidquid Movetur ab Alio Movetur," *The New Scholasticism*, 42 (1968), 401-421, and the reply to this by J. A. Weisheipl, *Ibid.*, 422-432.

[5]Part I, q. 2, a. 3.

[6](Cambridge, Mass.: Harvard University Press, 1957), pp. 241-264.

[7]*Summa contra Gentiles*, Book 1, chap. 13, *Quorum primum; Compendium theologiae*, Part 1, chaps. 3-4.

[8]*Physics* VII (Eta), chap. 1, 241b24-242ba16; the best English translation is that of H. G. Apostle, *Aristotle's Physics* (Bloomington: Indiana University Press, 1969), pp. 127-128.

[9]*The Five Ways*, p. 19.

[10]See Nicholas Rescher and Michael E. Marmura, *The Refutation by Alexander of Aphrodisias of Galen's 'Treatise on the Theory of Motion,'* translated from the Medieval Arabic Version, with an Introduction, Notes, and an Edition of the Arabic Text. (Islamabad, Pakistan: Islamic Research Institute, n.d. [1969]). Rescher and Mamura reconstruct Galen's arguments from explicit citations of his text by Alexander of Aphrodisias.

[11]Rescher and Marmura, p.34.

[12]*Ibid.*, p. 18.

[13]The first manuscript is analyzed by Solomon Pines in the article cited in fn. 4; the second manuscript, and how it relates to the first, is described by Rescher and Marmura (fn. 10), pp. 3-6.

[14]Rescher and Marmura, pp. 1-14.

[15]*Ibid.*, pp. 15-16.

[16]*Ibid.*, pp. 19-21, 26-28.

[17]*Ibid.*, pp. 49-51.

[18]Simplicius, *Commentaria in octo libros Aristotelis . . . de physico auditu . . .* (Venice: Hieronymus Scotus, 1546), Lib. VII, comm. 2, fol. 38.

[19]*Ibid.*, fol. 38 rb.

[20]*Ibid.*, fol. 38 ra.

[21]Avicenna, *Opera [philosophica] in lucem redacta ac . . . per Canonicos emendata . . .* (Venice: Bonetus Locatellus, 1508). *Sufficientia*, Lib. II cap. 1, fol. 23v-24v.

[22]This interpretation is followed by W. D. Ross, *Aristotle's Physics* (Oxford: Clarendon Press, 1936), p. 669, and by Kenny, *op. cit.*, p. 19; neither, however, mentions Avicenna.

[23]Aristotle, *Physica, cum commentario Averrois* (Padua: [1472-1475?]), Lib. VII, comm. 1-3. For John of St. Thomas's explanation of Averroës' terminology, see *The Material Logic of John of St. Thomas: Basic Treatises*, tr. Y. Simon, J. J. Glanville, and G. D. Hollenhorst (Chicago: University of Chicago Press, 1955), pp. 495-500.

[24]*Ibid.*, comm. 2.

[25]Augustinus Niphus, *Aristotelis physicarum acroasum, hoc est, naturalium auscultationum liber . . .* (Venice: Bonetus Locatellus, 1508), Lib. VII, fol. 185vb.

[26]Thomas Aquinas, *In octo libros physicorum Aristotelis expositio* (Rome-Turin: Marietti, 1954), Lib. VII, lect. 1, pp. 449-451.

[27]*Ibid.*, n. 889 (p. 451); an English translation is available in Aquinas' *Commentary on Aristotle's Physics*, ed. R. J. Blackwell et al. (New Haven: Yale Univ. Press, 1963), p. 424, but unfortunately it is defective because of the translation of the Latin *conditionalis* as "condition," whereas it should be rendered as "conditional."

[28]*Ibid.*

[29]*Ibid.*

[30]*Ibid.*, Lib. II, lect. 5, n. 183, p. 93.

[31]*Op. cit.* (fn. 25), fol. 184v-186r.

[32] *Ibid.*, fol. 184vb-185rb.

[33] *Ibid.*, fol. 185rb-vb.

[34] (Princeton: Princeton Univ. Press, 1971), originally a dissertation written under the direction of Richard McKeon.

[35] Niphus, *op. cit.*, fol. 184vb.

[36] *Ibid.*, fol. 185v.

[37] In two volumes: Vol. I. *Medieval and Early Classical Science* (Ann Arbor: University of Michigan Press, 1972); Vol. II. *Classical and Contemporary Science*, to appear in 1973.

[38] One can interpret Einstein's theory of general relativity along lines favorable to this thesis; see A. S. Eddington, *Space, Time and Gravitation* (Cambridge: Cambridge Univ. Press, 1920), pp. 95-96, and Max Jammer, *Concepts of Space* (Cambridge, Mass.: Harvard Univ. Press, 1954), p. 20. For a general exposition of the role of matter in Aristotle's theory of demonstration, see the latter part of Robert Sokolowski, "Scientific and Hermeneutic Questions in Aristotle," *Philosophy and Rhetoric*, 4 (1971), 242-261. My own emphasis on material causality is obviously not meant to exclude the traditional arguments through efficient causality, and in fact points the way to such arguments. Thus my procedure is very much like that of William Harvey, who first demonstrated the circulation of the blood using a material cause, i.e., the quantity of the blood (or matter) involved, and then sought the efficient cause of the circulation in the pumping action of the heart.

NEWTONIAN ANTINOMIES

AGAINST THE 'PRIMA VIA'

T HE proof of God's existence from motion in the universe, as originally proposed by Aristotle [1] and as later presented by St. Thomas,[2] was intended to be understood by physical scientists. The terms in which it was couched were technical terms with clearly defined meanings, and their application was straightforward and rigorous. Yet the proof, for all its technical elegance, no longer convinces the scientific mind. By and large, its terminology is unintelligible to modern scientists, and as a consequence the argument is now commonly rejected as having no scientific importance or validity.

There are many possible explanations for this enigma, most of them reducible to the patent equivocation in the use of the word " science " through the past three centuries. Prior to the

[1] *Physics,* Book VII.
[2] *Summa Theologiae,* I, q. 2, a. 3.

seventeenth century, science was commonly understood as a body of certain and evident knowledge known to be true through causes. Physical or natural science was further considered as having two main parts: a fundamental or generalized part, dealing with the common features of natural things presupposed to other studies, and a specialized part in which detailed investigation was made of the various types of natural things. The Galilean-Newtonian revolution drastically affected this understanding; it placed the accent on intensive specialized investigation, minimized the search for causes, and in its place substituted a methodology based largely on mathematical correlations.[3] From that time until the present day, the meaning of the term " science " has still not crystallized, but the prevailing modern opinion places the emphasis on specialized investigation using a uniform postulational procedure that engenders only probable knowledge. Thus causality, certitude and truth are no longer the hallmark of science. Moreover, there is no fundamental or generalized study of physical reality prior to detailed experimental work. Such considerations, if they are thought of at all, are usually relegated to the broad field of philosophy, and they are not regarded as essential to the intellectual equipment of the scientist.

The *prima via*, or the proof of God's existence from motion, is refractory to the modern mind simply because it is based upon these fundamental, generalized concepts that are no longer considered a part of science and hence are not taught to scientists. And the situation is further complicated by the fact that modern specialized terminology frequently employs the same terms as pre-Galilean science, but with more restricted meanings than these terms enjoyed in the traditional fundamental understanding. Thus the modern scientist finds considerable ambiguity in the classical statement of the demonstration, and this constitutes an almost insurmountable barrier to his acceptance of its conclusion.

[3] E. F. Caldin, "Science and the Map of Knowledge," *Blackfriars*, XXXVI (1955), 563-569.

Yet there is a ray of hope for one who would reinstate the *prima via* to its rightful place as a classical scientific demonstration. Oddly enough, this springs from the very man whose genius distracted later generations from becoming interested in the fundamental science of nature that rigorously establishes the demonstration, namely, Sir Isaac Newton. Being at the beginning of a new line of thought, Newton appreciated the terminology of his predecessors and properly formulated his own contribution so as not to be misunderstood by his contemporaries. But, as frequently happens, the scientists who are now most indebted to Newton are generally unacquainted with his original works, and thus have lost contact with this valuable part of his writings. They miss the point of the very title of his main contribution, the *Mathematical Principles of Natural Philosophy*, possibly because they are unaware of any other principles with which Newton might be contrasting the ones he there proposes. Even worse, in some instances they misrepresent his teachings, and use their own misconceptions to argue against the premises of the *prima via*.

This situation has given rise to the so-called Newtonian antinomies against the *prima via*.[4] They are not Newton's arguments against this classical demonstration, but rather are difficulties that present themselves to those who are acquainted with Newton's laws of motion, and cannot see how these can be reconciled with the analysis of motion presupposed to the proof for God's existence. Although these antinomies appeal immediately to anyone who has only a rudimentary knowledge of Newtonian mechanics, moreover, they are quite difficult to resolve, and have proved extremely bothersome to philosophers and theologians who teach the *prima via* to students of modern science.

The present study is an attempt to remove these difficulties

---

[4] R. Garrigou-Lagrange, O. P., has already considered one such antinomy in an appendix to *God: His Existence and His Nature* (London: B. Herder, 1936), II, pp. 447-452. More recently, E. T. Whittaker has invoked a Newtonian antinomy to reject the *prima via* in his *Space and Spirit* (London: Thomas Nelson and Sons, 1946).

at their source by evaluating them in the light of Newton's original doctrine. It aims to rediscover, for those acquainted with the terminology of modern Newtonian physics, the physical import of the celebrated *Principia*, to show how this work presupposes a fundamental science of nature based on generalized physical principles, and how in the light of these presuppositions answers can still be given to the basic problems Newton raised about the physical world. And in thus removing the apparent difficulties now contained in the Newtonian antinomies, it proposes to insinuate, at least, that the *prima via* still remains a classical demonstration for scientists, that it is in fact the monumental achievement of physical science for anyone who can learn the generalized concepts on which it is based and rigorously apply them to all he knows with certitude about the physical world.

The three antinomies selected for resolution are based upon each of Newton's three laws of motion. They are directed not only against the conclusion of the *prima via*, but also against its two basic premises, namely, the motor causality principle which states that whatever is moved is moved by another, and the regress principle which rules out either an infinite series or a re-entrant series of corporeal movers.

Thus the first law of motion, which enunciates the principle of inertia, would seem to affirm that the inertia of a body is the sufficient explanation of that body's motion, and therefore invalidates the principle that whatever is moved is moved by another. Again, one consequent of the second law, which itself seems to be an operational definition of force, mass and acceleration, is the inverse-square law of gravitational attraction. This law would seem to affirm that mutually attracting bodies are the sufficient explanation of gravitational motion, and thus they invalidate the regress principle by invoking a closed chain of moved movers. And finally, the third law of motion, stressing the universality of action and reaction between movers and the moved, would seem to exclude the very possibility of an unmoved incorporeal Mover as being the first cause of motion.

More complex antinomies may have occurred to some readers, and others could undoubtedly be excogitated with little effort, but it is believed that the basic difficulties are contained in these three. These also have the advantage that they can be solved to an appreciable extent by reference to Newton's original writings. From the viewpoint of textual analysis, it matters little in which order these be considered. Their resolution can best be accomplished, however, by first answering the antinomy arising from the law of gravitational attraction, then using the concepts developed therein to reply to the antinomy based on the principle of inertia, and finally by resolving the action-reaction antinomy.

$$* \quad * \quad * \quad * \quad *$$

FIRST ANTINOMY: *In gravitational motion, all bodies mutually attract each other with a force given by the inverse-square law. But this force adequately accounts for gravitational motion without the presence of an extrinsic mover. Therefore the two or more bodies are the mutual cause of each other's motion, and they form a closed system in which no extrinsic mover is needed, let alone a first unmoved Mover.*

This antinomy obviously presupposes the reality of gravitational attraction as a physical force that exists outside the mind and is actually the cause of the falling motion otherwise identified as gravitational. Most scientists today will accept this presupposition, for they commonly refer to the pull of gravity as if it were something real, and some even discuss quite seriously the problem of shielding gravitational attraction in some way analogous to that in which magnetic and electrical fields are shielded.[5] Whether or not this is a *true* presupposition, however, is another question. In fact, whether Newton would subscribe to such an understanding of the attraction concept he proposed presents an even more interesting problem, and one that will be fruitful to investigate at the outset in order to prepare for the resolution of this antinomy.

[5] The Gravity Research Foundation, New Boston, N. H., has repeatedly offered prizes for the best essay on this subject.

Newton's conception of gravitational attraction can best be understood in terms of the distinction that he made between physical and mathematical principles at the very beginning of his *Principia*. In the first sentence he states: " I have in this treatise cultivated mathematics as far as it relates to philosophy." [6] He then goes on to outline the entire content of the work, and stresses the role that mathematical demonstration will play in the science he is presenting:

I consider philosophy rather than arts and write not concerning manual but natural powers, and consider chiefly those things which relate to gravity, levity, elastic force, the resistance of fluids, and the like forces, whether attractive or impulsive; and therefore I offer this work as the mathematical principles of philosophy, for the whole burden of philosophy seems to consist in this—from the phenomena of motions to investigate the forces of nature, and then from these forces to demonstrate the other phenomena; and to this end the general propositions in the first and second Books are directed. In the third Book I give an example of this in the explication of the System of the World; for by the propositions mathematically demonstrated in the former Books, in the third I derive from the celestial phenomena the forces of gravity with which bodies tend to the sun and the several planets. Then, from these forces, by other propositions which are also mathematical, I deduce the motions of the planets, the comets, the moon, and the sea.[7]

Newton's use here of the term " philosophy " is to be understood in the sense of the term " physics," as they were used interchangeably in his time. He is quite clear in pointing out that he is concerned with natural phenomena, and not merely with calculations that respect artifacts, such as levers and the like, which were treated mathematically by the ancients. And his mathematical principles are not the abstract principles of pure mathematics; they have an intimate connection with physical reality and are primarily ordered to explaining that reality. He stresses this again in the introduction to the third Book, where he says:

[6] I. Newton, *Mathematical Principles of Natural Philosophy* (Great Books of the Western World, vol. 34; Chicago: Encyclopedia Brittanica Inc., 1952), p. 1.
[7] *Ibid.*, pp. 1-2.

In the preceding books I have laid down the principles of philosophy, principles not philosophical but mathematical: such, namely, as we may build our reasonings upon in philosophical inquiries. These principles are the laws and conditions of certain motions, and powers or forces, which chiefly have respect to philosophy. . . . It remains that, from the same principles, I now demonstrate the frame of the System of the World.[8]

Thus Newton's approach to physical reality was not completely physical, nor was it completely mathematical, but it was rather a mixture of the two, and so it would be more proper to designate it as physico-mathematical. Moreover, in his development of this new science, which has with good reason come to be known as mathematical physics, he is not always concerned with purely physical considerations. Since we are interested now in his attitude towards " gravitational attraction," it will be well to trace here his development of the inverse-square law in an attempt to identify the physical and mathematical elements present in his reasoning process.

After stating his definitions and laws of motion, Newton begins immediately to treat of the motions of bodies, and the whole of Book I is devoted to this subject. He begins this treatment, however, not with one body attracting another body in any physical sense, but with the notion of one body alone tending to a mathematical center. The first ten sections are thus devoted to theorems which describe mathematically the motion of such a body, and no reference is made whatsoever to any attracting body that might be regarded as the physical cause of the motion. Then, in the eleventh section, he takes up the motions of bodies *tending to each other,* and it is only in the twelfth section, where he considers the attractive forces of spherical bodies, that he derives the inverse-square law in the second proposition.

It should be obvious from Newton's procedure that he considered the mathematical aspects of gravitational motion as something that could be derived while abstracting completely

[8] *Ibid.*, p. 269.

335

from the physical causes of the motion, for otherwise he could not possibly have followed this method of derivation. But the question arises whether he himself actually thought that the "attracting" body was a necessary physical presupposition, or whether the entire derivation could be made rigorously while remaining quite indifferent as to what might be the physical cause of the motion. Or, to put it somewhat more generally, could his new science be developed without necessary reference to physical causes as they might exist in the real world, as long as they did not contravene the mathematical principles that successfully describe such motion?

Reference to Newton's original text will again throw light on the matter. At the very outset, in his comments on Definition VIII, he makes quite clear what he intends by the "quantities of forces" to which he will have reference throughout the three Books:

These quantities of forces, we may, for the sake of brevity, call by the names of motive, accelerative, and absolute forces; and, for the sake of distinction, consider them with respect to the bodies that tend to the center, to the places of those bodies, and to the center of force to which they tend; that is to say, I refer the motive force to the body as an endeavor or propensity of the whole towards a center, arising from the propensities of the several parts taken together; the accelerative force to the place of the body, as a certain power diffused from the center to all places around to move the bodies that are in them; and the absolute force to the center, as endued with some cause, without which those motive forces would not be propagated through the spaces round about it; whether that cause be some central body . . . or anything else that does not yet appear. For I here design to give only a mathematical notion of those forces, without considering their physical causes and seats.[9]

The last sentence of the citation gives express indication that Newton himself was abstracting from physical factors involved in all types of motion attributable to such forces. That he also had in mind gravitational "attraction" is beyond all doubt, for he goes on to say:

---

[9] *Ibid.*, p. 7.

I likewise call attractions and impulses, in the same sense, accelerative and motive; and use the words attraction, impulse or propensity of any sort towards a center, promiscuously, and indifferently, one for another; considering those forces not physically, but mathematically; wherefore the reader is not to imagine that by those words I anywhere take upon me to define the kind, or the manner of any action, the causes or the physical reason thereof, or that I attribute forces, in a true and physical sense, to certain centers (which are only mathematical points); when at any time I happen to speak of centers as attracting, or as endued with attractive powers.[10]

This makes it quite clear that centripetal " attraction," for Newton, was simply a mathematical way of looking at the phenomenon, which in no way was intimately connected with any physical presupposition as to why the phenomenon took place. And he recurs to this theme immediately after deriving the inverse-square law, where he again points out:

I here use word *attraction* in general for any endeavor whatsoever, made by bodies to approach to each other, whether that endeavor arise from the action of the bodies themselves, as tending to each other or agitating each other by spirits emitted; or whether it arises from the action of the ether or of the air, or of any medium whatever, whether corporeal or incorporeal, in any manner impelling bodies placed therein towards each other. In the same general sense I use the word *impulse*, not defining in this treatise the species or physical qualities of forces, but investigating the quantities and mathematical proportions of them.[11]

This was a point that was evidently misunderstood in Newton's own day, so when he came to write the *Optics* some years after the *Principia*, he returned again to the question of gravitational " attraction " at the end of the tract on light, and tried to make his position yet more explicit:

How these attractious may be performed I do not here consider. What I call attraction may be performed by impulse, or by some other means unknown to me. I use that word here to signify only

---

[10] *Ibid.*, p. 8.
[11] *Ibid.*, pp. 130-131.
[12] *Optics* (Great Books of the Western World, vol. 34), p. 531.

in general any force by which bodies tend towards one another, whatsoever be the cause.[12]

Thus an unprejudiced study of Newton's presentation of mathematical physics indicates that he thought it quite valid to discuss the mathematical laws and properties of motion, while abstracting completely from the physical factors that are the adequate cause of such motion. Does this mean that in Newton's mind there were no proper physical causes for the motion, or that these were out of the ambit of scientific consideration? Could his mathematical physics be said to deny causality, or at least to place it in the realm of meaningless questions? Far from committing himself to such an attitude, Newton frankly states that there *must* be a cause for gravitational motion; indeed, he should like very much to know what it is, but he has never been able to answer the problem to his own satisfaction, and he does not want to venture an explanation that is purely hypothetical. Thus he states at the end of the *Principia*, in the General Scholium where he summarizes his views on the physical universe:

Hitherto we have explained the phenomena of the heavens and of our sea by the power of gravity, but have not yet assigned the cause of this power. This is certain, that it must proceed from a cause. . . . But hitherto I have not been able to discover the cause of those properties of gravity from phenomena, and I frame no hypotheses.[13]

The last words cited, *hypotheses non fingo*, have often been quoted as Newton's great contribution over that of the scholastic thinkers, but its context seems completely forgotten in the minds of many moderns.

The more one studies Newton's works, the more one becomes convinced that Newton used the " attraction theory " only as a convenient mathematical device for deriving his laws and equations of motion, but that he inclined to the opinion that there was an inherent power in the bodies themselves that caused them to gravitate, and not to be pulled by something

[13] *Mathematical Principles*, p. 371.

outside. This would seem to be confirmed by his method of derivation in the first ten sections of Book I mentioned above, where he starts off initially with the notion of bodies tending towards a center. There are also express indications in his writings that he favored the impulse concept when he was speaking physically, as opposed to mathematically, as witness his statement at the beginning of Section XI of Book I:

I shall therefore at present go on to treat of the motion of bodies attracting each other; considering the centripetal forces as attractions; though perhaps in a physical strictness they may more truly be called impulses. But these propositions are to be considered as purely mathematical; and therefore, laying aside all physical considerations, I make use of a familiar way of speaking, to make myself the more easily understood by a mathematical reader.[14]

Further, when he comes to mention various causes at the physical level, he first names the action of bodies themselves before considering other possibilities.[15] He also defines motive force " as an endeavor or propensity of the whole towards a center." [16] Later, when speaking of the motions of planets, he prefers to speak actively rather than passively and mentions, " That all the planets gravitate one towards another, we have proved before." [17] These are not absolutely convincing in themselves, but when we consider them with some comments Newton made in a letter to Professor Bentley in which he expressly rejects the " attraction " concept, it seems that they give the best explanation consistent with his other statements. For Newton wrote to Bentley after the first edition of the *Principia*:

That gravity should be innate, inherent, and essential to matter, so that one body may act upon another at a distance through a vacuum, without the mediation of anything else, by and through which their action and force may be conveyed from one to another, is to me so great an absurdity, that I believe no man, who has in

---

[14] *Ibid.*, p. 111.
[15] *Ibid.*, p. 130.
[16] *Ibid.*, p. 7.
[17] *Ibid.*, p. 281.

philosophical matters a competent faculty of thinking, can ever fall into it.[18]

It is true that Newton's reasoning here is based on his abhorrence of a void, but the overall argument has cogency today in view of the rejection of a Newtonian " ether " on the basis of the Michelson-Morley experiment.

The only difficulty in Newton's mind about attributing to bodies an inherent power which caused them to gravitate was that such a power, from all the evidence he possessed, was occult, and he had no predilection whatsoever for occult powers. It is interesting in this connection to read Roger Cotes' implicit answer to this difficulty when he wrote, at Newton's invitation, the Preface to the second edition of the *Principia*. He there makes this statement:

But shall gravity be therefore called an occult cause, and thrown out of philosophy, because the cause of gravity is occult and not yet discovered? Those who affirm this, should be careful not to fall into an absurdity that may overturn the foundations of philosophy. For causes usually proceed in a continued chain from those that are more compounded to those that are more simple; when we have arrived at the most simple cause we can go no farther. Therefore no mechanical account or explanation of the most simple cause is to be expected or given; for if it could be given, the cause were not the most simple. These most simple causes will you then call occult, and reject them? Then you must reject those that immediately depend upon them, and those which depend upon these last, till philosophy is quite cleared and disencumbered of all causes.[19]

Cotes here gives implicit preference for the natural impulse explanation for gravitational motion. And this explanation being quite consistent with Newton's various remarks on the subject, we have excellent reason to reject the " attraction " notion as of mathematical utility but of little physical significance, and to look, therefore, for a proper physical cause for gravitational motion.

[18] Letter to Bentley, 1692/3, in Eddleston, *Correspondence of Sir Isaac Newton and Professor Cotes* (London, 1850), p. 159.

[19] R. Cotes, Preface to the Second Edition, *Mathematical Principles* (Chicago: Henry Regnery Co., 1951), p. xviii.

The foregoing analysis of Newton's work centers attention on the fact that the use of mathematics in this science can well obscure factors that pertain to physical causality. It is well to insist on this, and to make quite clear what the contribution of mathematics is for Newtonian science, for otherwise there is danger in replacing its physical aspects by an all-consuming mathematicism that confers great exactness and rigor on a description, but is not at all sure about what reality is ultimately described.

The most significant word in the vocabulary of the mathematician is the term " equation." The use of mathematics in a physical science is immediately directed towards the writing of equations that describe particular classes of phenomena. And this in turn makes it necessary to equate quantities. The only difference between mathematical physics and pure mathematics from the point of view of these quantities is that the former is concerned with quantities that are the result of measurements performable on various physical bodies and their qualities, while the latter is concerned with quantities that are pure numbers. The former considers numbers with a dimensional tag attached, while the latter considers numbers alone. The dimensional specification introduces an additional step into the calculations of the mathematical physicist, for he not only has to be sure that his equations are numerically correct, but also that they equate on the score of dimensional analysis. But he still must equate. If mathematics applied to physical problems can produce no equations, it is sterile and does not generate mathematical physics. It is only in terms of equations that the hybrid science becomes intelligible.

Now the peculiar thing about an equation is this: if it does not express a tautology, then the only way it can equal two things that are not identical is by *abstracting* from certain features that are not common to both. In fact, abstraction must be made from everything that would either disturb the equality, or does not enter into it essentially. An equation that is not a tautology, by the very fact that it is an equation, must of necessity give only a partial account of physical reality. This is not to say that such a partial account may not be an important one; it may well be extremely fruitful and useful in describing the properties and relations that obtain between particular phenomena. But it must abstract from some physical considerations—whether they be known or unknown in the mind of the mathematical physicist is immaterial at this point —it must equate parts, and thus of its nature it gives only a partial account of the physical world.

When Newton's second law is given mathematical formulation, for instance, there are only three things that enter the equation: force, mass and acceleration. Whatever be the physical situation to which it is applied, every physical aspect other than those which can be ascertained by these three measurements is unimportant. More than that, every other aspect *must* be neglected at the price of disturbing the equality. A boy pulling a sled cannot be equated to the sled. There is no doubt that he is the physical cause of the sled's motion, and yet there is no way of showing this in the Newtonian equation. All that the equation can say is F equals ma. Granted the motion, whatever be its physical cause, the relation between certain measurable aspects of the bodies involved will be expressed accurately by the equation. But the price of the very writing of the equation is the neglect of some factors that are physically necessary to an understanding of the phenomenon. The question of physical causality is by-passed at the point where mathematical physics begins.

If this were all that could be said for modern physics and its knowledge of the physical universe, however, the *prima via* would be a quite hopeless undertaking. The fact is that recent years have shed light on the inadequacy of a mathematical physics that equates quantities numerically and dimensionally, and then stops at that. Modern scientists are returning to the concept of a mathematical physics that uses its equations as a tool, as a starting point to ask questions about the physical reality that lies beneath the description, which Newton clearly espoused.[20]

One sign of this is the tendency, in certain quarters, to distinguish between mathematical physics and theoretical physics. According to this conception, the mathematical physicist may well restrict himself to writing equations, to investigating the consequents of certain postulates and the mathematical formulation of hypothetical constructions, and yet be withal divorced from questions immediately respecting the physical world. He may be two steps closer to that world than the pure mathematician, and one step closer than the applied mathematician who "tailors" equations for him, but he still refrains from passing judgment on the physical reality that lies behind his final results. Not so the theoretical physicist. He now is approaching the classical conception of the integral physicist. He not only knows the final results of the mathematical physicist, but he knows what they *mean* in terms of the physical world. Mathematics is one of his most powerful tools, but it is only a tool; there are still physical questions that can be asked, and it is his business to find the answers.[21]

It is to such a theoretical physics, developed in the light of the principles of a generalized physical science already known to Aristotle and Saint Thomas, that the solution of the problem of gravitational attraction must be referred.[22] The inverse square law, on the face of it, is powerless to say what is the cause of gravitational motion. Recourse must be had to physi-

[20] *Mathematical Principles* (Great Books of the Western World, vol. 34), p. 131: "In mathematics we are to investigate the quantities of forces with their proportions consequent upon any conditions supposed; then, when we enter upon physics, we compare those proportions with the phenomena of Nature, that we may know what conditions of those forces answer to the several kinds of attractive bodies. And this preparation being made, we argue more safely concerning the physical species, causes, and proportions of the forces."

[21] Cf. W. H. Kane, B. M. Ashley, J. D. Corcoran, R. J. Nogar, *Science in Synthesis* (River Forest, Ill.: Albertus Magnus Lyceum for Natural Science, 1953), pp. 36, 37.

[22] Cf. Pope Pius XII, "Science and Philosophy," Address to the Pontifical Academy of Sciences, April 24, 1955. *The Pope Speaks*, Vol. 2, No. 2 (1955), pp. 113-120.

cal concepts to find the answer, and since Newton himself seems to have inclined to the natural impulse explanation, it offers a convenient concept with which to begin the search.

Nature, taken in a strict technical sense, is a principle of motion that exists *within* a primary unit.[23] It is the source from which proceed all movements that are called " natural," and thus such movements are conceived as originating in some way within the moving body, and not imposed on it completely from without. Natural motions are therefore different from compulsory motions, which are the result solely of extrinsic agents acting on the body.[24]

When studying the local motions of fishes and birds and other living things, there is no great difficulty in recognizing a natural motion and distinguishing it from a compulsory motion. If a fish is taken and thrown into a bucket, there cannot be much question that its motion, as it flies in a graceful arc through the air, is not natural for a fish; " thrown " motion is compulsory motion, and it matters little whether the thing thrown be a fish or a baseball, because the cause of the motion is quite clearly from without. And if the fish be seen swimming in an aquarium, there is also no great difficulty in identifying this motion as natural. That is one of the ways you go about identifying fishes and various species of living things; their characteristic motions manifest their natures, and thus have a primary claim to being termed natural.[25] Somewhat the same thing may also be said for the motions that proceed from inorganic primary units, particularly when the motions considered are alterations and fundamental changes. For instance, it is natural for radium to break down to lead by radioactive disintegration. The very fact that such a phenomenon is referred to as *natural* radioactivity is a tacit admission of the validity of this view. But when the problem is raised about the

[23] St. Thomas, *II Physic.*, lect. 1; Aristotle, 192 b 22.

[24] Compulsory motion is also called violent motion. Cf. *IV Physic.*, 214 b 33, lect. 12.

[25] Cf. W. H. Kane, " Comment on Dr. Foley's Paper," *Proceedings of the American Catholic Philosophical Association*, XXVI (1952), pp. 144-146.

local motion of inorganic bodies, and particularly about gravitational motion, the answer is not so obvious. Is gravitational motion a compulsory motion, something imposed on the body completely from without, or is it a natural motion that proceeds in some way from within the falling body itself? This is the basic issue at stake in the question of gravitational attraction; it must be faced squarely if an answer is to be given in terms of fundamental physical principles.

The most simple way to solve the difficulty, of course, is to enumerate the various features of natural motions that are found in more obvious cases, and then to apply them to the case under consideration. If all can be verified of gravitational motion, then there is strong reason for holding that the latter is a natural motion. If, on the other hand, this motion has nothing in common with other motions that are known to be natural, then the presupposition that it is only a compulsory motion should be favored, and the search started for the compelling agent or the physical causes that properly produce the compulsion.

Natural motion can be identified from these conditions that accompany the work of nature: it is from within,[26] spontaneous, uniform in its action,[27] and always directed to a definite goal or term.[28] Furthermore, the term to which it is directed is characteristic of the particular primary unit having that nature. Moreover, all these conditions are verified in gravitational motion, and thus it should be regarded as a natural motion.

Gravitational motion is from within. No matter what extrinsic factors may affect the motion, the single most important cause of the motion is the characteristic of the body that makes it ponderable. We refer to this as its gravity, and measure it by the various operational procedures for determining weight or mass. But there is something *within* the body that we are measuring, and this is the most fundamental source of its motion.

[26] Cf. *II Physic.*, 199 b 26, lect. 14.
[27] Cf. *VIII Physic.*, lect. 15.
[28] Cf. *II Physic.*, 198 b 10, lect. 4, lect. 12.

Further, because gravitational motion is from within, it is spontaneous. As soon as the props are taken out from under a heavy object, it immediately and spontaneously falls to the ground. As soon as any massive body is left to its own devices, it immediately and spontaneously seeks its proper place in the physical environment in which it happens to be. There is no sluggishness, no indifference as far as the manifestation of the tendency is concerned. All that is required is the removal of the impediments restraining the tendency, and the material body will unhesitatingly seek a physical place compatible with its nature.

Again, gravitational motion is always uniform in its action. Bodies of any particular chemical element, to make the case simple, will follow exactly the same path, will fall with exactly the same velocity in a given medium as they seek their natural place. If this were not the case, all of Newtonian physics would have to be rejected immediately. Obviously, the particular details describing the motion will vary for different chemical elements, for different chemical compositions that might characterize various bodies, but given the same type of body it will always follow a characteristic path. Nature acts uniformly unless it is impeded by an outside agent, and this is also seen to be the case in gravitational motion.

Finally, gravitational motion is always directed to a definite goal or term that is characteristic of the falling body. This is not to say that every body has an absolute point in empty space to which it tends. The term referred to here is not a mathematical entity, but rather a term that is understood in a physical context. If a gas chamber contained atoms of all the elements in the periodic table, and the atoms were allowed to reach equilibrium at a given temperature, all of them would seek definite levels of stratification characteristic of their particular natures. In fact, that would be one way of sorting out the various elements and classifying them, and has been so used by Aston in his mass spectrograph. Similarly, bodies composed of various elements would seek definite places in any physical

346

environment determined by the proportions of the elements of which they were composed. The term sought in any particular environment is the natural place of the body, and when it is attained, the body comes to rest. This, too, is characteristic of natural motions, for nature is the principle of motion and *rest*, as has been clearly asserted by Aristotle.[29] Thus gravitational motion gives all the indications of being a natural motion.

It might be objected at this point that these arguments are convincing enough, but they do not *prove* that gravitational motion is a natural motion in the sense that they remove all doubt, nor do they completely exclude the hypothesis of another body or a corporeal medium acting outside the falling body and causing its motion. The objection is valid, but there is a twofold difficulty involved in it that needs elucidation.

First of all, to say that a motion is a natural motion is not to eliminate the need for an efficient cause of that motion. Nature is a principle of motion *within* the body undergoing motion, but it is a principle in the order of formal or material causality, not in the order of efficient causality. Thus, even a body that is naturally in motion must have an efficient cause of that motion, it must be moved by an agent distinct from itself. This is no less true of motions that proceed from active principles within living organisms, than it is of non-living things having only a passive principle of motion within them. But the mover in the case of a natural motion has to be one that can move the body *naturally*, i. e., in accordance with its nature. It cannot be a violent agent that leaves no determination to the thing moved by pushing it or pulling it from without in haphazard fashion.

Secondly, the identification of the efficient cause of a natural motion is a problem that is considerably more difficult than recognizing that particular motion as natural. But it does not require *proof* of the naturalness of a motion before it can be discussed. In fact, that any motion is natural cannot be proved in a strict sense; it can only be discovered. Nature is itself

[29] *Ibid.*, 192 b 22, lect. 1.

347

such a fundamental principle that there is nothing more fundamental in terms of which it can be demonstrated, and the same
thing is true of natural motions. In general, however, when
nature is known to be the first principle of motion that proceeds
from within a body, the first question that should be asked
about any motion is whether or not it can be properly explained
by this principle. Hypothetical conjectures about extrinsic
movers are all right in their place, but they have no place
obscuring the proper order of investigation into the world of
nature. That any motion is natural cannot be demonstrated,
but it can be recognized, and when the available evidence is
in its favor, it is quite unscientific to overlook this evidence
for a hypothetical mechanical explanation that neglects the
most obvious features of the motion.[30]

Yet for those who remain unconvinced that gravitational
motion is a natural motion, it is still possible to argue against
this antinomy by questioning the physical reality of gravitational attraction, for this is something that has never been
proved. One of the best indications of this is that Newton, who
first used the concept, over and over again explains that it is
only a mathematical device, to which he sees no reason for
assigning a physical reality. If he thought that its physical
existence could not be proved, and repeatedly warned against
accepting it as a reality, it is foolhardy for his students to urge
such a " reality " against the *prima via*.

Moreover, as far as the antinomy itself is concerned, Newton
and the founders of mathematical physics would never have
subscribed to it. Far from being convinced that the inverse-
square law made God unnecessary, they were quite convinced
that gravitational motion could only be explained by ultimate
reference to God. As one Newtonian scholar has written:

He (Newton) points to the necessary existence of some active
principle of force which would conserve and compensate lost motion.
Newton did not take very seriously the attempt to explain this
conservation mechanically, as has been noted above from his

---

[30] *Ibid.*, 193 a 2, lect. 1.

letters to Bentley, saying that gravitation must be caused by an agent following certain laws. He is willing to have Cotes refer to the fact that it is the Creator who by his will produces gravitational action. The same references are to be found in the words written by Newton himself, and in the writings of Newton's best defenders; also Samuel Hosley, the editor of Newton's *Opera*, says that the originator and sustainer of gravity is not material but divine, and that Newton did not explain his laws of motion in terms of repulsion but in terms of immaterial causes, not perceivable to the sense, but manifested to the spirit and effect of God.[31]

A confirmatory argument in the rejection of gravitational attraction, and one of particular appeal to those who favor facts over the endless multiplication of hypothetical constructions, is the fact that such an attraction has never been shielded. It is all well and good to speak of magnetic and electrical attraction, for these have physical meaning; the influence of a magnet or a charged body can be and has been shielded many times over in the laboratory. This gives indisputable evidence of the physical existence of such attraction. But the remarkable thing is that for all the advances that have been made in every field of physical research in the two and a half centuries since Newton's *Principia* first appeared, not the slightest evidence has been obtained of gravitation ever being shielded. This may be due to our appalling ignorance of facts concerning the physical world, it is true, but it is certainly no less likely that it is due to a fundamental misconception of gravitation itself.

Further, if any additional proof be needed for those who would identify mathematical concepts with the physical reality they so accurately describe, new developments in theoretical physics also disregard the theory of gravitational attraction. For instance, " least action " concepts as developed by Hamilton can be used to give a very elegant treatment of gravitational phenomenona, with no mention of attractive forces. One of Hamilton's basic notions is that all bodies try to reach a place of least potential energy, and in so doing, seek

[31] A. J. Snow, *Matter and Gravity in Newton's Physical Philosophy* (London: Oxford Univ. Press, 1926), pp. 162-163.

the path that involves the least work. This is the principle of least action, which Bertrand Russell has named the "law of cosmic laziness." When the energy equations are written and calculations are made of the paths of falling bodies, for instance, exactly the same results are attained by Hamilton's method as by the use of Newtonian equations.[32] This again reveals the superfluous character of attraction concepts.

Another development along the same line, perhaps more startling in its experimental confirmations, is Einstein's theory of General Relativity. This theory does not regard gravitational motion as something initiated by a pull extrinsic to the body itself, but rather conceives the whole motion as an "event" in the space-time continuum. A physical evaluation of this theory will not be attempted here; it suffices to note only that its mathematical formulation is made without reference to any attractive forces. And yet calculations made with Einstein's equations give results that not only approximate Newton's predictions, but in three now classical experiments give a more accurate description of phenomena.[33]

The solution to the first antinomy should thus be clear. It is based on a false, or at best, an arbitrarily taken supposition, namely, that gravitational motion is a violent or compulsory motion caused solely by the mechanical pull of another body. A more penetrating analysis of all that is involved in this type of motion reveals that it is properly a natural motion, proceeding from an intrinsic principle within the body. And like all other natural motions, it requires physical pre-motion by the Author of Nature, either directly or at least through an intrinsically subordinated chain of moved movers, at each instant of its motion.[34] It is possible that this causality be exercised

[32] Cf. A. G. Van Melsen, *The Philosophy of Nature* (Pittsburgh: Duquesne Univ. Press, 1953), p. 161.

[33] The three experimental verifications offered by Einstein were: (1) the advance of the perihelion of the planet Mercury, (2) the deflection of a beam of light passing the limb of the sun, and (3) the shift of spectral lines in the gravitational field of the sun. Cf. G. Rainich, *The Mathematics of Relativity* (New York: John Wiley, 1950), pp. 159-167.

[34] The details of this proof constitute the positive exposition of the *prima via,*

instrumentally through some corporeal medium, or even through surrounding physical bodies. But these can never be the adequate efficient cause of gravitational motion, any more than a baseball bat, of and by itself, can be the adequate efficient cause of the motion of a baseball.

Moreover, there can be no conflict between this explanation and the methods used by Newton to derive the inverse-square law. This particular law, as a physico-mathematical relation between various measurable properties following on gravitational motion, *abstracts* completely from an efficient mover.[35] It does not deny the existence of such a mover, it does not reject one mover or even a system of movers. It merely states an equality that is found to obtain when the resulting motion is described mathematically. Therefore it does not follow that a mutual " attractive force " gives an adequate physical explanation of gravitational motion. The inverse-square law does not dispense with a single mover in an intrinsically subordinated chain, let alone manifest the superfluity of God, and anyone who would speak as though it did is only creating for himself an apparent difficulty.

*　*　*　*　*

SECOND ANTINOMY: *According to Newton's first law of motion, a body in uniform rectilinear motion will continue in that motion indefinitely unless acted upon by an external force. But such a body is sufficiently moved by its own inertia and does not require an external mover. Therefore it is not true that whatever is moved must be moved by another, and thus the proof for God's existence based on this principle must be rejected.*[36]

which can be illustrated and understood on its own merits, quite apart from the peculiar difficulties associated with gravitational motion. Cf. *Summa Theol.*, I, q. 2, a. 3; *I Cont. Gent.*, c. 13; *VII et VIII Physic.*

[35] Cf. J. A. Weisheipl, O.P., " Natural and Compulsory Movement," *The New Scholasticism*, XXIX (1955), 80, and also the two other excellent articles by the same author: " The Concept of Nature," *ibid.*, XXVIII (1954), 377-408, and " Space and Gravitation," *ibid.*, XXIX (1955), 175-223.

[36] This is basically Whittaker's rejection of the *prima via*. Cf. *Space and Spirit*, p. 47.

This antinomy is built around the concept of inertia in much the same way as the first antinomy employed the concept of gravitational attraction. In a sense, however, it presents a more straightforward argument. The force of the objection would seem to follow directly from the principle of inertia, enunciated as the first law of motion, and not from a particular interpretation of an equation such as the inverse-square relation. Further, since no equation is mentioned explicitly, it would appear that the distinction between physical and mathematical principles invoked in the solution of the first antinomy cannot be applied in this case. Finally, the first law of motion is simply stated by Newton at the beginning of his technical exposition of the *Principia,* with no detailed derivation and with no extended argumentation in its justification. Thus it would appear that he thought it sufficiently obvious and self-evident to be accepted immediately at the beginning of the tract. Therefore the arguments that were used in the solution of the first antinomy drawn from Newton's own admissions would not seem to be applicable in this case.

These observations highlight the additional difficulties present in the second antinomy, and at the same time point out the main problems that have to be solved before the antinomy can be resolved. As in the preceding solution, the textual approach will serve as a good introduction to these problems, so it will be convenient to begin with a discussion of the first law of motion and the position it occupies in Newton's *Principia.*

Newton entitled his work, as will be recalled, the *Mathematical Principles of Natural Philosophy.* Yet he did not write it as a modern textbook with a long list of equations functioning in each derivation. Rather he started out with a few definitions of basic concepts, then stated the three laws of motion and their corollaries, and immediately launched into the various propositions that could be deduced reasonably from these principles and their consequents. Some propositions functioned for him as theorems and lemmas, and others were introduced

352

merely as problems. But all propositions were stated in words; except for an occasional proportion, all his derivations are described in the expositive form of an essay without the mathematical derivations that characterize present-day treatises on mechanics. The point is of historical interest, but it also accents a significant detail. The absence of an explicit mathematical equation does not indicate the absence of a mathematical principle. Because a principle or law is stated in words does not indicate that it is not basically mathematical, or at least founded on mathematical presuppositions.

Newton stated the first law of motion, which was the very first of his " Mathematical Principles," in these words:

Law I: Every body continues in its state of rest, or of uniform motion in a right line, unless it is compelled to change that state by forces impressed upon it.[37]

On face value, there is nothing in this statement that would seem to imply that it is a mathematical principle. It should be noted, however, that this law has been preceded in Newton's text by eight Definitions and one Scholium, though of all the terms mentioned in the law, only one is considered in the definitions, viz., " forces." Yet this may be of some significance, for Newton does state in Definition VIII: " I here design only to give a mathematical notion of those forces, without considering their physical causes and seats." [38] This may be a clue to the solution, but at best it is only a clue, for the term " forces " does not seem to enter essentially into the statement of the first law. It plays only a negative or accidental role. What the first law states is that *without* these forces, even mathematically considered, a body will continue in its state of rest or of uniform motion in a right line. The real problem is the first part of the principle of inertia. How is this to be conceived? Is it physico-mathematical or purely physical, and if the former, in what precise sense does mathematics enter into it? This is the key problem involved in the principle of inertia

[37] *Mathematical Principles*, p. 14.
[38] *Ibid.*, p. 8.

from the viewpoint of a foundational physics, and quite funda-mental to the solution of the second antinomy.

There can be no doubt that the principle of inertia, as we shall henceforth designate the first law of motion, is not a physico-mathematical principle in the sense that it will ever enter explicitly into an equation of mathematical physics. There is no way of writing it in the form of an equation, and it does not seem to express an equality that could be of any use in any other equation. At best it tells what can be left out of another equation, and this is hardly a positive contribution. As far as the positive, formal principles that bear directly on the derivation of conclusions of mathematical physics are con-cerned, the principle of inertia should not be included among them.

Yet the principle itself has some positive content. Moreover, it states what obtains in a *limiting* case, and thus presupposes the use of a limit concept in its derivation. And since such limit concepts pertain more to mathematical modes of reasoning than to physical ones, the principle of inertia is more physico-mathe-matical than it is physical. Thus Newton was justified in enumerating it first among the mathematical principles of natural philosophy.

As a matter of fact, the concept of a body proceeding in a uniform motion in a straight line to infinity is mentioned by Newton in his explanation of Definition V even before he states it in the first law. In the discussion following this definition, which defines a centripetal force as that by which bodies tend towards a point as to a center, he also gives clear indication of the reasoning which led to the statement of the principle of inertia. He says in part:

That force ... by which the sling continually draws back the stone towards the hand, and retains it in its orbit, because it is directed to the hand as the center of the orbit, I call the centripetal force. And the same thing is to be understood of all bodies, revolved in any orbits. They all endeavor to recede from the centers of their orbits; and were it not for the opposition of a contrary force which restrains them to, and detains them in their orbits, which I therefore call centripetal, would fly off in right lines, with an uniform motion. A projectile, if it were not for the force of gravity, would not deviate towards the earth, but would go off from it in a right line, and that with an uniform motion, if the resistance of the air was taken away. It is by its gravity that it is drawn aside continually from its rectilinear course, and made to deviate towards the earth, more or less, according to the force of its gravity, and the velocity of its motion. The less the gravity is, or the quantity of its matter, or the greater the velocity with which it is projected, the less will it deviate from a rectilinear course, and the farther will it go.[39]

Before giving the rest of this citation, it will be well to point out that the last sentence states the empirical basis for the first law, for it states something that can be observed experimentally. It also shows how this empirical basis is to be used in reaching a limit concept, insofar as the approach to the limit is stated as a proportion. The less the gravity or the greater the velocity, Newton notes, the less the deviation from rectilinearity and the farther the projectile will go. This is a true observation as far as it goes, and it sets up the conceptual framework for approaching the limit. Newton continues:

If a leaden ball, projected from the top of a mountain by the force of gunpowder, with a given velocity, and in a direction parallel to the horizon, is carried in a curved line to the distance of two miles before it falls to the ground; the same, if the resistance of the air were taken away, with a double or decuple velocity, would fly twice or ten times as far. And by increasing the velocity, we may at pleasure increase the distance to which it might be projected, and diminish the curvature of the line which it might describe, till at last it should fall at the distance of 10, 30 or 90 degrees, or even might go quite round the whole earth before it falls; or lastly, so that it might never fall to the earth, but go forwards into the celestial spaces, and proceed in its motion *ad infinitum.*[40]

Here he continues to apply the proportion, increases the velocity at pleasure and at the same time allows the air resistance to go to zero, and thus concludes to the limiting case: the projectile will proceed in its motion *in infinitum.* This

[39] *Ibid.*, p. 6.   [40] *Ibid.*

reasoning process is not completely original with Newton; Galileo, in his "Discourses on Two New Sciences," had discussed similar situations and had shown how limit concepts could lead to interesting conclusions.[41] But Newton's genius consisted in this: he did not restrict himself to the mathematical proportion involved in approaching the limit, but rather concentrated on the limiting case itself. He stated the limiting case as a general principle for all local motion when he formulated the first law.

As should be evident from this analysis, the principle of inertia is actually a conclusion, an inference drawn from a physico-mathematical approach to a limit, and for this reason is not a purely physical principle but is itself physico-mathematical. A more rigorous statement of the approach to the limit that is actually involved would be this: the distance a projectile will travel in a resistive medium under a given impulse is an inverse function of the resistance of the medium. Similarly, the limiting case might be stated: as the resistance of the medium goes to zero, the distance travelled goes to infinity.

Examining the principle of inertia in the light of this analysis, then, it can be seen that it is neither a self-evident principle nor demonstrable. The reason why it is not self-evident is simple enough. It is never found in ordinary experience that a body in uniform motion continues in such motion indefinitely. All the bodies met with in ordinary experience encounter resistive forces in their travel, and sooner or later come to rest. Nor does refined experimentation and research supply any instances where such resistive forces are absent. The best vacuums attainable in well-equipped laboratories are still quite gross, and present-day information about so-called " empty " interstellar space indicates that the rarest matter density that can be expected there is one nuclear particle per cubic centimeter. So it would appear that resistive media are a quite universal phenomenon.

[41] E. g., *Discourses,* Third Day, prob. IX, prop. 23, Scholium.

But it might be objected that this is to overlook the second half of the principle enunciated explicity by Newton, viz., " unless it is compelled to change that state (uniform motion) by forces impressed upon it." When this is taken into account, although it might be conceded that the first part is not evident to sense experience or to laboratory measurement, the entire principle seems evident to reason, to rational analysis. Unfortunately, however, this type of self-evidence must be rejected too. The second half of the statement cannot be taken as confirmatory of the first half, even when rationally considered. When the first half is considered in the light of the second half, all that is left is the statement, made notorious by Eddington, that " every particle continues in its state of rest or uniform motion in a straight line, except insofar as it doesn't." [42] Literally correct, no doubt, but hardly a first principle on which to build a mathematical physics.

The principle of inertia is not self-evident, then; furthermore it cannot be demonstrated, for there is no way of proving that it is true. Another way of saying the same thing is that the principle of inertia is a dialectical principle, and this by reason of the limit concept involved in its verification. The principle, as has already been noted, is an inference from observational data by means of a limit concept. The observational data are certainly true, but the only way in which it may be maintained that the limiting case is also true would be by maintaining that what is verified in the approach to a limit is also verified at the limit itself. The latter statement, however, cannot be maintained, because it is not universally true. There are many instances in mathematics where it is known to be violated. One illustration is the approach of polygon to circle as the number of sides is increased indefinitely. All through the approach to the limit, assuming the simple case where all figures are inscribed in the limiting circle, every figure constructed that has a finite number of sides is a polygon. The

[42] *The Nature of the Physical World* (New York: The Macmillan Company, 1937), p. 124.

limiting case is a figure of a different species, it is no longer a polygon, but a circle. It is not true to say that a polygon is a circle; the difference is as basic and irreducible as that between the discrete and the continuous. In this case, what is verified in the approach to the limit (polygon), is not verified at the limit itself (circle).

Now if it is not *always* true that what is verified during the approach is necessarily verified at the limit, and indeed there are excellent arguments to show that it can *never* be true,[43] then the fact that the observational base for the principle of inertia is true cannot be used to prove, or demonstrate, that the limiting case stated in the principle is also true. Thus it remains that the first law as stated by Newton is neither self-evident nor demonstrable, and as such is not certainly verifiable of physical phenomena in the real world.[44]

But this does not necessarily derogate from the utility of the principle of inertia as a physico-mathematical principle. What it does indicate is that this principle does not have the broad applicability of a generalized physical principle that would be universally verified in all real motions. Rather it gives an idealized account of local motion that abstracts from extrinsic factors present in the real world and affecting such motion. And since it abstracts from extrinsic factors acting on real bodies moving in a physical enviroment, it should not be surprising that it also abstracts from efficient causality influencing the body in its motion.

In point of fact, in all observable cases in the real world, an extrinsic mover is needed in order to have a motion that is exactly uniform. The reason is obvious from what has been said above about resistance being present throughout the known universe, and therefore the need for such a mover is quite consistent with the statement of the first law. Resistance is always encountered from objects extrinsic to the thing moved, and to

[43] Cf. J. Lalor, O. F. M., *The Concept of Limit* (unpublished doctoral dissertation; Quebec: Université Laval, n. d.).

[44] Cf. Weisheipl, " Natural and Compulsory Movement," *loc. cit.*, p. 72.

overcome the decelerating effect of this, an extrinsic force will have to continue to be applied to the object being moved. Of course, it is possible to *abstract* from this resistance, and *conceive* of a body moving uniformly without reference to its external physical situation. But when one does this, it is very analogous to conceiving of a body at some arbitrary temperature in the real world that maintains this temperature indefinitely despite any changes of temperature occurring around it. It is all well and good to conceive of insulators that suppositionally isolate it from the real world, but all physicists know that such insulators do not exist in practice. Making the supposition eliminates the problem of a heat source to maintain the body at the given temperature, but it does this only in the mind of the physicist. The same thing goes, *mutatis mutandis*, for idealized local motion. If one makes a supposition that eliminates thinking about extrinsic movers, then for him they do not exist, but that does not eliminate their necessity in the real world.

It might be objected that what has been said here is true enough if one wishes to be a rigorist and speak of motions that are *exactly* uniform. However, it would seem that Newtonian physics does not attempt to give an exact account of the physical universe, but only an approximate account. Therefore, if the motions of stars and planets are considered, or of projectiles in very rare media, they will actually decelerate slightly, but the resistance is so small that in practice it can be neglected. Thus the motion that is in practice referred to as uniform, though in fact slightly decelerated, does not require an extrinsic mover, but is sufficiently accounted for by the inertia of the moving body.

The answer to this further difficulty, like the basic answer to the difficulty of gravitational attraction, must be given in terms of a generalized science of nature such as that developed by Aristotle and Saint Thomas. In fact, there is a marked similarity between the two cases, as will become apparent in the development below. But there is also a considerable difference, and it will be well to make this clear at the outset.

Inertial motion is universally taken as opposed to gravitational motion. The latter is usually referred to as " free " or natural motion, while the former is " forced " or compulsory motion. In the strict understanding of natural motion, it is called such because it proceeds from the nature of the body itself, it proceeds in some way from within the body undergoing the motion. Compulsory motion, on the other hand, is imposed from without; it is violent, it is contrary to the natural inclination of the body being moved. The reason why it is recognized as not being a natural motion is that it does not fulfill the conditions mentioned above as associated with all natural motions, viz., it is not from within, nor spontaneous, nor is it uniform in its action, nor does it always tend to the same term characteristic of the particular body. Obviously, if a motion is a composite of gravitational and inertial components, care will have to be taken to isolate what comes from nature from what is imposed from without. But assuming, in the spirit of the difficulty that has been proposed, an inertial or compulsory motion in which gravitational tendencies can be neglected, these conditions will also be lacking. The inertial motion does not originate from within, but rather from without. It is not spontaneous, but is initially forced and sluggish. It is not uniform in its action for any particular body, for the same projectile may be thrown fast or slow, it may be rolled or spun, it may be juggled back and forth. And it is not directed to a place determined by the particular body and its physical environment, for it may be directed now up, now down, now in any direction conceivable for a three-dimensional vector. Thus inertial motion is not natural motion.

Yet there seems to be something about inertial motion that is similar to natural motion. When a projectile is thrown, it appears that an impulse is imparted to it by the thrower, and impulse further appears to be in some way the source of its motion. Again, once initiated, the motion proceeds in a uniform fashion for that particular impulse, and moreover, it proceeds in a very determined direction. It is true that it does not seek a compatible place in a particular physical environment, but there does not seem to be any doubt of an inherent tendency in a particular direction. And this direction is not necessarily that intended in the mind of the thrower, but appears to be objectively realized in the thing thrown; otherwise it is extremely difficult to understand how there can be such a thing as poor marksmanship. What is objectively realized does not have the perfectly determined tendency of a nature, but it nonetheless has an inherent tendency sufficient to make the physicist realize that momentum is a vector.

These reasons impel us to argue that there is associated with inertial motion an impulse that is analogous to the impulse of gravity found in natural gravitational motion.[45] In a sense, this impulse is a sort of " second nature." It is not natural as coming from within the body itself. Rather, it is more like a behavior pattern induced in animals from without, by training or by continued application of certain stimuli. Still it is different from this, because all material bodies have an *immediate* susceptibility for the impulse of inertial motion. And further, once it has been imparted to a body, there appears to be no reason to believe that it would not perdure endlessly, unless overcome by something extrinsic encountered in the course of its motion, which however is always the case in our experience.[46]

Now, granted the existence of such an impulse associated with inertial motion, it is important to realize that even this impulse needs an extrinsic mover in order to sustain the motion efficiently. The reason is basically the same as that advanced for an extrinsic mover in natural gravitational motion. Just as

---

[45] Cf. Dominicus de Soto; *Super octo libros Physicorum Quaestiones* (Salamanca, 1551), Lib. VIII, q. 3, fol. 104v-105v.

[46] The precise entitative status of this impulse is disputed among Thomists, as is the subject of its inherence, some maintaining that it is in the medium surrounding the projectile, others that it is in the projectile itself. For a summary of opinions, cf. A. Rozwadowski, S. J., " De motus localis causa proxima secundum principia S. Thomae," *Divus Thomas Piacenza*, XVI (1939), 104-114; P. Hoenen, S. J., Cosmologia (4th ed., Roma: Aedes Pont. Univ. Gregorianae, 1949), pp. 482-501. Father Weisheipl has a good evaluation of these opinions in " Natural and Compulsory Movement," *loc. cit.*, pp. 52-61.

the nature itself requires an extrinsic mover, so the " second nature " which is a modification of the nature must be actuated from without. Both are principles in the order of formal or material causality, and both therefore require actuation in the order of efficient causality in order to be continually operative.[47]

When abstraction is made from such an efficient agent, of course, it is possible to conceive of the impulse itself as an inertia, as some type of explanation of the compulsory motion, and it is possible to speak also of measures of this, such as momentum. Such measures will be useful in accounting for the apparent uniformity of the motion, for estimating the potentiality of the thing moved in originating other motions, etc. But neither inertia nor momentum sufficiently accounts for the entire motion any more than a body's gravity can completely account for its fall.

Further, far from the principle of inertia disproving the existence of God, the more one tries to verify this principle, the more one is led to affirm the existence of an infinite Mover. If all the idealized concepts that have been discussed be granted, and the idealized case be considered as physically real, then not only is *some* extrinsic mover required, but also one of infinite power, and this can only be God. The reason for this is based on the proportionality that must exist between cause and effect. If it be maintained that a finite impulse can impart a motion that will perdure *ad infinitum,* this is to hold that an infinite effect can proceed from a finite cause.[48] Since such a position is untenable, if the principle of inertia in this understanding is to be maintained, it must be held that the cause is finite from the part of the formal cause (the impulse), but infinite from the part of the efficient mover that sustains the motion. And such an infinite efficient mover would be none other than God. Thus the principle itself, taken in the most realistic sense possible, leads to the postulation of a first unmoved Mover.

[47] Cf. Weisheipl, " The Concept of Nature," *loc. cit.*
[48] Cf. R. Garrigou-Lagrange, O. P., *God: His Existence and His Nature* (London: B. Herder, 1938), II, 447-452.

Now it may come as a surprise to the modern physicist, but this explanation that has been offered is quite consistent with what Newton himself thought about inertial motion. It is true that he does not explicitly mention an extrinsic principle for such motion in his discussions throughout the *Principia*, apart from what he says generally about God as the universal Mover and to which we will refer in the solution of the third antinomy. But in his animadversions on mechanics that occur at the end of the *Optics*, he does explicitly clear up any misunderstanding that might exist about his position on inertial motion, quite apart from his reservations on gravitational motion. He states:

The *vis inertiae* is a passive principle by which bodies persist in their motion or rest, receive motion in proportion to the force impressing it, and resist as much as they are resisted. By this principle alone there never could be any motion in the world. Some other principle was necessary for putting bodies into motion; and now they are in motion, some other principle is necessary for conserving the motion.[49]

A clearer statement could not be made about the necessity of an extrinsic mover, not only at the beginning of inertial motion, but also at every instant throughout that motion. The evidence is thus indisputable that Newton would not have rejected the fundamental principle, " whatever is moved is moved by another," on the basis of the law he was first to enunciate.

The solution to the second antinomy should therefore be clear. The first law of motion and the concept of inertia that it involves state only partial truths. They are not verified of an entire physical reality, but rather abstract from efficient causality and its relation to compulsory motion. Although not explicitly mathematical, they nevertheless are based on a physico-mathematical reasoning process and invoke a limit concept in their verification. Because of the dialectical aspect of the approach to the limit, the principle of inertia cannot be proved to be true in a complete and self-sufficient sense. Nor is it

[49] *Optics*, p. 540.

evident either to experiment or to reason. Consequently it cannot be invoked as a certain argument against the validity of the foundational principle: whatever is moved must be moved by another.

Further, looking at the truth contained in the first law from the vantage point we have now attained, it can be seen that the former attains its full stature and most intelligent justification when understood as requiring the continued application of an extrinsic mover. The latter mover's influence may not be directly measurable, but it is knowable. Although it is not known to modern physicists, moreover, it was known to Newton, the father of their science, who knew better than they the limitations of the principles he first formulated. Far from undermining the motor causality principle, it furnishes yet another instance of its universal verification. The principle still stands, and along with it the proof for God's existence from motion in the universe—motion both gravitational, *and* inertial.

*   *   *   *   *

THIRD ANTINOMY: *To every action, there must correspond an equal and opposite reaction. But there can be no such interaction between any body and an incorporeal mover. Therefore it is impossible that motion proceed from an incorporeal mover, and any proof that would terminate with such a mover must be rejected.*

The third antinomy does not contain difficulties of the magnitude of those presented by the first two. It is not, like them, directed at the fundamental principles which function as the premises of the *prima via*. Rather it raises a question about the term of the proof, and this in a general way. It proposes that there can be no such thing as an incorporeal mover, and thus jeopardizes the proof by maintaining that it reaches a nonsensical conclusion.[50]

[50] The attitude of mind underlying this objection is characteristic of logical positivism and operationalism, both of which would categorize an incorporeal mover as a "meaningless concept."

The answer to this antinomy, as to the preceding ones, is suggested by Newton's treatment of the problem in his development of the *Principia*. Actually, he does not state the action-reaction principle in the very broad and general way in which it is employed in the antinomy, but restricts it specifically to actions where two bodies are involved. His original statement of the third law is this:

Law III: To every action there is always opposed an equal re-action: or, the mutual actions of two bodies upon each other are always equal, and directed to contrary parts.[51]

His explanation of the law also makes clear that he is except-ing the case of incorporeal movers from its ambit, for the only illustrations he furnishes in justification of the action-reaction principle involve corporeal movers. Thus he states:

Whatever draws or presses another is as much drawn or pressed by the other. If you press a stone with your finger, the finger is also pressed by the stone. If a horse draws a stone tied to a rope, the horse (if I may so say) will be equally drawn back towards the stone; for the distended rope, by the same endeavor to relax or unbend itself, will draw the horse as much towards the stone as it does the stone towards the horse, and will obstruct the progress of the one as much as it advances that of the other. If a body impinge upon another, and by its force change the motion of the other, that body also (because of the equality of the mutual pressure) will undergo an equal change, in its own motion, towards the contrary part.[52]

It is interesting to note here that of the three instances that Newton uses for exemplification of the principle, two concern cases where bodies are in physical contact, and the third is clearly an instance of an intrinsically subordinated instrumental motion, viz., the case of the horse pulling a stone by means of a rope. We shall have occasion to return to this later, but for the moment it will suffice to note that all are concerned with corporeal movers.

[51] *Mathematical Principles,* p. 14.
[52] *Ibid.*

Now it may be maintained that Newton restricts himself to corporeal movers in this principle because he is convinced that these are the only type of movers that exist, and so it would be nonsensical to refer to incorporeal movers in his *Principia*. Or the possibility suggests itself that he himself might have *believed* in incorporeal movers, but that he did not think they had any place in physical science, and therefore left them out of consideration. Both of these hypotheses, however, are untenable in the light of explicit citations from the great scientist.

As to the existence of incorporeal and immaterial entities in the physical universe, he takes the general position that such things do exist. For instance, in discussing his meaning of attraction in one of the texts already referred to, he states: "I here use the word *attraction* in general for any endeavor whatever . . . whether it arises from the action of the ether or of the air, or of any medium whatever, whether corporeal or incorporeal." [53] Again, in a letter to Bentley after the first edition of the *Principia* had appeared, he mentions: "Gravity must be caused by an agent acting constantly according to certain laws; but whether this agent be material or immaterial, I have left to the consideration of my readers." [54] A person who was convinced that material movers were the only type that existed would never make the allowances explicit in these statements.

Beyond this, it is further evident that Newton attributed actual dominion to the supreme Being over all the workings of the physical universe, and this for him also included motion. Insofar as God was the mover and governor of the universe, He also pertained to the realm of physical science. Newton makes these ideas explicit in the General Scholium which he wrote at the end of the third book of the *Principia*, where he is at pains to exclude the type of interpretation of his opus which is at the root of the antinomy now under discussion. Some citations which bear this out are the following:

[53] *Ibid.*, p. 130.
[54] *Correspondence of Sir Isaac Newton and Professor Cotes*, p. 159.

It is not to be conceived that mere mechanical causes could give birth to so many regular motions. . . . This most beautiful system of the sun, planets, and comets, could only proceed from the counsel and dominion of an intelligent and powerful Being.[55]

It is the dominion of a spiritual being which constitutes a God. . . . And from his true dominion it follows that the true God is a living, intelligent, and powerful Being; and, from his other perfections, that he is supreme, and most perfect.[56]

In him (God) are all things contained and moved; yet neither affects the other: God suffers nothing from the motion of bodies; bodies find no resistance from the omnipresence of God.[57]

He (God) is utterly void of all body and bodily figure, and can therefore neither be seen, nor heard, nor touched; . . . We have ideas of his attributes, but what the real substance of anything is we know not . . . all our notions of God are taken from the ways of mankind by a certain similitude, which, though not perfect, has some likeness, however. And thus much concerning God; to discourse of whom from the appearances of things, does certainly belong to Natural Philosophy.[58]

The very last sentence indicates the relevance of God to physical science in Newton's estimation, for his use of the term "natural philosophy" was equivalent to our understanding of physics and astronomy. And the citation stating that God moves all things, "yet neither affects the other: God suffers nothing from the motion of bodies, etc.," supplies his direct answer to the third antinomy.

As should be clear now from the distinctions that have been made in the solution of the previous difficulties, the action-reaction principle is a physico-mathematical relation that holds only between quantified bodies that are already being moved by some physical agent. It merely stresses the mathematical symmetry involved in the transmission of mechanical impulses, and this is wholly consistent with what one would expect in terms of more fundamental principles. If bodies are in contact and an impulse is being transmitted, obviously its metrical aspects are the same whether it be looked at from the viewpoint

[55] *Mathematical Principles*, p. 369. [57] *Ibid.*
[56] *Ibid.*, p. 370. [58] *Ibid.*

367

of the transmitter or the receptor. And the same thing is true if a physical case is being considered where a motion is being transmitted by a series of connected instruments. Here, as can be seen on a moment's reflection, there is specifically only one motion involved. One should therefore not be surprised if its metrical aspects will be the same in each of the transmitting instruments.

It is further true that the action-reaction principle, precisely as physico-mathematical, can also be extended to the two-body problem in the case of gravitational motion. For instance, if two bodies in a given physical environment approach each other in seeking their natural places in accordance with the inverse-square law, there is a certain mathematical symmetry about the phenomenon. As far as the mathematics is concerned, it makes no difference whether one is conceived at rest while the other approaches, or the second is at rest while the first approaches, or both approach each other. And if either of the first two cases are to be conceived in terms of " attractive forces," evidently the latter will manifest the same equality as the motions. Thus the action-reaction principle can be applied to " attractive forces " in gravitational motion, and it will be found to be operationally verifiable.

But while this is a valid principle of mathematical physics, it is not true when the total reality is considered, it cannot be taken as a strict physical principle of universal validity. The reason is simple enough. If there is a strict equality between agent and receptor, there can be no motion. Nothing dynamically new can proceed from strict equality. One rope, of and by itself, cannot pull another rope. That is the reason Newton, in explaining the third law as cited above, makes a slight excuse for the example of the horse drawing a stone by a rope. He says, ". . . the horse (if I may so say) will be equally drawn back towards the stone. . . ." The reason he inserts " if I may so say " is that there is a big difference between the horse and the rope and the stone when all three are considered physically. A rope, of and by itself, cannot pull a horse, but a horse can pull not only the rope but also something tied to it. If abstraction is to be made from this fact for the purposes of noting physico-mathematical equalities, all well and good. But the physical reality contains much more than the physico-mathematical equality.

The obvious answer to the third antinomy then is that it is based on a misunderstanding of the third law of motion. The physico-mathematical character of the action-reaction principle accents the fact that it abstracts from efficient movers considered in their physical totality. It neglects all movers except bodies already in local motion, and then only seeks an equality that is verified of the moving parts. It abstracts from the movers that form the subject matter of the *prima via*, but it does not reject them. Indeed, it presupposes them, for Newton's third law of motion, like his other two, has its only solid foundation and ultimate justification in the physical movers which lead their discoverer inexorably to the existence of God.

* * * * *

This completes the resolution of the three Newtonian antinomies. Apart from their utility in penetrating the *prima via* through a more thorough understanding of local motion, they also contain a message for the modern physicist. For it should be clear now that the scope and intent of the science Newton proposed never was clearly grasped by his successors. The many generations of physicists who now are referred to as " classical physicists " concentrated on the physico-mathematical aspects of his *Principia,* to the neglect of the further ordination that Newton made of the new science to discovering true physical causes. Flushed by early successes in predicting the details of many macroscopic phenomena, they saw the physico-mathematical technique for the powerful tool that it was, and then forgot that it was only a tool. Not possessing the traditional foundation in which Newton himself was grounded, they read too much into the father of their science. They took his mathematical principles as the total explanation of physical reality, and were content to stop where he had begun.

369

Needless to say, such men were not prepared for the rise of the new physics. Having slipped into the error of mathematicism, not appreciating the methodological use of mathematics in physical science, their illusions of a facile explanation for the entire gamut of physical experience were quickly dashed to the ground. Later generations of physicists seemingly profited by their mistake, and so began anew. But the pendulum did not swing to center; its momentum carried it to the other extreme. The philosophers of the new physics still failed to grasp the importance of a generalized physical science which could give true and certain knowledge of the universe; they claimed now that *nothing* could be certain or absolute. They were content to settle for a provisional explanation of reality; hypothetical constructions and mathematical models were the " ultimate " they were willing to concede. Their concern became manifest when the rapid multiplication of postulational systems soon involved them in contradictions, and so they turned to the problem of logical consistency. Here the logical positivists began to have their day, for a super-mathematicism has become the vogue, and this in turn is nothing more than logicism.

Amid present confusions as to what is logic and what is mathematics, there are very few scientists who have intelligent notions on the basic question of what is physics. But the question has been raised anew, and there is hope that the present generation of physicists may start to work on the answer. Of all the attempts made so far, the foundational physics of Aristotle and St. Thomas alone gives full meaning to the term " physical," as opposed to " mathematical " and " physico-mathematical." Newton had sufficient knowledge of this to orient his new science properly at the outset. His sons would do well to return to where he began. Not only will they find there the answer to the nature of their science, but they will learn how such science can lead them to their God.

BIBLIOGRAPHY

The following is a list of the principal publications of the author, William A. Wallace, relating to the history and philosophy of science.

1956a: "Newtonian Antinomies Against the *Prima Via*," *The Thomist* 19 (1956), 151-192, reprinted as Essay 16 of this volume.
1956b: Review of *De Noetica Geometriae, Origine Theoriae Cognitionis*, by Peter Hoenen, *The Thomist* 19 (1956), 381-391.

1957a: "Some Demonstrations in the Science of Nature," *The Thomist Reader 1957*, 90-118, reprinted as Essay 7 of this volume.
1957b: Review of *The Manner of Demonstrating in Natural Philosophy*, by Melvin Glutz, *The Thomist* 20 (1957), 365-369.

1959a: *The Scientific Methodology of Theodoric of Freiberg*. Studia Friburgensia, New Series, No. 26. Fribourg: The University Press, 1959, pp. xviii + 395, with index.
1959b: Review of *The General Science of Nature*, by V. E. Smith, *The Thomist* 22 (1959), 434-437.

1961a: "St. Thomas Aquinas, Galileo, and Einstein," *The Thomist* 24 (1961), 1-22, reprinted as Essay 4 of this volume.
1961b: "Gravitational Motion According to Theodoric of Freiberg," *The Thomist* 24 (1961), 327-352.
1961c: "Theology and the Natural Sciences," *Theology in the Catholic College*, ed. R. Masterson, Dubuque: The Priory Press, 1961, 167-204.

1962a: *The Role of Demonstration in Moral Theology*. Texts and Studies, No. 2. Washington: The Thomist Press, 1962, pp. x + 244.
1962b: "The Cosmogony of Teilhard de Chardin," *The New Scholasticism* 36 (1962), 353-367.
1962c: "Natural Philosophy and the Physical Sciences,"

Philosophy and the Integration of Contemporary Catholic Education, ed. G. F. McLean, Washington: The Catholic University of America Press, 1962, 130-157, 292-297.

1963a: *Einstein, Galileo and Aquinas. Three Views of Scientific Method.* Washington: The Thomist Press, 1963, pp. 37.

1963b: "Existential Ethics: A Thomistic Appraisal," *The Thomist* 27 (1963), 493-515.

1963c: "The Thomistic Order of Development in Natural Philosophy," *Teaching Thomism Today,* ed. G. F. McLean, Washington: The Catholic University of America Press, 1963, 247-270, 333-338.

1963d: "Modern Science: A Challenge to Faith?," *Proceedings of the Society of Catholic College Teachers of Sacred Doctrine* 9 (1963), 96-117.

1963e: "Nuclear Weapons, Morality, and the Future," *Dominicana* 48 (1963), 7-21, reprinted as Essay 12 of this volume.

1963f: "Radiation and Social Ethics," *America,* Vol. 108, No. 25, June 22, 1963, 880-883.

1963g: "A Thomist Looks at Teaching Machines," *Dominican Educational Bulletin,* 4 (1963), 13-23.

1964a: "The Reality of Elementary Particles," *Proceedings of the American Catholic Philosophical Association* 38 (1964), 154-166, reprinted as Essay 9 of this volume.

1964b: "Theodoric of Freiberg on the Structure of Matter," *Proceedings of the Tenth International Congress of History of Science 1962,* Paris: Hermann, 1964, 2 vols., Vol. 1, 591-597.

1964c: "St. Thomas and the Pull of Gravity," *The McAuley Lectures 1963: Science and the Liberal Concept,* West Hartford, Conn.: St. Joseph College, 1964, 143-165, reprinted as Essay 8 of this volume.

1964d: "Cybernetics and a Christian Philosophy of Man," *Philosophy in a Technological Culture,* ed. G. F. McLean, Washington: The Catholic University Press, 1964, 124-145, 307-314, reprinted in part as Essay 11 of this volume.

1965a: "The Measurement and Definition of Sensible Qualities," *The New Scholasticism* 39 (1965), 1-25, reprinted as Essay 5 of this volume.

1965b: "Some Moral and Religious Aspects of Nuclear Technology," *Journal of the Washington Academy of Sciences* 55 (1965), 85-91.

1967a: *Cosmogony. Summa Theologiae of St. Thomas Aquinas, Vol. 10, in English translation, with Notes and Appendices.* New York: McGraw-Hill, 1967, pp. xxiii + 255, with glossary and index.

1967b: *The New Catholic Encyclopedia,* New York: McGraw-Hill, 1967:
"Action at a Distance," 1:96-97
"Atomism," 1:1020-1024
"Color," 3:1030-1031
"Cybernetics," 4:557-562
"God and Modern Science," 6:568-572
"Hylomorphism," 7:284-285
"Hylosystemism," 7:285
"Logic, Symbolic," 8:962-964
"Measurement," 9:528-531
"Science (Scientia)," 12:1190-1193
"Science, Philosophy of," 12:1215-1219
"Sound," 13:474-476
"Theodoric (Dietrich) of Freiberg," 14:22-24
"Thomas Aquinas," 14:102-115
"Uncertainty Principle," 14:385-387

1967c: "The Concept of Motion in the Sixteenth Century," *Proceedings of the American Catholic Philosophical Association* 41 (1967), 184-195.

1968a: "The Enigma of Domingo de Soto: *Uniformiter difformis* and Falling Bodies in Late Medieval Physics," *Isis* 59 (1968), 384-401.

1968b: "Elementarity and Reality in Particle Physics," *Boston Studies in the Philosophy of Science,* eds. R. S. Cohen and M. W. Wartofsky, New York: Humanities Press, 1968, 236-271.

1968c: "Toward a Definition of the Philosophy of Science," *Mélanges à la mémoire de Charles De Koninck,* Quebec: Laval University Press, 1968, 465-485, reprinted as Essay 1 of this volume.

1968d: "Philosophy of the Physical Sciences: Some New Perspectives," *Philosophy and Contemporary Man,* ed. G. F. McLean, Washington: The Catholic University Press, 1968, 50-64, reprinted as Essay 2 of this volume.

1968e: "Thomism and Modern Science: Relationships Past, Present, and Future," *The Thomist* 32 (1968) 67-83.

1969a: "The 'Calculatores' in Early Sixteenth-Century Physics," *The British Journal for the History of Science,* 4 (1969), 221-232.

1969b: Reviews of *Nicole Oresme: Le Livre du ciel et du monde,* by A. D. Menut and A. J. Denomy, and

Nicole Oresme and the Medieval Geometry of Quali-
ties and Motions, by M. Clagett, *Isis* 60 (1969),
562-564.

1970a: "The Case for Developmental Thomism," Presiden-
tial Address, *Proceedings of the American Catho-*
lic Philosophical Association 44 (1970), 1-16.
1970b: "Albertus Magnus" and "Aquinas, Thomas," *Dic-*
tionary of Scientific Biography, New York:
Charles Scribner's Sons, 1970, Vol. 1, 99-103,
196-200.

1971a: "Mechanics from Bradwardine to Galileo," *Jour-*
nal of the History of Ideas 32 (1971), 15-28.
1971b: "Dietrich von Freiberg," *Dictionary of Scienti-*
fic Biography, 4 (1971), 92-95.

1972a: *Causality and Scientific Explanation. Vol. 1.*
Medieval and Early Classical Science. Ann Arbor:
The University of Michigan Press, 1972, pp. xii
+ 288, with index.
1972b: "The Cosmological Argument: A Reappraisal,"
Proceedings of the American Catholic Philosophi-
cal Association 46 (1972), 43-57, reprinted as
Essay 15 of this volume.

1973a: "Experimental Science and Mechanics in the Middle Ages," *Dictionary of the History of Ideas,*
New York: Charles Scribner's Sons, 1973, 2:196-
205.
1973b: "Lax, Gaspar," *Dictionary of Scientific Bio-*
graphy, 8 (1973), 100.

1974a: *Causality and Scientific Explanation. Vol. 2.*
Classical and Contemporary Science. Ann Arbor:
The University of Michigan Press, 1974, pp. xi +
422, with index.
1974b: "Three Classics of Science," *The Great Ideas*
Today 1974, Chicago: Encyclopaedia Britannica,
1974, 211-272.
1974c: "Theodoric of Freiberg: On the Rainbow," *A*
Source Book in Medieval Science, ed. E. Grant,
Cambridge, Mass.: Harvard University Press, 1974,
435-441.
1974d: "Galileo and the Thomists," *St. Thomas Aquinas*
Commemorative Studies 1274-1974, 2 vols., Toron-
to: Pontifical Institute of Mediaeval Studies,
1974, Vol. 2, 293-330.
1974e: "Aquinas on the Temporal Relation Between Cause
and Effect," *The Review of Metaphysics* 27 (1974)

569-584, reprinted as Essay 6 of this volume.

1974f: "Aquinas on Creation: Science, Theology, and Matters of Fact," *The Thomist* 38 (1974), 485-523.

1975a: "The First Way: A Rejoinder," *The Thomist* 39 (1975), 375-382.

1975b: "Soto, Domingo de," *Dictionary of Scientific Biography*, 12 (1975), 547-548.

1976a: "Galileo and Reasoning *Ex suppositione:* The Methodology of the *Two New Sciences*," *Proceedings of the 1974 Biennial Meeting of the Philosophy of Science Association*, ed. R. S. Cohen et al., Dordrecht-Boston: D. Reidel Publishing Company, 1976, 79-104.

1976b: "Buridan, Ockham, Aquinas: Science in the Middle Ages," *The Thomist* 40 (1976), 475-483.

1976c: "Six Studies of Causality on the Bicentennial of David Hume," *The Thomist* 40 (1976), 684-696.

1977a: *The Elements of Philosophy: A Compendium for Philosophers and Theologians.* New York: Alba House, 1977, pp. xx + 342, with index.

1977b: *Galileo's Early Notebooks: The Physical Questions. A Translation from the Latin, with Historical and Paleographical Commentary.* Notre Dame: University of Notre Dame Press, 1977, pp. xiv + 321, with index of names.

1978a: "Galileo Galilei and the *Doctores Parisienses*," *New Perspectives on Galileo*, eds. R. E. Butts and J. C. Pitt, Dordrecht: D. Reidel Publishing Company, 1978, 87-138.

1978b: "The Philosophical Setting of Medieval Science," *Science in the Middle Ages*, ed. D. C. Lindberg, Chicago: The University of Chicago Press, 1978, 91-119.

1978c: "Causality, Analogy, and the Growth of Scientific Knowledge," *Tommaso d'Aquino nel suo settimo centenario*, 9 vols., Naples: Edizioni Domenicane Italiane, 1978, 9:26-40, reprinted as Essay 10 in this volume.

1978d: "Galileo's Knowledge of the Scotistic Tradition," *Regnum Hominis et Regnum Dei*, ed. C. Bérubé, Rome: Societas Internationalis Scotistica, 1978, Vol. 2, 313-320.

1978e: "Causes and Forces in Sixteenth-Century Physics," *Isis* 69 (1978), 400-412.

1979a: *From a Realist Point of View: Essays on the*

        Philosophy of Science, Washington: University
        Press of America, 1979, pp. xii + 376.

1979b: "Medieval and Renaissance Sources of Modern
        Science: A Revision of Duhem's Continuity Thesis,
        Based on Galileo's Early Notebooks," *Proceedings*
        of the Patristic-Medieval-Renaissance Conference
        1977, Villanova, Pennsylvania: Augustinian His-
        torical Institute, 1979, 1-17.

1979c: "Immateriality and Its Surrogates in Modern
        Science," *Proceedings of the American Catholic*
        Philosophical Association 1978, expanded as
        Essay 14 of this volume.